Graphic arts
PROCEDURES

The Offset Processes
includes strike-on and
film composition

R. Randolph Karch
Graphic Arts Consultant
Author of Textbooks and Technical Magazine Articles
Formerly *teacher* of Graphic Arts,
Technical Supervisor Department of Publishing and
Printing, Rochester Institute of Technology,
Principal of Graphic Arts High School, Cincinnati,
and *Director of Publications,* Pennsylvania

Edward J. Buber
Member, International Printing
Pressmen and Assistants Union of North America
And *Assistant Director* of Publications, Pennsylvania
Formerly: *Offset Instructor,* Glen Mills Schools,
Pennsylvania

American Technical Society
CHICAGO · USA

Library of Congress Catalog Card Number: 66-12164
PRINTED IN THE UNITED STATES OF AMERICA

PREFACE

Financial growth and technical progress in the Graphic Arts industry has been extraordinary. All evidence points to even greater growth for this dynamic industry. This means there is now a great need and will be an increasing need for trained men and women in all the printing trades. Although growth for the entire industry has been great, offset-lithography has grown at twice the rate of the industry as a whole. The need for trained personnel is correspondingly great.

This introductory book on the offset processes has been prepared to help the nation meet this need. It has been carefully designed to lead the student by planned steps to a sure understanding of offset work, including the latest technical developments in strike-on, film composition and computerized typesetting.

The Offset Processes is built around a basic and essential educational concept: that the understanding of the whole leads to a firmer grasp of the parts of the whole.

The Offset Processes encompasses the whole of the offset craftsman's task. Beginning with the origin of lithography, the student goes by sure steps through copy preparation, cold type, offset photography, platemaking, inks, fountain solutions and blankets into actual press operating practices and on to paper and bindery operations. *The Offset Processes* includes operating practices for six of the smaller offset presses. This material follows the recommended practices of the manufacturers. In providing these practices and procedures, the book emphasizes the functional similarities of the equipment without slighting the operational differences. This serves to provide the student with a working knowledge of the concepts as well as the presses themselves.

Edward J. Buber and R. Randolph Karch have a combined experience with offset equipment of more than 50 years. They also pool their experience to make a total of more than 30 years of teaching in the classrooms of the nation. Mr. Karch has taught and administered vocational educational programs at all levels of education.

We feel fortunate in being able to draw on this combined experience and knowledge in producing Graphic Arts Procedures — *The Offset Processes*.

The Publishers

Contents

PAGE

1 **Origin of Lithography** 1

   Senefelder's discovery   Early methods   Early power driven presses
   Offset printing today   New machines

2 **Processes and Methods** 8

   Basic methods and process   The contribution of letterpress to offset
   Letterpress printing and hot type   Letterpress printing plates
   Photoengravings   Duplicate letterpress printing plates   Preparing
   type forms for letterpress   Other major processes in the graphic arts
   Office copiers and offset platemakers   Proofreaders' marks

3 **Copy Preparation for Offset Printing** 46

   Typographic layout   Office forms   Preprinted artwork   Shading
   media   Foto-Chase

4 **Cold Type** 68

   Contrast between cold and hot type   Growth of the cold type
   processes   Kinds of cold type devices   Photographic typesetting
   Lettering devices   Paper and plastic type   Photographic line
   composers   Modification devices   Tape-operated cold type devices

5 **Offset Photography** 141

   Parts of a camera   Types of cameras   Film   Types of film
   Adjustments of the camera   Lights   Halftone photography
   Screened snapshots   Rescreening   Color separation   Duotones
   Combination line and halftone   Dropout halftone   The darkroom
   Development fixing and washing   Analysis of halftone negatives

6 **Offset Platemaking** 207

   The offset plate   General steps in plate-making   Plate graining
   Counter etch   Coating solution   Vacuum printing frame   Photo-
   composing machines   Developing ink   Caustic solution   De-
   sensitizer   Gum Arabic   Asphaltum   Zinc plate   Pre-sensitized
   plate   Deep etch plate   Materials and qualities of offset plates
   Other methods of platemaking   Care and cleaning

7   **Related Press Data**   256

   *Press fountain etches Zinc plate solutions Offset blankets
   Preparing the new blanket for the press Care and cleaning Offset
   printing inks The pigment The vehicle Other ingredients*

8   **Offset Presswork**   273

   *Basic press operation Ditto Offset Duplicator A. B. Dick Offset
   Duplicator, Model 360 Multilith Offset Duplicator, Model 1250*

9   **ATF Chief "15" and the Davidson Dual "500"**   366

   *ATF Chief "15"—Inking system Operating controls Adjust-
   ments Davidson Dual—Inking system Operating controls
   Adjustments Other methods of printing*

10 **Harris Offset Model LUH-120**   453

   Operating controls Press adjustments Press maintenance

11 **Printing Paper**   478

   *Raw material Pulp Bleaching Coated and enameled paper
   Watermarks Papermaking machine Classes and kinds of paper
   Paper cutting Weights of paper Testing for grain Humidity*

12 **Bindery Operations**   491

   *How sheets of paper are fastened Folding paper Stapling and
   stitching Collating and gathering Drilling and punching holes
   Jogging Padding Round cornering Perforating Gold stamping Cutting paper Paper ruling Embossing Book-edge
   treatment*

Review Question Answers   510

Acknowledgments   518

Dictionary of Technical Terms   529

Appendix   561

Index   565

CHAPTER 1

The Origin of Lithography

The word lithography was derived from two Greek words, "lithos" which means "stone" and "graphein" which means "to write." From this we get the original meaning of the word, "stone writing," or "writing from stone." Although the exact date is not known, the discovery of lithography was made about 1796 by a German musician and playwright, Alois Senefelder (Fig. 1-1). Senefelder, in seeking a cheap method to reproduce his music and plays discovered the lithographic process. Prior to this discovery, illustrations had been made on copper as early as 1446. It was in this year that Maso Finiguerra of Florence, Italy, discovered the art of copperplate engraving. At the time that Senefelder discovered lithography, William Blake was engraving on copper and printing on a flatbed press in England.

Fig. 1-1. Alois Senefelder, a Munich playwright and musician, discovered lithography in the year 1796.

Senefelder's Discovery. The exact story of Senefelder's discovery is clouded by conflicting reports. One version is that he had no paper on which to write his laundry list, so he wrote on a stone with a greasy crayon. Another report is that while near his home in Bavaria, he picked up a limestone formation and wrote a small memo to himself with a crayon. Still another story is that he had invented a greasy ink which he used to write his notes for music, and he chanced to write with the ink on stone.

It was while putting this image on stone that the idea occurred to Senefelder to try to transfer the image to paper. He placed a piece of paper on the stone, applied pressure and succeeded in transferring the image from the stone to the paper. Many experiments followed until another idea came to him. If it is possible to transfer an image from stone to paper, might it be possible to transfer an image on paper to the stone, and then from the stone back to the paper? He tried and succeeded.

He interested an artist friend, Strixner, in the process. Together they made a drawing on paper, placed it face down on the stone and put it through a crude copper-plate press. They were successful in transferring the image from the paper to the calcareous stone. This stone, containing calcium carbonate or calcite (which includes common limestone, chalk, and marble), has an affinity to both grease and water. Senefelder and Strixner decided to apply more ink to the image on the stone to transfer it back to the paper. At this point they probably noticed the ink spread beyond the image area. Observing that this stone could hold both the greasy ink and water, they decided to moisten the stone first and then apply the ink. After doing this, they placed a piece of paper over the image on the stone and ran it back through the press. The image was transferred back to the paper. The experiment was a success and lithography was born.

The news of this discovery spread rapidly throughout continental Europe and England. Soon artists in various countries took up the art. They tried many techniques. Among them were the use of chalk, ink, pen, and wash, covering the entire stone with ink and scraping away the ink to form the image in reverse, and the combination of one, two, or even all of these devices.

Early Methods. Two basic methods were employed in lithography. One was placing the image on the paper first, transferring it to the stone and then back to the paper, or placing the image on the stone and then transferring it to the paper. The second method was to engrave or cut the reverse of the image desired directly into the stone. Both methods had advantages and disadvantages. To place the image on the stone directly either by drawing or engraving was a very slow and tedious process requiring a great amount of time, because the image had to be done in reverse or backward. The advantage of this method was that the artist knew his image existed and that it would reproduce during the process. Drawing the image on paper first, however, was faster. Transferring the image to the stone was a disadvantage since the artist could not be sure the full image would be successfully transferred. Special paper was needed and preferably thin. The back side of the paper had to be moistened and pressure applied in order to transfer the image from the paper to the stone. To visualize this more clearly, imagine yourself trying to place a "tatoo" on your arm. The "tatoo" is on a thin piece of paper. You place the "tatoo" face down on your arm, and while wetting the back of the paper you apply pressure. It isn't until you remove the paper from your arm that you actually know whether the "tatoo" is transferred. Anyone who has tried, knows that the full image does not transfer successfully every time. Since the transfer method could not guarantee the artist a proper image, the most popular method eventually became engraving the image directly into the stone.

The lithographic stone itself was another disadvantage to the artist. The stones ranged in size from approximately 6 by 8-inches to 44 by 62-inches and 3 to 4 inches thick, great weight was involved. Moreover, before the stones could be used they had to be processed. The top of the stone had to be very smooth and level. This was accomplished by grinding the stone with sand and then with pumice stone and emery. The bottom of the stone also had to be smooth and parallel with the top. If it was not, the possibility existed that the full image would not be reproduced, or the stone itself might chip or break when pressure was applied.

The lithographic flatbed press made reproductions very slowly.

Before a reproduction was made, the stone required dampening and inking. The stone could travel only in one direction while the impression was taken, and then it traveled back again to the starting position where the stone was dampened and inked again. This procedure lost at least fifty percent production time. With this press, the artist was able to reproduce only about 600 copies an hour.

Early Power-Driven Presses. In 1814, R. Hoe and Company built the first steam-operated press to be used for printing. "The Times" of London was the first printing by this press. The press was equipped with an impression cylinder, and ink fountain, one set of ink rollers at each end of the stone and one set of water rollers.

With the development of the zinc plate came the invention of the offset and rotary press. In 1904, Ira W. Rubel from Rutherford, New Jersey, invented the offset press. Before too many of these were manufactured, Alex Sherwood had built and was operating a new kind of rotary press in Chicago in 1905. This press produced 1100 impressions per hour. A man named Dickinson, who sold machinery for the Harris Brothers, saw this press and suggested that they try to make an offset press. But they were in fact, already working on one. The first Harris offset press was delivered to a company in Pittsburgh in July of 1906. Today the Harris Company is one of the leading manufacturers of offset presses.

The Offset Process. Offset printing, which eventually took the place of direct lithography, involves the same basic principle (Fig. 1-2) except that metal plates replace the stone and the plates

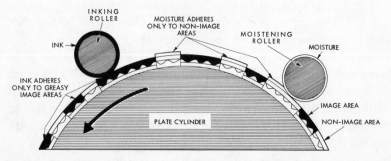

Fig. 1-2. The lithographic process is based on the well-known fact that grease and water will not mix.

rotate in a circular motion instead of the forward and backward movement of the flatbed press. The process is basically the same and based on the well known fact that grease and water do not mix. The ink that is used to cover the image on the plate contains a grease base. We know that if we roll ink over the entire plate that it would become completely covered with the ink. To prevent this, a water solution is applied to the plate before the ink is applied. The image, already containing a grease base, will attract the ink and repel the water. The water being applied is repelled in the image area keeping the non-image areas of the plate clean. An equal balance of ink and water must be maintained to insure accurate reproduction.

The term "offset printing" was derived from the nature of the process itself. The thin metal plate, containing the image to be reproduced, is clamped around the plate cylinder. After the water and ink have been automatically applied, the image is transferred to a rubber blanket on another cylinder. The image is then "offset" to the paper as it passes between the blanket and impression cylinder.

Offset printing today is a photo-mechanical process. The image to be reproduced is photographed on a sensitive film which, when developed, will show the image as being transparent, the rest of the film will be black or opaque. The film negative is placed on a prepared light-sensitive metal plate where the image is transferred by means of a strong light. The plate is then clamped on the offset press where the printing process is completed. Offset presses can produce 9000 impressions per hour or more. Rotary newspaper presses are capable of printing as much as 1,200 feet per minute from a roll of paper.

Recent surveys show that there are approximately 6,000 offset printing plants and over 23,000 combination letterpress and offset printing plants in the United States, excluding newspapers. The United States Department of Commerce, Bureau of Census, estimates that over a period of 9 years from 1958 to 1967, the monetary value of printing by offset will increase 98% as compared to letterpress estimated to increase only 19%.

Newspapers which have been dominated by letterpress are

changing to offset at a much faster pace due to the advancement of cold type composition equipment.

In 1960 it was reported that over 170 daily and over 1,500 weekly newspapers were printed by offset. Reports in 1967 now indicate there are more than 4,000 newspapers, both dailies and weeklies that have converted to offset printing. Although not all newspaper plants will change to offset, these reports indicate the trend in the Graphic Arts Industry.

Many improvements have been made through the years, too numerous to write about here, and offset printing still continues to show improvements and advancement with the years.

New Machines. In recent years we have seen the development of new machines, such as Photon, Fotosetter, Linofilm, ATF Phototypesetter, Headliner, and many others. These machines have enabled the offset process to compete with letterpress, especially in copy preparation. With the constant improvements of these photocomposing machines and the offset press, the offset process has definitely found a place in the printing industry of today and tomorrow.

Review Questions

Instructions: Do not write in the book unless instructed to do so by your instructor.

Questions are in several forms: multiple choice, true or false, fill-in, or matching. For multiple choice questions, select from the list of statements or words the most logical answer. To answer true-false questions place "T" in the space provided if the statement is true; "F", if it is false. Use one or as few words as possible in fill-in answers. In matching questions, select the letter which corresponds to the correct answer.

1. About what year was lithography discovered?

    a. 1596   c. 1796

    b. 1696   d. 1896

2. Who invented the offset press?

   a. Harris Brothers   d. Rubel
   b. Webendorfer   e. Sherwood
   c. Dickinson   f. Senefelder

3. Who was active in the development of the early offset presses? (*Use answers under 2.*)
4. Stones used in lithography had to have an affinity for both ink and water. True or False
5. Paper receives the ink from the zinc plate in offset printing. True or False
6. Who discovered lithography?
7. Who assisted the inventor of lithography?
8. People in what activity welcomed the new process?
9. What were the two basic methods employed in lithography?
10. The term used to describe the kind of stone used in lithography is _____ .
11. What company developed the first steam operated lithography press?
12. When and where?

CHAPTER 2

Processes and Methods

What are the methods employed in the graphic arts and what are the processes employed in each of the methods? Why do we have as many as nine processes, and at least 27 methods? Why not one process and one method? Why should we know about the processes and methods?

This chapter acquaints the graphic arts student with all of the present methods of placing images on objects. We use the word "objects" because images may be "printed" on materials other than paper. For example, how do you "print" on a radio cabinet and on a milk bottle? We have the many methods, subdivided into the many processes, because of the nature of the work to be accomplished. For example, where each sheet printed is to be sequentially numbered, the letterpress method is used. Newspapers usually are printed letterpress or offset, but newspaper magazine sections are printed by gravure, because it is economical to do the jobs in this way, and "soft" illustrations are possible with extremely fine halftone screens. Full-color art objects are printed by the photogelatin process where large quantities are not needed, because it is least expensive to print them in this way. "Tin" cans cannot be printed by letterpress, so cans are printed by offset. Because the letterpress and offset processes cannot do a good enough job printing white ink on black paper, screen process is used. Quantities printed are a factor. A thousand letterheads would hardly be printed on a gravure press at speeds up to 1200 feet per minute from a roll of paper, but rather on a small letter-press or offset press. Flexographic (Letterset) and gravure methods are better suited to printing on cellophane (as on candy wrappers) than are letterpress or offset. What press would be large enough to print 20-foot political posters? A built-on-the-spot screen process "press" can do the work. Examples are endless to account for the many methods and processes.

The graphic arts student is urged to learn to differentiate among the methods and processes of the graphic arts so that he will know what methods and procedures are to be used in the production of the many types and kinds of printed products.

Of the many methods and procedures used in the graphic arts, letterpress and offset-lithography account for 66.1% in monetary value. Letterpress leads with 43%, and offset-lithography is second with 23.1%. However, it should be noted that offset-lithography is growing faster than letterpress.

The graphic arts is a small-shop industry. Only about 1,000 plants employ more than 100 employees, and the average is 17. A total of about 40,000 shops employ about 800,000 people. There are 1,761 daily newspapers with a total daily circulation of 70,400,000. More than 1,500 weekly newspapers are now being printed by the offset process. It should be noted that printing news-papers by offset is not generally less expensive than printing by letterpress. Letterpress stereotype plates can be melted down and the metal used again; stereotype matrices cost about 32 cents each. Offset negatives cost 84 cents each. Ink used in letterpress costs slightly over a nickel a pound; offset inks cost more than 35 cents. Newsprint paper used in letterpress is inexpensive; the offset process requires a more expensive paper because of the impression adjustment and the water-and-ink balance.

However, the quality of the product—the newspaper—is generally better when printed offset than when it is printed by letterpress, particularly in the use of pictures because offset allows the use of a finer screen. In addition, hot type need not be used in any form whatever. Previously printed material can be "picked up" for offset production, eliminating the setting of type.

Whether use of offset-lithography will one day exceed that of letterpress remains to be seen. Letterpress is the older process, being more than 500 years old. Most of the newspapers, magazines, and books, and over 50% of commercial printings are at present produced by letterpress.

Offset-lithography, however, was conceived about 1900, and gained impetus in the 1920's. Only 50 years since its conception, it has grown tremendously. The future holds much for the process and its workers.

The last 50 years have seen more technical advancement in the graphic arts than in the 500 preceding years. This is true in almost every method and process.

Basic Methods and Processes

The student of offset-lithographic techniques and procedures should be acquainted with other methods. Most are highly competitive. The basic methods of placing images on objects are quite varied, and each method can be divided into processes for making multiple copies.

Although we are concerned with offset-lithography, the reader should know the competing processes for the reasons stated in the introduction to this chapter. The eight basic methods, and their associated processes are listed in Table I, and the more important are briefly discussed.

The Products of the Processes

Generally, particular printed products are manufactured by specific processes:

Newspapers, Magazines	Letterpress
Bank checks and deposit slips	Offset
Tax Stamps, Packaging materials	Dry Offset
Sunday newspaper supplements	Gravure
Wedding invitations	Copperplate printing, thermography
Art subjects	Photo-gelatin
"Tin" cans	Offset
Candy wrappers	Flexographic

TABLE I: BASIC METHODS OF PRINTING

RELIEF SURFACES

ACCOUNTING MACHINES	POSTAGE METERS	EMBOSSING: ""BLIND" IMAGE OR IMPRESSED PRINTING
AUTOMATIC TYPEWRITER, TAPE OR WIRE OPERATED	RUBBER STAMPS: HAND OPERATED	
	SPOT CARBONIZING	ENCODER: MAGNETIC-INK PRINTING, USED IN CHECKS
BLIND STAMPING: BOOK-COVER TITLES	METALLIC STAMPING: BOOK COVERS	
DIE-CUTTING: FOLDING BOXES, DISPLAYS	THERMOGRAPHY: RAISED LETTER PRINTING	FLEXOGRAPHIC: RUBBER PLATES
		IMPRINTER: PERSONALIZED CHECKS, SIGNATURE MACHINE
DRY OFFSET: ETCHED PLATE TO BLANKET	TICKOMETER: CHECK ENDORSING	LETTERPRESS: TYPE, SLUGS PLATES

PLANE SURFACES

DECALCOMANIA MANUFACTURING	PHOTO-GELATIN (COLLOTYPE)
OFFSET-LITHOGRAPHY	SPIRIT DUPLICATION

SUNKEN SURFACES

COPPERPLATE ENGRAVING	GRAVURE, SHEET FED AND ROTARY
DRY-POINT ETCHING (ART ACTIVITY)	STEELPLATE DIE STAMPING
ETCHING, ACID (ART ACTIVITY)	

OTHERS

ELECTROSTATIC	XEROGRAPHY, APECO, COPYTRON	LAMINATING, VINYL APPLIQUE
ELECTRO-CHEMICAL	THERMOFAX	PRESSURE-SENSITIVE STICKER
PAPER RULING	PEN RULING: COLORED, RULED LINES	MIMEOGRAPH, GESTETNER, ETC.
PHOTOGRAPHIC	MARBLING, STAINING, GILDING	SCREEN PROCESS ("SILK SCREEN")

It should be remembered, however, that many jobs of printing can be and are manufactured by more than one process. An example is the letterhead, which may be printed by die stamping, offset, letterpress and/or thermography.

The Contribution of Letterpress to Offset

Letterpress type is often used as the text matter for offset plates. This is the major contribution of letterpress to the offset process. Only a few prints, called reproduction proofs, are made from the letterpress type. This is done to insure that the plate will be perfect. If errors are found in the type set-up, they are corrected before the offset plate is made. Other products of the letterpress which concern the offset printer are:

  a. Previously-printed office forms, books and the like, printed by letterpress can often be photographed then printed by offset-lithography. This eliminates the cost of type composition.
  b. Conversion methods can convert standing letterpress plates

or type forms to negative to be used in offset-lithography.

c. Letterpress type can be printed on offset masters and printed by the offset process.

d. Letterpress printed halftones (pictures) in books can often be "picked up" as line shots, or rescreened for printing by the offset-lithographic process.

Offset for Directories. Periodic revisions and reprintings of lists by hot type and letterpress soon finds the printer concerned with a variety of thickened type lines caused by wear on the press contrasted with the light, new hot type lines for new line insertions in the type form.

When books containing lists subject to change are printed by offset, all reproductions of pages are the same in appearance, and no thickening of lines is possible. Changes are made by stripping new film on the old film.

Another method that eliminates thickening is the sequential card camera used in composing pre-typed cards.

Letterpress Printing and Hot Type

Letterpress printing is produced from raised surfaces which are inked and pressed against paper in a variety of printing presses. See Fig. 2-1.

Hot type composition is done in several ways. Single characters

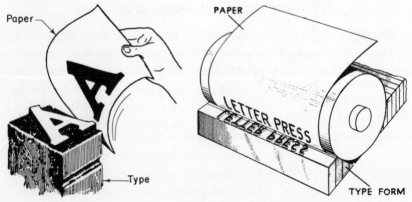

Fig. 2-1. Letterpress printing is done from raised type.

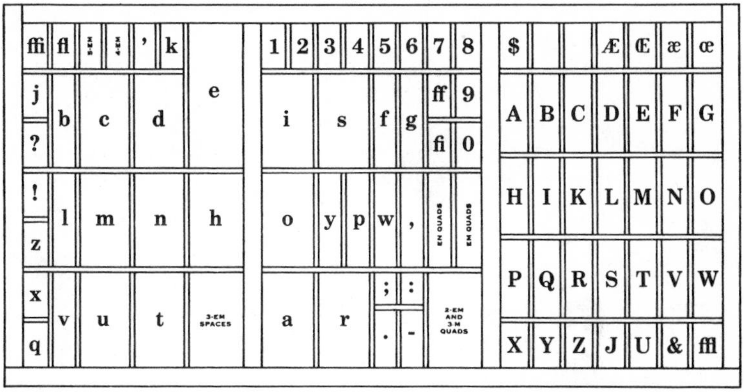

ffi	fl	⁞	⁞	’	k			1	2	3	4	5	6	7	8		$			Æ	Œ	æ	œ
j		b	c	d	e			i		s	f	g		ff	9		A	B	C	D	E	F	G
?														fi	0								
!		l	m	n	h			o	y	p	w	,	2-EM QUADS	3-EM QUADS		H	I	K	L	M	N	O
z																							
x		v	u	t	3-EM SPACES			a	r	;	:	2-EM AND 3-M QUADS		P	Q	R	S	T	V	W
q										.	-			X	Y	Z	J	U	&	ffl

Fig. 2-2. Hand-set type is obtained from a job case like the one shown here.

Fig. 2-3. Type from the job case is assembled in a composing stick.

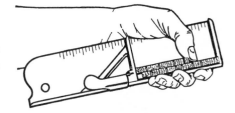

Fig. 2-4. Machine-set type is cast in lines, as shown here, or by individual letters.

may be set by hand from type cases, see Figs. 2-2 and 2-3. Slug lines of letters may be set on Linotype and Intertype machines, see Fig. 2-4.

A third hot-metal linecasting machine similar to the Linotype and Intertype is the imported Mentype. It includes a hydraulic, push-button system for changing magazines. Five main magazines are featured on the machine. Lines may be cast from hand-assembled matrices on a Ludlow Typograph, see Fig. 2-5. Mono-

Fig. 2-5. The Ludlow-Typograph is a type casting system that uses hand-assembled matrices.

Fig. 2-6. The Monotype keyboard punches a perforated tape, the tape in turn activates the Monotype caster.

type is another system which uses a perforated tape to activate a caster which casts individual characters in justified columns, see Figs. 2-6 and 2-7.

Although the term "typesetting machine" is used, no device "sets" type, the devices *create* either individual types or complete lines of characters, usually referred to as a "slug."

In the letterpress process, the hot type slugs are assembled by hand into "forms" and "locked up" in frames called "chases." The chases are then placed in "platen" presses; or "cylinder" presses,

Fig. 2-7. The Monotype caster assembles letters individually.

for printing directly from the type. Sometimes duplicate plates are made for long press runs. Duplicate plates often wear longer than type forms.

"Makeready" is done by the pressman to achieve the best possible type impression on the paper. This includes the "shimming-up" of low areas in a form, with overlays of tissue paper.

Letterpress flatbed cylinder presses make two revolutions to print one sheet. Offset presses print a sheet with every revolution of the cylinder and therefore generally produce more sheets per hour than letterpress presses.

Letterpress Printing Plates

Letterpress printing may be divided into two groups: originals and duplicates. Originals may be used on the presses, or duplicates may be made from the originals to save the latter from wear on long press runs.

Original plates include:
1. Photoengravings: line, halftone, combination, and color.
2. Electronically-made halftones and line plates.
3. Dycril plates.
4. Hand-cut rubber plates.

Duplicate plates for letterpress include:
1. Electrotypes.
2. Wax engravings.
3. Stereotypes.
4. Molded rubber plates.
5. Plastic plates.

Photoengravings

The chemical action of light on a film makes photoengraving possible. Photoengravings may be "line," which involves only black and white, see Fig. 2-8; as contrasted with "halftones," see Fig. 2-9, which appear to have gray shades, although printed in black ink. Both line and halftone may appear in the same plate, which is then called a "combination" plate, see Fig. 2-10.

The traditional method of making photoengravings is accomplished as follows:

    1. Copy is placed on a camera, and shot same size, reduced, or

line

Fig. 2-8. Line engravings involve only black and white.

halftone

Fig. 2-9. Halftone engravings use black ink in a pattern of dots so that the illustration appears to have gray shades.

combination

Fig. 2-10. Combination engravings involve both line work and halftone patterns.

"blown up" on film. A flat is made by reversing the film on plate glass. The flat is placed face-down on zinc or copper plate which has been made sensitive to light. A powerful light is used in a vacuum frame to transfer the image to the plate.

2. The plate is then etched in an acid tank which eats away the non-image areas in the metal plate. Four brushings, in different directions, with "dragon's blood" are made before four or more successive "bites" in the etching tank.

3. The photoengraving is then fastened to a wood base to make it type high.

Copy of continuous tone photographs and other copy is photographed through a screen to break up the picture into a multitude of fine halftone "dots" which allow gray shades in the final plate. Screens may be 50, 65, 85, 100, 120 or 133 or finer depending upon the paper to be used to print the picture.

Dow Etch (Powderless Etching). This is a much speedier process for making photoengravings, requiring one "bite." The plate is placed face down above a tank of etching acid. Paddles throw the acid upward against the rotating plate, see Figs. 2-11 and 2-12. No etching occurs on the sides of the images because the nitric acid strikes these areas at a lesser angle. Hence, plates can be made in about one-sixth of the time required by the traditional method.

Dycril Plates. In this process of making original letterpress plates the photopolymer plate is sensitive to ultra-violet light, which hardens the image areas. See Fig. 2-13. The plate is then washed out with a dilute solution of caustic soda. The areas not

Fig. 2-11. A powderless etching machine.

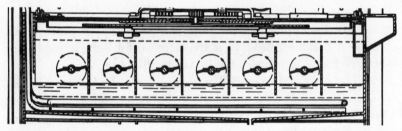

Fig. 2-12. The paddles in a powderless etching machine throw acid from the tank to the plate as it whirls.

Fig. 2-13. Dycril photopolymer devices. The plate conditioning cabinet (*left*) processes the plates to make them ready for exposure. The rotary plate exposure unit (*center*) exposes the plate. The automatic washout unit (*right*) develops the plate, removing all of the unexposed, unhardened polymer.

hardened (or polymerized) wash away, leaving the printing (or image) areas in relief. Dycril plates can be made in about a half hour.

The Kodak Relief Plate. The plate is a photopolymer for letterset (offset with no water) of the wrap-around type. It is only .025-inch thick, made up of a layer of emulsion, a white pigment, a .013 layer of acetate and a steel plate .010-inch thick. The relief depth is .011-inch. After the plate is exposed (as for Dycril) the acetate is removed by immersion in an alkaline solution. Plates are still good after a half-million impressions.

Electronic Platemakers. These devices make halftones directly from the original photographs. No cameras or negatives are used. The copy is placed on one cylinder of the machine, and a plastic or metal plate is placed on another cylinder. The Scan-a-Sizer (see Figs. 2-14 and 2-15) is one make of electronic platemaker. It pro-

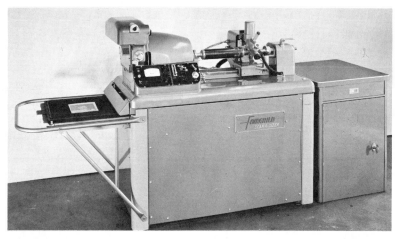

Fig. 2-14. The Fairchild Scan-a-Sizer uses electronic impulses to produce reduced or enlarged letterpress plates.

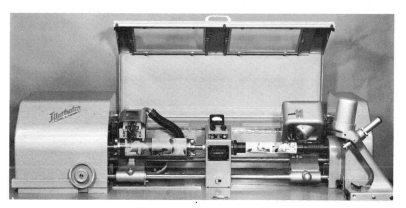

Fig. 2-15. The Fairchild Scan-a-Graver uses electronic impulses to produce electronic plates.

vides *plastic* halftone plates. The copy is "read" by an optical system, and amplified electrical charges direct a heated stylus to penetrate a plastic plate 640 times a second. The stylus produces halftone dots on the plate.

The Scan-a-Sizer reduces or enlarges directly from original copy. It produces halftone letterpress plates up to $12\frac{3}{4} \times 16$ inches. Two screens are available. The Scan-a-Sizer Cadet produces same size halftones as original copy up to 6×8 inches. The

Scan-a-Graver Dual Screen model permits coarse screens for newspaper printing, and a fine screen for job shop work. The Scan-a-Graver Journalist makes both halftone and line plates. An optical system "reads" the photograph, and a heated stylus is directed to penetrate the plate to be printed, producing halftone dots. Some devices make plates same size, some reduced and enlarged plates, and still others make either line or halftones. These machines include the models of Scan-a-Graver, Klischograph, Photo-Lathe and Elgramma.

Plastic Plates. Used during World War II because of the metal shortage, the plastic plate weighs much less than its counterpart, the electrotype. Plastic plates, used for some book printing, are being improved at the present writing.

Rubber Plates. These plates are used mainly on flexographic letterpress machines or for printing multiple business forms, such as snapout forms and continuous forms, candy bar wrappers, foil printing, holiday wrappings, and like work. Applications allow even printing upon razor blades and English walnuts.

A plastic mold is made first, and the same machine is used to vulcanize rubber with the mold. Printing by this method is often confused with that of offset-lithography because rules (lines) make no visible impression on the reverse side of the paper.

The Bista Plate is a lightweight, plastic-backed, curved, electrotype plate applied to folding carton and periodical printing yielding up to 7 million impressions. The plates are laminated with the printing surface, plastic body, and a perforated aluminum shell. The electrotype shell is backed up with plastic rather than the usual lead alloy. The Bista plate weighs about ⅓th as much as a conventional electrotype. Higher press speeds are possible, and less makeready is needed.

Chem-o-Type Duplicate Plates. A newer development in duplicate platemaking is Chem-o-Type. In the process, a liquid is poured over a plastic matrix made of a letterpress type or plate form. The batter-like substance is then spread thinly and evenly. After one minute in an open preheater press, a reinforcement mat and backing sheet are added. Then the entire assembly is heated and later bonded in a cold press. The plate is peeled off and trimmed, which produces a flexible plate for flat or rotary printing.

Duplicate Letterpress Printing Plates

Duplicate letterpress plates include the electrotype, plastic duplicate, stereotype and molded rubber plates.

Duplicate plates are made to save more expensive originals, such as photoengravings, to print in "gangs," i.e., to print more than one form on a sheet, and to allow the same form to be printed in more than one locality at the same time, as newspaper advertisements.

Electrotypes. An impression of a type form is made in vinyl, plastic or lead. See Fig. 2-16. This mold is then sprayed with silver to make it electrically conductive. Placed in an electroplating bath, the mold receives a thin coating of copper, called a shell. The shell is backed up with molten metal which produces a cast about three-sixteenths of an inch thick. After it is mounted on wood base, or planed for mounting on steel patent base, or curved to print on rotary letterpresses, the electrotype is ready for printing.

Stereotypes. This plate is cast in metal from an impression

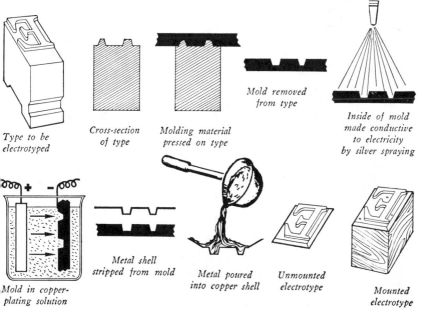

Fig. 2-16. The steps in making an electrotype.

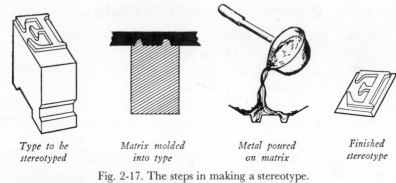

Type to be stereotyped   *Matrix molded into type*   *Metal poured on matrix*   *Finished stereotype*

Fig. 2-17. The steps in making a stereotype.

Fig. 2-18. The stereotype cast may be used flat or be curved for use on rotary presses.

Fig. 2-19. Hot metal is being used here to make a stereotype.

made in a paper-like matrix. See Fig. 2-17. The cast, see Fig. 2-18 and 2-19, may be flat or curved depending upon its use.

Wax Engraving. Now largely passé, this type of plate was used in the printing of maps, cross-ruled work, and the like. Copy was drawn or photographed on a wax-covered metal plate, and hand or machine ruled. The plate was made in like fashion for an electrotype.

Preparing Type Forms for the Letterpress

These procedures are followed by the letterpress shop after type has been set.

a. Make-up. The hand compositor assembles his hot type and spaces it according to layout (plan) of the job at hand.

b. A proof is taken and read by the proofreaders, who compare it to the original copy. Necessary corrections are made either on the machines or by hand.

c. The form of hot type is locked up in a chase with "furniture" (blocks of wood or metal) and quoins by the lock-up man, often called a "stone man." Figure 2-20 shows a small type form being locked in a chase for letterpress printing. The quoins (wedges)

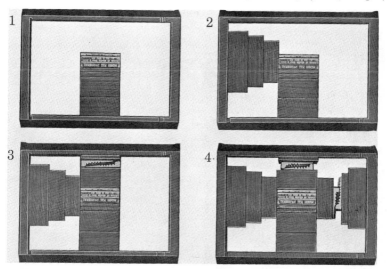

Fig. 2-20. A form is locked in a chase using wood furniture and quoins.

hold the form in place by pressure. Because of innate inaccuracies in the wooden furniture surrounding the form, and sometimes of the printing materials, some printing surfaces may be slightly lower or higher, necessitating makeready ("shimming" up low areas in the impression). Also, the letterpress printer may be plagued by "work-up": i.e., spacing material rising upon the press impression and printing on the paper. The operation above is comparable to "stripping" in offset printing. This includes lock-up and imposition; i.e., the locking up of pages in such a manner that they can be printed 16 or 32 at one time, so that when folded, the 16 or 32 pages "come out right."

　　d. The pressman sets up his press and "makes ready" the work. Certain adjustments are made for handling the sheets on the press. Then, usually, the makeready procedure follows, which consists of allowing for the press pressure required for printing properly. Low areas are built-up so that all parts of the form of type and plates transfer the right amount of ink to the paper. Makeready can be mechanical, as shown in Fig. 2-21 with the 3 M makeready machine. A press proof is fed into the device, and within a few seconds the sheet returns with gradations of rise (adding to thickness from .001 to .004 inches) where more impression is needed for the type to print properly. This eliminates hand-cut tissue

Fig. 2-21. The 3M makeready machine.

paper overlays which delay production. Makeready is often done by cutting out very thin paper on areas marked on a trial sheet. The trial sheet is then buried in the packing of the press. This operation may be a time-consuming job and is not encountered in offset-lithography.

Platen Presses Used in Letterpress Printing. The Chandler and Price Automatic platen press now removed from manufacture, (see Fig. 2-22) has sizes of 10 × 15 and 12 × 18 inches. Top speeds are 4500 and 4000 sheets per hour, respectively. The 10 × 15 will take sheets up to 11 × 17; the 12 × 18 will take sheets up to 13 × 19. Minimum sheet sizes for both are 1⅓ × 3⅜ inches. Impression and line-up of platen and bed are hand-wheel controlled. Small sheets and envelopes may be printed two up.

The Original Heidelberg Platen Press (see Fig. 2-23) is manufactured in 10 × 15 and 12 × 18 inch sizes. Top speed of the former is 5,000 impressions per hour; the latter, 4,000 per hour.

Figure 2-24 illustrates an automatic Kluge Press, size 12 × 18.

Cylinder Presses Used in Letterpress Printing. Figure 2-25 shows a Miehle Vertical letterpress which prints sheets up to about 4,000 per hour. Maximum sheet size is 14 × 20 inches.

Original Heidelberg Cylinder Presses are available in sheet sizes of 15 × 20½, 21 × 28, 21¼ × 30¼ and 22 × 30¼. Presses may be one-color or two-color. Wrap-around relief plates are used on the two-color presses. Zinc, magnesium, copper or Dycril plates are used. Top speed of the 15 × 20½ is 5,000 impressions per hour.

Fig. 2-22. The Chandler-Price automatic plate press.

Fig. 2-23. The Original Heidelberg platen press.

Fig. 2-24. An automatic Kluge press.

Fig. 2-25. A Miehle Vertical letterpress.

Fig. 2-26. A Harris "Wrap-Around" sheet feed press.

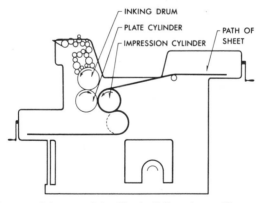

Fig. 2-27. The essential parts of the Harris "Wrap-Around" press are shown in in this schematic diagram.

The Harris "Wrap-Around" sheet-fed letterpress, shown in Fig. 2-26, uses shallow-etched relief plates which are wrapped around the plate cylinder (see diagrammatic sketch). The sheet size is 23 × 30 inches, it is stream fed and attains a speed of 8,000 impressions per hour. Figure 2-27 is a diagrammatic sketch of the Harris "Wrap-Around" sheet-fed letterpress. Note that the inking drum is the same diameter as the plate cylinder.

Rotary Presses Used in Letterpress Printing. Figure 2-28 illustrates a Goss rotary 192-page magazine press which prints from curved electrotypes by letterpress. Note (lower left) that signatures (folded pages) are delivered ready for binding.

Figure 2-29 shows how electrotype plates are attached to the cylinders of rotary letterpress.

Numbering. The serial numbering of each sheet or card is a letterpress process. See Fig. 2-30. Offset printers add "numbering heads" to their offset presses, but inasmuch as the number changes with each sheet, the numbering cannot be placed on an offset blanket. Typographic numbering machines are used on letterpress machines. The numbering head sinks into the machine upon impression, and when it rises again the number is changed. Both frontward and backward machines are in use. Figure 2-31 is a

Fig. 2-28. This pictorial diagram shows the operation of the Goss 192 page magazine press.

Fig. 2-29. An electrotype is being attached to the cylinder of a rotary letterpress.

Fig. 2-30. Serial numbering devices, like those shown here, are used only on letterpress.

Fig. 2-31. A serial numbering head is shown here.

numbering machine of the type used on small offset presses. Note that the digits are curved to match the curve of the press cylinder.

Sign Machines. Often used in department stores, sign ma-

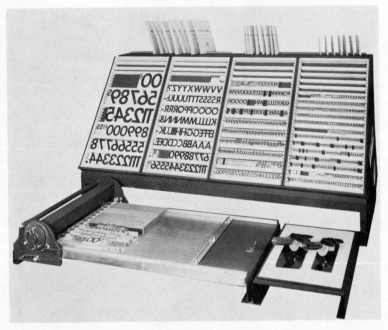

Fig. 2-32. Machines such as this Morgan Line-O-Scribe are often used in department stores for making "in-the-store" signs.

chines use the letterpress process for making one or more signs on thick display board. See Figs. 2-32, 2-33 and 2-34. The Morgan Line-O-Scribe Model shown will print signs up to 14 × 22 inches. Note the metal type above, and the form in the press below. A press adjustment allows thin or thick material to be printed. Forms can be inked in colors with several ink brayers shown at bottom, right. Type from 24 point to 144 point is generally used.

Other Major Processes in the Graphic Arts

Dry Offset. A shallow-etched relief plate transfers the image to a rubber blanket on a cylinder. The press needs no moistening rollers. Millions of printed impressions are gained in this method. Tax stamps and other work used in great quantities are printed by this process.

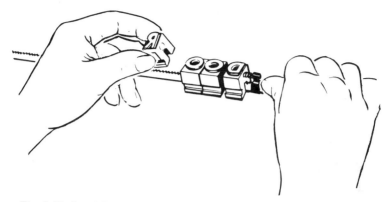

Fig. 2-33. Specially cast type is assembled one letter at a time on a bar.

Flexographic. This process involves the use of rotary (web or roll fed) printing from rubber plates, (see Fig. 2-35) which are usually duplicates of letterpress plates of hard metal. The older name for this process is "aniline" printing. Plates are of various types: two-faced or sticky-back for application to the plate cylinder, plates molded directly to sheets of brass, controlled sheets of rubber with shrink-controlled material in the center of the plate, rubber molded to a fabric-and-rubber backing, and rubber plates molded

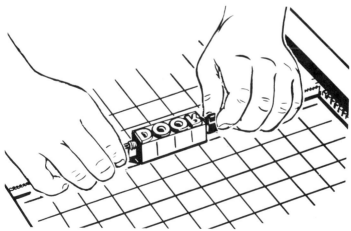

Fig. 2-34. The bar is then placed on the bed of the press. When all copy is assembled, the sign can be printed. (See Fig. 2-32.)

Fig. 2-35. Rubber plates are made in the flexographic process in a device like the one shown here.

in a special mold having a locking ridge on the back. Typical products include office forms, tax stamps, labels, packaging materials, razor blades, and one application includes printing on English walnuts.

Thermography. This process is often referred to as "process engraving" and "raised letter printing." See Fig. 2-36. The sheets are usually delivered directly to a belt which carries them under a cascade of resin-like powder which adheres to the ink. The sheets are then passed through a heater which fuses and raises the ink, thus simulating copperplate or steelplate engraving. Some of the products are wedding invitations, special business and personal stationery, calling cards and greeting cards.

Copperplate engraving and Die Stamping. In this process "lines of type" are cut into a copper or steel plate usually by machine. See Fig. 2-37. The entire surface of the plate is inked on the press, and the surface of the plate is wiped clean by mechanical means. During press impression, the ink leaves the recesses in the plate and adheres to the paper, presenting a raised effect. Products are

Fig. 2-36. Thermography or process engraving uses a resin-like powder to produce a raised letter effect. The one shown here is an ATF offset press in line with a Virkotype thermograph machine (right).

Fig. 2-37. Copperplate engraving uses a steel or copper plate such as the one shown here.

Fig. 2-38. A gravure press is shown here.

usually paper money, stock certificates, postage stamps, society and wedding printing, invitations, name cards, and the like.

Gravure. In this web or sheet-fed process the ink leaves cells which are etched into a cylinder (intaglio) and is printed on the paper at great pressure. See Fig. 2-38. The entire cylindrical plate is inked, but a "doctor" blade on the press scrapes away any ink on the surface of the plate. Both type and illustrations are finely screened. Products include magazines, Sunday newspaper supplements, stamps, mail order catalogs, food and candy wrappers, and foil-printed products.

Screen Process. Often called "Silk Screen," this process uses both hand-cut and photographic screens. The non-image areas are blocked out, and ink is forced through fabric or metal mesh screen with a rubber blade called a squeegee onto the object being printed. Printing is accomplished by hand (see Fig. 2-39) or with a screen process press (see Fig. 2-40). The frame and fabric screen can be made almost any size, even to 12 feet or more. The process prints on almost anything: paper of any thickness, wood, cloth, bottles, and the like. Both line and halftone work can be printed. Products include paper and board too large for conventional presses (over 80 inches), odd-shaped objects, posters, signs, white ink on black paper, radio cabinets, "printed" electrical circuits and cloth book covers.

Fig. 2-39. Screen process printing is often done by hand.

The screen process is important in the printing of textiles, which include shower curtains, tablecloths, napkins, dry goods, draperies and neckties. Printed in long bolts, the material is processed on tables often 300 feet long, in widths from 4 to 6 feet. Movable stops are mounted on rails along two sides of the table to help to register colors. Hand-painted or reinforced photographic screens are generally used. The printing is usually done by two men who move the screen from stop to stop, using the squeegee to print each section.

Wallpaper is traditionally printed from rollers on webs (rolls) of paper. After being "grounded," that is, having a base color printed as a background, a separate roller applies each color of the pattern. Drying is accomplished by blowing hot air on a draped web of the paper. Specialty presses are used, which are often as tall as 12 feet. However, the screen process has lately made inroads into wallpaper manufacturing. Printing is done similarly to that of textiles.

Decalcomania. This process involves the building up to successive layers of ink on base paper to gain a predetermined thickness. Offset-lithography or screen process is generally used. When moistened, the built-up image leaves the paper base and can be affixed to glass, marble, wood, and the like. Typical products include "decals" or "stickers" for adherence to glass.

Photogelatin. Also called "collotype," this process features illustrations carrying no screen pattern found in other processes. An aluminum or Monel metal plate supports a layer of gelatin, and the plate controls the density of the ink. Type is not printed by this process, and press runs usually do not exceed 5,000. Products include art objects, displays, greeting cards, and catalog illustrations.

Paper Ruling. This process uses pens or discs which print or rule

Fig. 2-40. Screen process presses are often used for printing on glass bottles.

Fig. 2-41. Presses like this one are used in printing ruled paper.

lines on paper, usually in a variety of colors. See Fig. 2-41. Usual products are stenographers' notebooks, school tablets, accounting forms, statements and invoices.

Office Copiers and Offset Platemakers

Many devices are used in business and industry to make single or multiple copies of letters, charts and the like, and also offset plates for small duplicators. It is obvious that if one copy is needed it is less expensive to make it on one of these devices than to typewrite, proofread, and correct copy. The devices make copies for a few cents each. These devices can be categorized as:

Electrostatic Printing. New developments allow printing on irregular surfaces, such as sandpaper, plastics, corrugated board; or smoother surfaces, such as glass and ceramic.

A 200-inch stainless steel screen is charged to 1,500 volts. A stencil made with the image area transparent is applied to the screen, and the material to be printed upon is placed behind the screen. The stencil (screen) printing surface "sandwich" is backed with a solid metal plate which has a polarity opposite that of the screen. A dry ink-resin mixture is then brushed into the screen with a rotating brush. The ink-resin particles acquire a charge, and are attracted electro-statically to the rear metal plate. Those particles over the transparent image area are drawn through the screen onto the material being printed. The image is fixed permanently by heat.

Electrostatic Printing—RCA Electrofax. The first step in electrostatic printing is placing a negative charge on the surface of a sheet. Then the sheet receives a latent image from copy through a lens or prism. Iron filings are brushed on the sheet, where positively-charged resin is attracted to the latent image. Heat melts the resin, which is permanently fused to the sheet.

Non-Contact Charged-Grid Printing. The charged grid principle of electrostatic printing involves a metal screen on which a stencil is adhered. A toner passes through the image areas on the screen. Electrons flow between the charged grid and a ground, and carry the toner on the object being printed. The two elements are not in contact.

Xography, providing three-dimensional printing which can be seen without benefit of special reading glasses, is a recent development. A special screen is placed before the film in the process, which divides the picture into many very small vertical "strips." Plates are made in a conventional manner. A special press applies a coating to the printed surface. The screen focuses upon the small "strips" and gives the illusion of depth. Thus far, advertisements specially printed for insertion in magazines, have been the only application of this process.

The Xerography Process. Figures 2-42 and 2-43 illustrate how the popular Xerography process makes plates and copies:

Fig. 2-42. The Xerox offset platemaker.

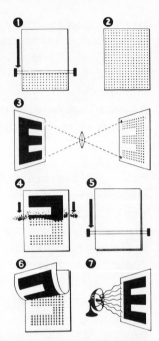

Fig. 2-43. The numbers in this illustration refer to the numbered steps in the text.

1. Surface of specially coated plate is being electrically charged as it passes under wires.
2. Shows coating of plate charged with positive electricity.
3. Copy is projected through lens in camera. Plus marks show projected image with positive charges. Positive charges disappear in areas exposed to light as shown by white space.
4. A negatively charged powder adheres to positively charged image.
5. After powder treatment a sheet of paper is placed over plate and receives positive charge.
6. Positively charged paper attracts powder from plate forming direct positive image.
7. Paper is heated for a few seconds to fuse powder and form permanent print.

The Xerox Model 2400 is so named because it can produce 2400 copies an hour. Copy is placed on a curved platen, and the operator dials the number wanted from one to 499. Size of originals can be up to 8⅞ × 14⁷⁄₁₆ inches.

Fig. 2-44. A Thompson National die-
cutting machine.

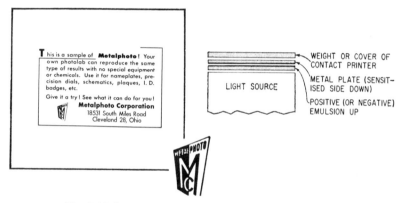

This is a sample of **Metalphoto**! Your
own photolab can reproduce the same
type of results with no special equipment
or chemicals. Use it for nameplates, precision dials, schematics, plaques, I. D.
badges, etc.

Give it a try! See what it can do for you!

Metalphoto Corporation
18531 South Miles Road
Cleveland 28, Ohio

WEIGHT OR COVER OF
CONTACT PRINTER

METAL PLATE (SENSIT-
ISED SIDE DOWN)

POSITIVE (OR NEGATIVE)
EMULSION UP

LIGHT SOURCE

Fig. 2-45. Metalphoto plates are made photographically.

Die-Cutting. This process, basically letterpress, is used to cut out
boxes, displays and the like from paper or paperboard. See
Fig. 2-44. It can be accomplished on both platen and cylinder
presses equipped with a steel plate against which the dies cut.
The "form" is made of a steel cutting rule, usually held in place on
plywood. High dies are used on such small work as labels, and are
not used on printing presses, but on special devices which use
tremendous pressure to drive the die through a "lift" of paper or
board.

Metalphoto Plates consist of anodized aluminum, and carry
images as found on dials, name plates, instruction panels, plaques,
badges, and the like. See Fig. 2-45. Made photographically, the
image is locked in a clear, hard, glass-like anodized layer. No

special skills other than that of photography are required in the manufacture.

Camera Produced Printed Circuits. In the production of printed circuits for electronic computers, exposures are made and negatives are produced on large cameras. The negatives are put in close vacuum contact with laminated plastic boards covered with a thin layer of copper and exposed to a highly intense light source. The boards are then placed in an etching machine which removes the unexposed copper, leaving a complete circuit.

Computers and Typesetting. Some newspapers are handling classified advertisements using a computer. First perforated on tape, the ad lines are fed via Data Phone to a computer which puts them on magnetic tape and sorts them into classified sequence. These are combined with another tape with ads that are continued from the previous day. "Dead" ads are killed. Billing is also prepared. The perforated master tape completes a column of ads in about 50 seconds. The tape is fed into a phototypesetting machine.

Electronic computers have information input, information output, a memory unit for data and instructions, a control unit and a mathematical unit. Input may be in the form of punched cards, punched tape or magnetic tape. The latter can condense several hundred characters to one inch. Tape can then go to a phototypesetting machine for swift composition of lines for offset printing. One device in research stage has the potential of revising the Manhattan telephone book and preparing it for printing in 24 hours.

Computers and Type Composition. Several devices vastly increase the speed of type composition by relieving the operator of keyboard justification (aligning the right-hand margin) and placement of hyphens for word divisions. These machines are applicable to both hot and cold type composition.

The RCA-301 computer accepts punched paper tape and produces a new tape, adding justification (otherwise keyboarded by the Teletypesetter operator). Four additional devices which properly divide words are used: a paper tape reader, punch, on-line printer, and a magnetic tape station. A memory system stores 30,000 word divisions following a dictionary, or a computer system may be used based on logic. The device can correct and justify final tape to fill a 21-inch newspaper column in 17 seconds.

The IBM 1620 computer justifies lines, hyphenates words and produces a new tape from the first tape which does not perform this work. The device can produce 4,000 hyphenated and justified 11-pica lines per hour.

The several computers can save as much as 50% of machine operator labor, because they:

1. "Read" unjustified punched paper tape.
2. Hyphenate (divide words) correctly.
3. Justify the type lines (with no loose or tight lines).
4. Make a new tape to operate linecasting machines.

In addition, the computer can handle the entire operation, including the making of corrections in hot metal or on film, and handle galleys or pages for adding corrections, divide the galleys into pages, and strip film into individual pages.

The Intertype Digital Computers. These devices "read" perforated tape, as from a Teletypesetter keyboard, which does not contain type justification codes or hypenations for word divisions. The computers divide the words and justify the lines automatically. See Fig. 2-46.

Fig. 2-46. The Harris-Intertype computer is used in typesetting; it divides words and justifies lines automatically.

One model hyphenates by searching a stored memory of over 10,000 "except" words, as well as using rules and logic of word division. Another model hyphenates through rules only. A third computer stops when a word is to be divided, and the decision is made by a monitor employee. The resultant tapes from the computers activate hot metal or photographic typesetters.

The Photon 900 Computer Phototypesetter (Zip Model) can produce 150 eight-inch lines per minute on film or on paper. The series of three devices uses a typewriter which produces tape, without benefit of proper spacing and justification. The system produces

✕	Defective letter	⊙	Colon	no ¶	No paragraph
⊥	Push down space	;/	Semicolon	wf.	Wrong font letter
ꓯ	Turn over	ꝟ	Apostrophe	stet.	Let it stand
℮	Take out	ꝟ"	Quotation	tr.	Transpose
⋀	Insert at this point	-/	Hyphen	Caps.	Capitals
✓	Space evenly	///	Straighten lines	S.C.	Small capitals
✳	Insert space	⊏	Move over	l.c.	Lower-case letter
‿	Less space	☐	Em quad space	ital.	Italic
⌒	Close up entirely	⌐¹	One-em dash	Rom.	Roman letter
⊙	Period	⌐²	Two-em dash	(?)	Verify
,/	Comma	₰	Make paragraph	◯	Spell out

Printing Educates

tr   Even if none of these boys should ever follow the craft   e/x
⊥   of the printer in years to come/ the education that they   ,/
wf   get in this department will prove of real value in prac-
℮   tical life, whatever /life of occpation or profession they   n/u
ꝯ   may later choose. The printing trade isa thoroughly prac-   #
     tical school of education in itself//It provides practical   °/Cap.
     lessons in the principles of language, composition, punc-
     tuation, and other everyday exercises, in addition to the   ⌒
     vast fund of general knowledge which passes under the
l.c.   Worker's observation.   ---An excerpt from an editorial
     in the <u>Portland Press Herald.</u> ⎫⎦ —*ital.*

Fig. 2-47. Standard proofreader's marks.

any combination of 264 characters in sizes from 6 to 14 point.

The Linotron accepts tape from IBM, RCA, Univac or Honeywell computers and provides the "print out" on film or paper, in sizes from 5 to 18 point from character grids with 256 characters. The speed ranges from 1,100 characters per *second* for 5 point to 250 characters per *second* for 18 point.

The Star Autojustifier is not a computer, but receives unjustified tape and produces from it justified tape in booklength lines. Word divisions are not machine produced.

Reading Machines. Both typewriter and hand-written manuscript can be "read" and converted to tape to operate hot and cold typesetting machines. The Sylvania devices can read up to 2,500 characters per *second.* Each character is scanned electronically 16 times vertically and 20 times horizontally. The Farrington Scanner scans horizontally three times and vertically six times.

The Electronic Retina Character Reader, which views constantly rather than intermittantly, can read printed or typewritten copy at 2,400 characters per second and produce punched paper type at 900 words per minute. The remaining words are stored on magnetic tape until the device producing the tape for composing machines can catch up.

More than one hundred computers manufactured by about a dozen manufacturers are now installed in printing plants. Among those presently in use are:

IBM 1620	Intertype
IBM 1400	Control Data 8080
IBM 709/7090	Fairchild Comp-Set
Linasec	Honeywell
Computographic	Digital Equipment PDP
RCA 301	NCR 315
RCA 30	Burroughs 280

Proofreaders' Marks

Figure 2-47 illustrates the standard proofreaders' marks used to indicate corrections. These symbols apply to corrections made in either hot or cold type in any of the printing processes.

Review Questions

Match the process at the right with the basic method at the left:

1. Blind stamping	a. Relief surfaces
2. Die Cutting	b. Plane surfaces
3. Dry Offset	c. Sunken surfaces
4. Embossing	d. Stencil
5. Gold leaf stamping	e. Electrostatic
6. Thermography	f. Electrochemical
7. Decalcomania	
8. Offset	
9. Photogelatin	
10. Copperplate engraving	
11. Gravure	
12. Die stamping	
13. Screen process	
14. Xerography	
15. Thermofax	

Match the press name at the left with the type of press at the right:

16. Chandler and Price	a. Platen
17. Kluge	b. Cylinder
18. Heidelberg	c. Rotary
19. Miehle Vertical	
20. Harris Wrap-Around	
21. Goss	

List four kinds of hot type compositions:

22. _____
23. _____
24. _____
25. _____

Name four types of photoengravings:

26. _____
27. _____
28. _____
29. _____

Name four types of duplicate letterpress plates:

30. _____
31. _____
32. _____
33. _____
34. Make-up in letterpress is called _____ in offset.
35. A doctor blade is used on a _____ press.
36. The most likely process used for printing on bottles is _____ .
37. Decalcomania may be printed by _____ or _____ .
38. Printing may be done without contact with the object being printed by the _____ process.
39. Printed electrical circuits may be produced by the _____ and _____ process.
40. The offset process is older than letterpress. True or False?
41. The last 50 years has seen more technological progress than the preceding 400 years. True or False?
42. Offset presses print one sheet for every two revolutions of the cylinder. True or False?
43. Powderless etching requires four acid bites. True or False?
44. The photopolymer plate is called Dycril. True or False?
45. The Scan-a-Sizer makes only halftone plates. True or False?
46. Makeready in letterpress can be accomplished mechanically. True or False?
47. Serial numbering can be done on an offset press blanket. True or False?
48. Dry offset uses no moistening press rollers. True or False?
49. Flexographic presses use rubber plates. True or False?
50. Thermography can be done by either letterpress or offset. True or False?
51. The photogelatin process uses a screen on halftones. True or False?
52. The Gestafax device makes mimeograph stencils and offset plates. True or False?
53. The average number of employees in U.S. printing shops is:

a. 17	c. 37
b. 27	d. 47

CHAPTER 3

Copy Preparation for Offset Printing

What does the term "copy" mean in offset-lithography? What kinds of copy are needed? What devices are needed to create the copy? How many methods can be used? What techniques are involved?

When copy* is photographed for offset printing, the resultant negative or positive film is used to make a press plate, which is placed on an offset press. Type may be set by hand or by machine (as in letterpress), and one proof pulled for use in making an offset plate. However, a great trend exists to accomplish all this work without benefit of hot type devices. Inking pens, paste pot and scissors, often take the place of the letterpress printers' type, leads and slugs, rules and photoengravings. This chapter will acquaint you with the methods and procedures used in this work.

Typographic Layout

Production of original printed matter by the offset process usually begins with a *layout,* or plan of the work, created by an artist or layout man. The layout man usually receives the reading matter in typewritten form, along with glossy photographs, line drawings or other artwork. He studies the material received and notes the customer's preferences for page size, kinds and sizes of type, final sizes and treatment of photographs or other artwork, colors of ink,

*The term "copy" or "camera copy" as it is used in offset-lithography means something to be photographed for the purpose of making offset plates from which duplicate copies are produced.

as well as any other preferences the customer may have. He may make several rough sketches for approval by his superior or the customer. He may, however, be permitted to proceed with the work on his own initiative.

After these initial steps, the layout man prepares his manuscript and artwork. He specifies type sizes and typefaces for composition. The artwork is marked for size and keyed for position in the completed job. The final assembly of the two will then be ready for the camera and ultimate completion of the job. (This final assembly of reading matter and artwork for the printer is called a *mechanical.*) *Accuracy is of prime importance:* Type must fit and photograph reductions must fit perfectly.

The layout man may choose to use proofs (also called proof-press prints). These proofs may be hand-set, machine-set or both. The type may be set "in-house" or obtained from a composition house. That is, the work may be done in the composition department of the offset printer or it may be obtained from a compositor who supplies reproduction proofs to offset printers (or type to letterpress printers). Another alternative is to use one of the many available cold type devices for composing type. Cold type is usually done in the offset printer's plant, but it too may be obtained from a composition house.

Photographs. It is usually desirable to *crop* photographs; that is, to indicate by marks (placed on the mounting material or in the margins of the photograph) the limits of the area to be reproduced on the finished page.

It is usually desirable to provide photographs which are larger than or at least the same size as the picture which will appear in the finished job of offset printing. This is also true of any artwork other than photographs. See Fig. 3-1.

Artwork. Original drawings, paintings, charts, graphs and the like come under the general heading of artwork. This material is often cropped in the same way as photographs.

Figuring Copy Reductions and Enlargements. Reductions and enlargements of photographs and artwork may be figured by three methods: The diagonal line method, by a formula, and by proportional scales and rules.

See Fig. 3-2. The diagonal line method:
1. Draw a rectangle ABCD (the original size of the copy)
2. Draw a diagonal line from the point C through point B to point F.
3. Measure the known width on the horizontal line CG.

Fig. 3-1. The lines shown here in the margins of this halftone are called crop marks. They indicate the limits of the illustration as it will appear in the finished job.

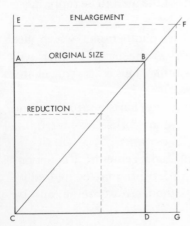

Fig. 3-2. The diagonal method of figuring reductions and enlargements is one of three possible methods.

4. Draw a vertical line to point F and then a horizontal line across to point E.

The above computes the height of an illustration when the width is known. To compute the width of an illustration when the height is known, the measurement is made on the vertical line and a horizontal line is drawn across to point F and then down to point G. Either an enlargement or reduction may be computed by this method.

The formula method:

Any reduction or enlargement may be computed by the following formula:

$$\frac{OW}{OH} = \frac{NW}{NH}$$

OW—Original width   NW—New width
OH—Original height   NH—New height

An example: An area four inches wide and six inches high is available for an illustration and the artist wants to draw the original eight inches wide. How high should the original be so that the copy could be reduced to fit into the available space?

$$\frac{OW}{OH} = \frac{NW}{NH}$$

$$\frac{4}{6} = \frac{8}{NH}$$

Cross-multiply

$$4NH = 6 \times 8$$

$$NH = \frac{6 \times 8}{4}$$

$$NH = \frac{48}{4}$$

NH = 12 inches, the height of the illustration

Proportional Scale Method. Several types of scales for finding proportional enlargements or reductions are available. One type

Fig. 3-3. This is one of the many types of proportional scales available. The problem given in the text is illustrated here.

is shown in Fig. 3-3. A sample problem solved by the scale as follows:

Artwork is five inches wide, to be enlarged to 10¾ inches:

1. Place 5″ on inner circle at point 10¾″ on outer circle.
2. Length of artwork is 4 inches. Find 4 inches on inner circle, which aligns with 8³⁄₁₆ inches on outer circle—which indicates the proportional depth of the artwork when enlarged.
3. The percentage of original size (enlargement), see arrow, is 215%. This is valuable information for the camera man.

Wax Coaters. To hasten the application of proofs on artwork, paste-up men often use wax coaters. One pass through the device coats the work so it can be affixed. Up to 90% of time is eliminated over the paper cement method. Excess cement, of course, need not be removed from the artwork. On the VariTyper Striped Adhesive Wax Coater, shown in Fig. 3-5, the roller width is 12 inches, and pieces as small as a half-inch square can be coated.

Fig. 3-4. Overlays are used to prepare copy for color printing. Register marks are used to position the second color.

Fig. 3-5. The wax coating prepares the back of illustrations so that they can be readily affixed to paste-ups.

Copy Preparation for Office Forms

Billions of office forms are produced by offset each year. Offset printing does not curl the ruled sheets which is often the case with letterpress. The letterpress rules (lines) indent the paper, causing a curl. Crossrules also look better when a form is printed by offset, because space does not occur where rules cross as it usually does in letterpress.

Forms to be printed by offset may be prepared in several ways. When the work is composed in hot type, it is customary to set all horizontal rules, pull a reproduction proof, and draw in the vertical rules with India ink on the proof. Vertical rules may be scribed on the negative rather than on the proof. Either method requires a drawing board, T-square, India ink and fine ruling pen.

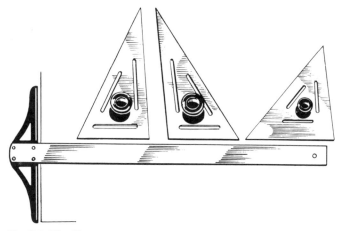

Fig. 3-6. The T-square and triangles may be used in ruling forms for offset-lithographic reproduction.

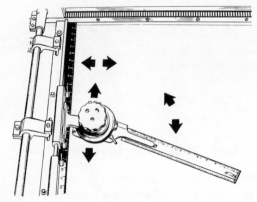

Fig. 3-7. The rotary angle T-square is often used to rule forms.

See Figs. 3-6 to 3-12. The first is often preferable, because if an error is made in ruling, one needs only begin again on another reproduction proof. However, if the negative is ruined, a new negative must be made, which involves expensive camera work.

Cold Type Forms Machines. Many forms are composed in actual size or for reduction on the camera using special "typewriter-like" composing machines. For example, the VariTyper 660 F machine may contain various styles of type in 6, 7, 8, 9, 10 and 12 point sizes. Type sizes are readily changed on the machine. In addition, segments are added to the VariTyper fonts of "type" which can automatically "rule" the copy paper with various widths and styles of lines. A "forms machine" is illustrated in Chapter 4.

Reproduction Proofs of Forms. Reproduction proofs are sold to offset printers in "kits" providing copy of form headings, bodies and body notes. Over 5,000 combinations make camera-ready copy available, thus eliminating a considerable amount of hot or cold type composition.

In addition to the VariTyper, other cold type machines provide paper prints by photographic means.

Pre-Printed Guideline Sheets. When lines of type are pasted-up to be photographed, the make-up man may use pre-printed forms as a base. Printed in a non-photographable light

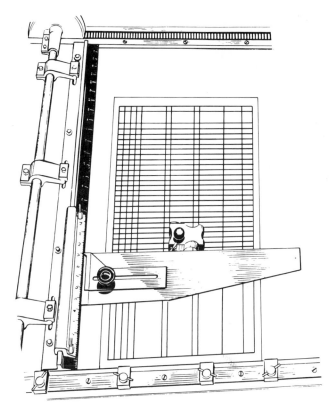

Fig. 3-8. The Jet Scriber is another tool for ruling forms.

Fig. 3-9. A close-up view of the stylus holder from the Jet Scriber is shown here.

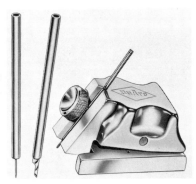

Fig. 3-10. The Paraliner line-up table is another tool used in ruling forms.

Fig. 3-11. The Hamilton Formliner uses a light under the circular area shown. This device is used in scribing lines on negatives.

Fig. 3-12. The handwheels on the Hamilton Formliner allow the rule to be moved in regular increments.

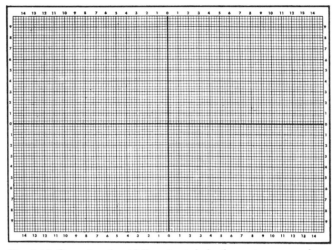

Fig. 3-13. Pre-printed guideline sheets help the paste-up man keep pages uniform in size.

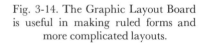

Fig. 3-14. The Graphic Layout Board is useful in making ruled forms and more complicated layouts.

blue ink, these forms insure that all pages will be the same size in the finished work. See Figs. 3-13, 3-14.

Projected Layout Guides. A substitute for the blue-lined sheet consists of a small positive print mounted overhead, and projected on a blank sheet of paper below. The paste-up man affixes reproduction proofs, typewritten materials and any line illustrations in accordance with the projected outlines. This device, called the

Fig. 3-15. The Optaliner projects outlines onto the layout sheet to provide guidelines.

"Optaliner," is invaluable when hundreds of pages are to be pasted up for camera work prior to offset printing. See Fig. 3-15.

Preprinted Artwork

The layout man may purchase a great amount of artist-drawn and printed illustrations. This material, especially for advertising printing, is cut from catalogs and pasted along with type matter.

Preprinted Graph and Chart Material. The offset printer may purchase, from many sources, a variety of preprinted artwork on paper or plastic material which may have an adhesive backing for instant application to existing artwork, or for providing original artwork. See Figs. 3-16 to 3-18.

Adhesive-backed transparent sheets, which contain type, arrows, shading media, bolts, nuts, springs, borders, ornaments and electronic symbols are also available. See Fig. 3-19. The images are cut from a backing sheet with knife or layout needle, placed on artwork and rubbed. Heat resistant material is available (for duplication in "hot" copymakers) and matte finish which can be drawn upon. See Fig. 3-20.

In addition to the "clip books" (art books) mentioned, "Modular" artwork is available. Modular art allows a selection

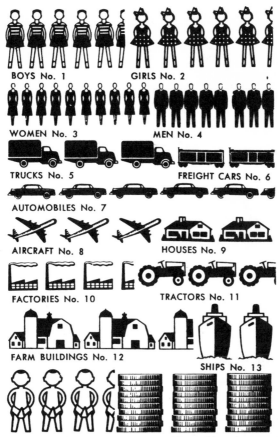

BOYS No. 1   GIRLS No. 2

WOMEN No. 3   MEN No. 4

TRUCKS No. 5   FREIGHT CARS No. 6

AUTOMOBILES No. 7

AIRCRAFT No. 8   HOUSES No. 9

FACTORIES No. 10   TRACTORS No. 11

FARM BUILDINGS No. 12

SHIPS No. 13

Fig. 3-16. Pre-printed artwork may be used in making charts and graphs.

Fig. 3-17. Chart-Pak pressure sensitive tapes are handy for making bar charts and graphs.

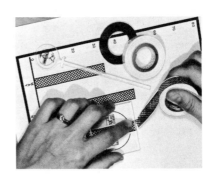

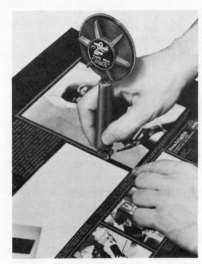

Fig. 3-18. The Brady Tape-Pen applies copy tape to artwork.

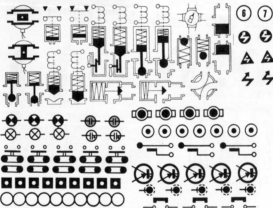

Fig. 3-19. Pre-printed symbols for preparing schematic drawings are available to the paste-up artist.

of heads looking left or right, and legs, arms and bodies in various positions. See Fig. 3-21.

Colored and designed pre-printed materials are available from many sources. Examples include four-color process work, often found on the front (or cover) page of folders or booklets, stock certificates and guarantees, already printed except for the type matter, envelopes of the same kind, and Christmas cards for imprinting.

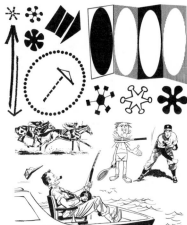

Fig. 3-20. Clip-books of ready-made art are available. These are often used in advertising.

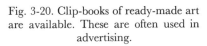

Fig. 3-21. Artype's modular art can be used for making figures in various positions.

Graph-Making Typewriter. The Siemag (West German) typewriter features special characters which produce designs for bar charts or graphs. Capital letters are available as shown in Fig. 3-22. An example of a bar chart made on the Siemag typewriter with a carbon ribbon attachment is shown in Fig. 3-22. A considerable number of designs are possible by combining characters.

Shading Media. Shading media can be applied to artwork by the artist or layout man. They include:

1. Pre-printed designs on adhesive sheets bearing many shaded or stippled images. The sheets are laid on the areas of the artwork

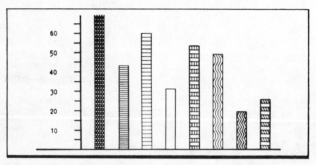

Fig. 3-22. The Siemag typewriter is specially designed for making bar charts and graphs. (*Top*) The keyboard of the Siemag typewriter is shown. (*Bottom*) This bar graph was made on the Siemag typewriter.

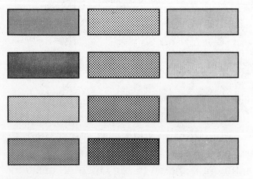

Fig. 3-23. Some of the many available patterns of shading media are shown here.

to be treated, rubbed slightly for adherence, then cut out with a knife blade and the excess pulled away. A thorough rubbing with a blunt instrument makes the shaded area adhere firmly to the work. See Fig. 3-23.

2. Drawing boards on which the surface is partly in relief and partly depressed, so a drawing is created which is made up of small black surfaces separated by white areas. When all the coating is scratched away, pure white remains. See Figs. 3-24, 3-25.

3. Chemically-treated single and double tone white board allows an artist to secure one or two kinds of shading in a drawing. The drawing is first pencilled, and then inked. A fluid developer is then applied with a pen or brush to the areas where the dark tone is wanted. The light tone is then applied to complete the shading in two different shades. See Fig. 3-26.

"Instantex" consists of specially-printed sheets of dry transfer

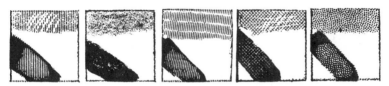

Fig. 3-24. Ross drawing board shading.

Fig. 3-25. Scratchboard shading.

Fig. 3-26. Craftint Double-Tone board permits chemical shading.

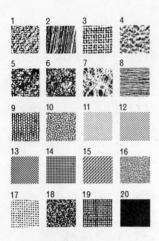

Fig. 3-27. Instantex is available in many patterns.

Fig. 3-28. Rubbing transfers the Instantex design to the artwork.

Fig. 3-29. Some samples of Instantex are shown here in use.

Fig. 3-30. When two colors are to be used the basic drawing is made first.

Fig. 3-31. The color is added on an overlay.

textures, tints, stipples and solid black. To apply the shading to artwork, the sheet is placed over it and a stylus, pencil or ball point pen is rubbed over the area to be treated. Rubbing transfers the design to the original artwork. See Figs. 3-27 through 3-29.

Shading Media for Colors. Figures 3-30 and 3-31 illustrate a drawing to which shading has been applied, and a piece of clear acetate to which shading material has been added to provide a second color.

In making the latter, a piece of clear acetate was placed over the drawing, and a solid (not shaded) medium was placed over the drawing, certain areas cut out, and reproduction proofs of hot type cut apart to provide curved lines as shown.

Illustration Medium. Transparent plastic films which bear removable deposits of pigments are available under trade names of Solotone, Colotone, Transopaque, and Bourges.

Solotone changes the contrast of black and white. Colotone is used in various colors to aid in color reproduction. Transopaque consists of overlay films bearing a transparent coating which is removable, and used to introduce solid color effects in conjunction with line originals. The color sheets consist of 12 basic colors, ranging from 10% to 100% in halftone value.

No airbrush or high skill is needed to phantom photographs since Solotone plastic sheets are available in five values of "gray." See Fig. 3-32.

A shows the original photograph.

B shows the photograph over which a 50% white overlay has been placed.

C shows the coating on the overlay removed with a stylus (lower right). Note how the background has been "phantomed" out.

D shows the complete work, ready for the camera. The photograph is uninjured and can be used again for other purposes when the overlay is removed.

When a dark area is to be emphasized, white Solotone is used. To emphasize a light area, a gray Solotone sheet is used.

Kits are useful in the preparation of pre-separated full-color process copy. A key drawing or high-contrast photography may be used. The coated plastic sheet of yellow is fastened with tape

Fig. 3-32. Illustration media like Solotone are used to drop out (or phantom) the background of photographs.

at the left of the drawing, the red is fastened at the top, and the blue at the right, so they can be interchanged while being worked upon.

Starting with the yellow transparent sheet over the black copy, unwanted color is removed with a stylus. A color remover liquid is used with cotton to remove large areas of color. The red and the blue are handled similarly. Stronger color may be added with modeling pencils, or with liquid color.

Each color sheet of plastic is photographed separately with the correct color filter in the camera. This art procedure is much less expensive than making color separations.

"Foto-Chase" makeup is an ATF development. See Fig. 3-33. Photographically-set copy is mounted on extremely lightweight plastic about ⁵⁄₁₆ in. thick, and a special cutter is used to make desired widths and lengths. Column rules are provided in various thicknesses. Make-up of pages needing periodic revision (classified

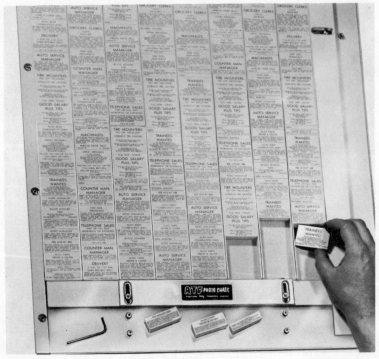

Fig. 3-33. Foto-Chase make-up is used for making up pages that need periodic revision, like classified advertisements.

advertisements, catalogs, and the like) can be accomplished faster than when hot-metal slugs are used. Pages are made up in a "Foto-Chase" with the right-reading material for making negatives for printing by any process.

Review

Name five items needed from the customer in the preparation of the copy for a job of offset printing:

1. _____
2. _____
3. _____
4. _____
5. _____

By what three methods can reduction proportion be determined?

6. _____

7. _____

8. _____

Aids for offset paste-up preparation include:

9. _____

10. _____

Name three illustrative materials which aid copy preparation for offset printing:

11. _____

12. _____

13. _____

Name three devices which allow easy shading of artwork:

14. _____

15. _____

16. _____

17. What device is used to indicate the position of colors? _____

18. The _____ machine not only types letters but also rules lines.

19. Phantom artwork eliminates airbrush work when _____ materials are used.

20. Full color may be prepared when _____ color kits are used.

21. What material is available to offset printers for aiding in the preparation of office forms? _____

22. "Mark up" involves the type specifications written on the manuscript or copy. True or false?

23. Hot type is often used for offset printing. True or false?

24. Cropping of photos means indicating by lines the area to be used. True or false?

25. Rules (lines) do not indent the paper, causing a curl in the paper, in letterpress printing. True or false?

CHAPTER 4

Cold type

How is typesetting divided into groups? What is the difference between cold type and hot type? What are the advantages of each? How is the typewriter used for offset? Which kind of ribbon is best? What are the names of the many kinds of cold type devices?

Typesetting is often divided into two groups: cold type and hot metal. Hot metal typesetting includes all of the several methods of type in which metal is directly involved in producing the text to be printed: hand set, Ludlow Typograph, Linotype, Intertype and Monotype are all classified as hot type methods of typesetting. Cold type is the second major category. The term cold type arose in the language of the printing crafts to fill the need for a term which would cover the methods of typesetting which do not involve molten metal (as in machine set type) or cold metal (as in hand set type).

Many offset printers look to hot type methods to provide prints called "reproduction proofs" of type for display (large letters) and for text (small letters). They either operate what is known as a "combination" shop, that is, they provide both letterpress and offset printing; or they buy reproduction proofs from "trade composition" houses which supply reproduction proofs or hot-cast metal forms to printers who do not choose to operate composing rooms for typesetting.

Figure 4-1 illustrates a typical reproduction proof press. After type has been composed by hand from type cases, usually combined with slug lines cast on Linotype or Intertype machines, and

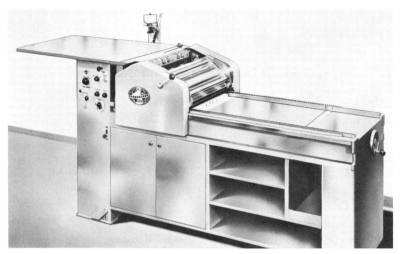

Fig. 4-1. The Vandercook Universal III proof press; proofs from a press like the one shown here are used as camera copy in offset printing.

spaced properly into pages or other forms, the proof press operator carefully pulls a number of proofs on the machine. When the ink has dried, the reproduction proofs are assembled to provide camera-ready copy and are photographed for offset printing.

Figure 4-2 illustrates letters "st" greatly enlarged from the 12-point type size. The letters on the left show how ink could be squeezed out by the letterpress process on the proof press. The letters on the right show an improved product for offset printers'

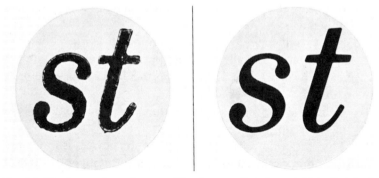

Fig. 4-2. The letters shown here are 12 point, greatly enlarged. Note that the ink in the letterpress letters (left) is squeezed out.

copy as enlarged on a cold type device, in this instance, the Inter-type Fotosetter.

A Contrast between Cold and Hot Type

Cold type composition has certain advantages over hot-metal type composition:

1. Sizes of type can often be varied using only one "font" of film fonts.
2. Longer lines can be set—in hot-metal, the usual line is five inches long; longer lines must be "butted," which results in double priced typesetting.
3. Tabular (columns of figures) matter can usually be produced faster and cheaper than by hot-metal methods.
4. Very often the cold type device is less expensive than a comparable hot type device.
5. Symbols and schematics can be composed by cold type.
6. Cold type devices have means for distorting, slanting, bouncing, condensing, expanding, outlining, enlarging, reducing, and even transforming a straight line into a complete circle.
7. Some cold type devices are "office machines" or "table top" devices—usually no heavy machinery is used as in hot type methods.
8. No heavy lifting (such as linotype magazines and pigs of metal) is required which enables women to operate cold type devices.
9. Many cold type devices are more easily learned than hot type devices. Usually no long apprenticeship is required to learn the operation, which results in a lower hour cost to the printer.
10. Cold type devices require one-third the space that hot type methods do.
11. The cost of power to operate cold type devices is much less than that required to keep metal pots at temperatures over 535 degress. Several cold type devices use only a 40-watt lamp.

12. Film storage is less expensive and takes less space than hot type forms. Only negatives need be stored when cold type devices are used.

13. Large cabinets, cases of type, spacing materials and imposing tables are not necessary when cold type means are used.

14. No large investment in type metal is necessary with cold type methods.

15. No reproduction proof press is needed in cold type operations.

16. White space is not "composed" with cold type machines. It is composed in hot type methods.

Hot type, however, has certain advantages over cold type. The advantages include the ease of making changes (particularly the respacing of lines), the assurance that the "fit" of type characters is correct, the advantage of an enormous number of type face designs in hot metal, and, in some instances, better type designs. For printing jobs requiring numbering, die cutting and perforating, the letterpress process with hot type is very often preferable.

Growth of Cold Type Processes

Factors responsible for the growth of cold type composition are:

1. *Cost.* The cost of reproduction (photographable) proofs from hot type for use in offset-lithography brought about the obvious question from offset printers, buyers of offset printing, letterpress shops installing offset equipment, and equipment manufacturers:

"Why must we prepare type forms permitting up to 50,000 letterpress impressions when the offset printer needs only a few copies to photograph? Could a less expensive method be used?"

The obvious answer is yes.

2. *Expendiency.* The rise of "do-it-yourself" offset-lithography by organizations, schools, businesses, professions, churches, and governmental agencies has been great. In addition to "stretching the budget," some of these activities enjoy deliveries of printed matter "when they want it." They are not dependent upon regular printers for delivery.

This is particularly important on close-deadline work and work of a confidential nature.

3. *Acceptance of inferior quality of printing.* Although many private shops produce excellent work comparable to commercial shops, in some instances management can accept inferior work at a saving in cost.

4. *Installation of offset equipment by "letter shops."* Letter shops, once using mimeograph-type equipment, added the offset process with light-weight machinery to expand and broaden their production, and to provide halftone and line illustrations.

5. Availability of simpler, relatively inexpensive offset machinery.

When office-type devices were available for almost all offset operations, aggressive salesmanship increased the growth of private offset shops, as well as installation in letterpress shops which wanted a second process. These devices included:

a. Special typewriters with proportional spacing simulating hot type.

b. Special typewriters allowing the right-hand margin to be aligned.

c. Small offset presses.

d. Small office-type folding machines, paper drills, and paper cutters.

e. Headline paper types and devices for making headline type faces by photography.

f. Simple, more direct means of making plates, and the increasing number of "trade" offset platemakers.

g. Typing directly on offset press "masters."

Kinds of Cold Type Devices

The methods, equipment, devices and procedures for producing a single copy of text (small) type for reproduction by offset printing are many and varied. They include typewriters, proportional spacing typewriters and certain accessories, an automatic justifying typewriter, and cold type composition machines which are the same, comparable to, or better than, the type designs of hot type.

The devices for providing display (large) type include manipu-

Fig. 4-3. The IBM Selectric has a standard typewriter keyboard.

Fig. 4-4. A single sphere-shaped element moves across the paper on a carriage for placing characters.

lated lettering machines, paper and acetate type fonts, photographic line-composers, modification devices, and sequential card cameras.

Other cold type machines provide both display and text type, and are capable of producing a comparable quality to that of hot type processes.

Typewriters for Strike-On Cold Type Composition (Typewriters). The IBM Selectric Typewriter, Fig. 4-3, features changeable typefaces on a sphere-shaped element which moves from left to right across the paper which remains stationary. There is no conventional carriage, Fig. 4-4. Figure 4-5 illustrates the IBM spherical element which contains the usual characters. Arrows indicate how the element moves to place the letter impressions on the paper. The element can be quickly substituted for other elements containing different type styles. Figure 4-6 shows a few of

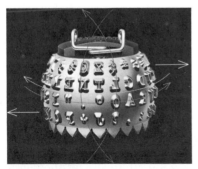

12 pt. Pyramid Medium
11 pt. Univers Bold
11 pt. Univers Medium
10 pt. Press Roman Italic
10 pt. Pyramid Medium
10 pt. Aldine Roman Italic
8 pt. Pyramid Medium
8 pt. Pyramid Italic
8 pt. Aldine Roman Medium
8 pt. Bodoni Book Medium
8 pt. Aldine Roman Italic

Fig. 4-5. This single sphere-shaped element of the IBM Selectric contains all the usual typewriter characters.

Fig. 4-6. A few samples of the many type faces and sizes available for the IBM Selectric typewriter.

3	4	5	6	7	8	9
i ;	I (	J	P y	B	A Y	M
j '	f)	a	S *	C	D w	W
l '	r !	c	b †	E	G ¾	m
. -	s /	e	d $	F	H ½	
,	t	g	h +	L	K &	
	:	v	k =	T	N %	
		z	n]	Z	O @	
		?	o		Q ¼	
		[	p		R –	

Fig. 4-7. The IBM Selectric Composer typewriter. Margins are automatically justified on second typing.

Fig. 4-8. IBM type is designed in a nine-unit system that permits seven different letter widths.

the type faces available for the Selectric in fonts from 7 points through 12 points.

The IBM Selectric Composer, Fig. 4-7, allows automatic justification of the right-hand margin with a retyping. Characters for these IBM machines are proportionately spaced as shown in Fig. 4-8. The spherical element contains 88 characters which approximates the character fitting of hot type. Leading between lines is dialed from 5 to 20 points.

The IBM Magnetic Tape "Selectric" Composer, Fig. 4-9, is a more sophisticated series of devices including one or more recorders on which copy is typed without regard to justification. The copy is first stored on magnetic tape which holds about 4000 words. A "tape reader" reads the magnetic tape at 20 characters per second. The operator sets up the control console (Fig. 4-9) and the Composer reads the tape automatically to produce camera ready copy at speeds up to 14 characters per second with automatic justification.

The "one-time" carbon ribbon makes a better impression than either cotton or silk ribbons. Most reproduction typewriters are equipped for large rolls of "one-time" carbon ribbon.

All characters are the same "set width" on the VariTyper Model 230. The right-hand margin is automatically justified with a second keyboarding of the line. See Fig. 4-10.

Regular typewriters are also used to prepare offset copy. For

Fig. 4-9. The IBM Magnetic Tape Selectric Composer. Recording units are shown in the background with the typewriters used to type rough copy which is stored on magnetic tape. On the left in the foreground is the tape reader, and on the right is the control console which produces camera ready copy from the tape.

Fig. 4-10. The VariTyper automatically justifies copy on the second typing.

Fig. 4-11. Many faces are available for the Remington electric typewriter.

example, the Remington electric, Fig. 4-11, has a one-time carbon ribbon for offset copy, and a regular fabric ribbon for other work. Only one type face is available on any one machine, but there is a large selection of typefaces from which to choose.

INTERNATIONAL   Ç ` ^ ¿ ~ ′ ¨

MATHEMATICAL   √ ∫ > Σ π ∞ < ≈

POPULAR GREEK   β δ λ σ α Υ θ Π

ENGINEERING   º ± ³ [π ÷ ²]

MEDICAL   ろ Ə ℳ ℞ ⅔ fl ℞ ā

Fig. 4-12. The SCM electric has provisions for special symbols which are readily changed on the typewriter.

Fig. 4-13. The SCM "250" is one of the smaller electrics with a full keyboard.

Special-purpose typewriters have been introduced to eliminate tedious drawing or pasting special characters on copy. The SCM Electric Machine 250 features changeable type in sets of eight which can be snapped on type bar units. Characters include symbols for mathematical, engineering and medical work, and Greek characters. See Figs. 4-12 and 4-13.

Typewriter Accessories. The "Doublebold" device, used on IBM typewriters allows an additional "type font," that of bold

DOUBLEBOLD will add a versatility to the office typewriter heretofore unmatched by anything less than a combination of expensive composing machines.

Fig. 4-14. Typewriter attachments are used to adjust the size, weight or position of characters on typewriter copy. The Doublebold attachment is used to create boldface typewriter copy.

Fig. 4-15. *Justi-Gage* is used in calculating the number of spaces needed to justify typewriter copy on the second typing.

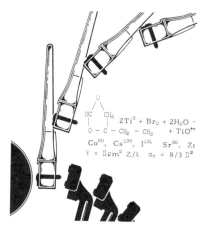

Fig. 4-16. Typit is shown in operation.

capitals and lowercase characters. To achieve the effect, two levers are flipped, and the words are retyped. See Fig. 4-14.

The Marginator is an attachment which can be used on various typewriters. This device makes possible the alignment of the right hand margin to simulate hot type composition. In the operation, the typist overlays the right-hand margin of the draft copy with a transparent scale, and visually selects a satisfactory column width, noting indicator settings marked on a scale. The Marginator is then set to the column width selected, and the operator sets the indicator for each line typed. The device extends or condenses each line to the required width.

The Fototype Justi-Gage is a plastic scale calibrated in IBM proportionately-spaced electric typewriter units. See Fig. 4-15. It has a self-adhesive back which keeps it mounted in position on the typewriter without clips or bolts. A built-in magnifier allows the typist to see at a glance exactly how many unit spaces are left over at the end of each line to guide in re-typing to align the right-hand margin. This eliminates the necessity to rule off the right-hand margin for the original typing, or to tap out some arbitrary sign to the end of the margin and count it for re-typing.

The need for special symbols is often critical in cold type composition. Electric typewriters may be adapted to make impressions of any one of hundreds of mathematical symbols, accent marks and other symbols which would otherwise be laboriously pasted by hand on cold type copy. See Fig. 4-16. A typewriter mechanic replaces the existing type bar on most makes of electric typewriters with a modified guide to hold and locate "Typits". The normal operation of the typewriter is not affected. In operation, a Typit with the desired symbol is selected and inserted in its holder next to the roll of the typewriter. A key is struck and the rising type bar forces a small slide into the platen, printing the special character. The Typit is then removed and normal typing is continued. The full operating time is about four seconds.

Strike-On Cold Type Composition (Proportional Spacing). Proportional spacing refers to different widths of characters on typewriters. For example, on regular typewriters, all characters are the same width, but proportional spacing typewriters allow less space for their letters, i, t, period, etc., a medium space for such characters as a, b, h, etc., and wider spaces for capital letters. Some cold type devices have three widths of characters, others have five.

The VariTypers. A series of strike-on cold type composing machines by VariTyper allow changing not only point sizes but also type face designs. Sizes range from a small-faced six point to a 13-point full point sized capital letter font. Hundreds of type designs are available. See Appendix.

Most VariTyper models allow the justification (aligning) of the right-hand margin. The operator keyboards the line until a dial indicates that the word count is close to the end of the line. A key

Fig. 4-17. The VariTyper is one of many devices which provide proportional spaced copy.

is then punched, which makes the carriage move to the left, and the entire line is re-keyboarded. Spacing is increased automatically for justification. A short explanation of each VariTyper model follows. A letter "F" following the model number indicates that the machine will rule lines in various thicknesses, or "leader" (making dotted lines) or both automatically by holding a key down. A key need not be struck for each segment of a line or leader, as on ordinary typewriters. Vertical lines may be made by turning the copy paper.

Models 660 and 660F have proportional spaced characters. Characters are either two increment, three increment, or four increment widths. Automatic justification is possible.

Models 270 and 270F have unit spacing, that is, all characters occupy the same space horizontally, as in standard typewriters. This model will justify the right-hand margin as explained.

Models 116 and 116F have unit spacing without the justification feature.

Model 900F is used for single line sequential card camera work (see Sequential Card Cameras), and Model 940F is used for one, two or three lines on individual cards.

Model 330 is used for branding codes on vinyl wire coverings, useful in electronic work.

Model 350 is used to place words on engineering drawings up to 12 feet wide and any length.

Leading (spacing) between lines can be varied to any point size, and one-time carbon ribbons are used to achieve good, black copy for negative making for offset printing. A repeat key is used to strike over a character any number of times to make it blacker.

Two 90-character fonts can be used on the machine. The fonts are changed by lifting a knob and turning a font into position for use, as in mixing roman and italic or any combination of type designs. Copy paper can be turned in any angle to place words directly on art work.

The IBM Model C Standard electric typewriter with proportional spacing is limited to one type face per machine. See Fig. 4-18A. By using the two and three unit space bars and typing the copy twice, a typist can justify (align the right-hand margin)

Fig. 4-18A. IBM's Model C electric typewriter.

4-18B. The Justi-meter is an attachment used on IBM typewriters to aid in justifying the right hand margin of typed copy.

We/have/found/it/convenient to use a digit be-   4
tween a comma and a/following/word/if/the/space   -5
is to/be increased by more than one unit, or if   1
instead of the usual four units after a/period,/it -2
may be desired to leave only two/units/of/space.   -3

4-18C. The first typing for preparing copy with the Justi-meter. Note the slanted lines.

We have found it convenient to use a digit between a comma and a following word if the space
is to be increased by more than one unit, or if
instead of the usual four units after a period, it
may be desired to leave only two units of space.

4-18D. This second typing shows the justified lines with the use of the Justi-Meter.

columns. Offset masters are produced using a one-time carbon ribbon. A few of the type faces available on the IBM Model C electric typewriter are shown in Fig. 4-19. Fonts of type are not interchangeable.

Figure 4-20 compares proportional spacing of the IBM Executive typewriter with the ordinary typewriter. Letters of the propor-

This is IBM Bold Face #1 Type. IBM's "proportional lettering" gives each character the amount of space it deserves, according to its width.

This is a sample of IBM Bold Face Italic Type. IBM's "proportional lettering" gives each character the amount of space it deserves,

This is a sample of IBM Registry Type. IBM's "proportional lettering" gives each character the amount of space it deserves, according to its width. 2345

THIS IS A SAMPLE OF IBM COPPERPLATE GOTHIC NO.1 TYPE. IBMs PROPORTIONAL LETTERING GIVES EACH CHARACTER THE AMOUNT OF SPACE IT DESERVES, ACCORDING

THIS IS A SAMPLE OF IBM COPPERPLATE GOTHIC NO.2 TYPE. IBM's PROPORTIONAL LETTERING GIVES EACH CHARACTER THE AMOUNT OF SPACE IT DESERVES, ACCORDING

This is IBM Directory Type. IBM's "proportional lettering" gives each character the amount of space it deserves, according to its

This is a sample of IBM Charter Type. IBM's "proportional lettering" gives each character the amount of space it deserves, according to its width. 234567890-@#$%¢&*()_qwertyuiop1QWERTYUIOP! asdfg

Fig. 4-19. A few of the many type faces available for IBM electric typewriters.

ORDINARY TYPEWRITER SPACING

iiiii
ooooo
wwwww
mmmmm

The quick brown fox jumps over

DIFFERENTIAL SPACING

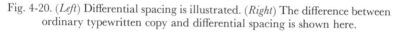

EXECUTIVE TYPEWRITER SPACING

iiiii
ooooo
wwwww
mmmmm

The quick brown fox jumps over

mai

Fig. 4-20. (*Left*) Differential spacing is illustrated. (*Right*) The difference between ordinary typewritten copy and differential spacing is shown here.

tional type consist of one of five different widths. Letters on an ordinary typewriter are, of course, all of one width. Hence, proportional spacing typewriters simulate hot type characters.

The Justi-Meter attachment allows the justification of right-hand margins on IBM proportional spacing typewriters for text type to be used in offset printing. Two typings are required. The meter is set, see Fig. 4-18B, for the desired column width. The lines are typed and the meter is checked by the operator to determine the plus or minus units. The units are then typed at the right-hand margin. See 4-18C and D. In the retyping of the justified line, the operator adds or subtracts units at the keyboard accord-

Fig. 4-21. Underwood's Raphael is another typewriter offering differential spacing.

ing to the slant lines previously marked in the copy by hand.

Unlike the ordinary typewriter, on which all characters have the same width, on the Raphael typewriter, Fig. 4-21, each letter occupies a space relative to its natural width. When the letter "a" is struck, the machine automatically allots a smaller space than it allows for a "w." The letter "i," occupies a still smaller space in keeping with the natural shape of the letter. Figure 4-22, shows specimens of six type faces available for an Underwood Raphael electric typewriter. Only one type face is available at one time on a single machine.

Automatic Strike-On Cold Type Composition (Automatic Justifying). The Friden Justowriter with Edge Card Punch and Reader hastens publication of directories, inventories, and like work. See Fig. 4-23. Cards are punched on the *recorder* and then sorted into a desired sequence. The cards are then run through the recorder again, which automatically "sets" the lines on paper or direct image plates at 100 words per minute. Cards can be

This is a specimen of WINDSOR type.

This is a specimen of KENT type.

This is a specimen of RAPHAEL type.

This is a specimen of AVON type.

This is a specimen of PINTORI type.

This is a specimen of BAUDIN type.

Fig. 4-22. Six type faces available for Underwood's Raphael.

Fig. 4-23. The Friden Justowriter Recorder (*left*) types the copy so that the operator can see it while it punches a tape. The copy is reproduced and automatically justified from the tape on the Justowriter Reproducer (*right*).

reshuffled in various sequences. Proofreading, being done on the cards, is eliminated on the copy or master plate. Offset newspapers may use a Justowriter which automatically sets justified copy from press wire tapes. Another model allows tape control for hot-metal line-casting machines.

Each Friden Justowriter cold type composition machine consists of a *recorder* (on which copy is typed in plain view) and a *controller ribbon* (which is punched with a series of holes for each character) and a *reproducer*. Because the typist can see what he types, corrections can be made or a line killed and re-keyboarded. The ribbon is then placed on the *reproducer* and the same typing is reproduced on paper or on plates at a speed of 100 words per minute automatically justifying and aligning the right hand margin. Tape can be filed for future runs. Characters are proportionately spaced, one to five units wide. Line spacing can be single, one and one-half, double, etc. Several sizes of "type" are available. The machine is in use for printing newspapers and books. Samples of Justowriter type designs, available in various sizes are shown in Fig. 4-24. Faces can be mixed, as in italic and roman, by using more than one machine.

"NHM" System. Manufactured by Aller, Copenhagen, Denmark, "NHM" refers to a "No Hot Metal" device, and uses typewriter composition on a roll of paper featuring side-hole

9 Point Galvin
ABCDEFGHIJKLMNOPQRSTUVWXYZ
abcdefhgijklmnopqrstuvwxyz
1234567890

10 Point Booktype
ABCDEFGHIJKLMNOPQRSTUVWXYZ
abcdefghijklmnopqrstuvwxyz
1234567890

10 Point Heritage
ABCDEFGHIJKLMNOPQRSTUVWXYZ
abcdefghijklmnopqrstuvwxyz
1234567890

10 Point Modern
ABCDEFGHIJKLMNOPQRSTUVWXYZ
abcdefghijklmnopqrstuvwxyz
1234567890

12 Point Galvin
ABCDEFGHIJKLMNOPQRSTUVWXYZ
abcdefhgijklmnopqrstuvwxyz
1234567890

12 Point Bold Face
ABCDEFGHIJKLMNOPQRSTUVWXYZ
abcdefghijklmnopqrstuvwxyz
1234567890

12 Point Bold Face Italic
ABCDEFGHIJKLMNOPQRSTUVWXYZ
abcdefghijklmnopqrstuvwxyz
1234567890

12 Point Documentary
ABCDEFGHIJKLMNOPQRSTUVWXYZ
abcdefghijklmnopqrstuvwxyz
1234567890

14 Point Commercial
ABCDEFGHIJKLMNOPQRSTUVWXYZ
abcdefghijklmnopqrstuvwxyz
1234567890

Fig. 4-24. A representative selection of Friden Justowriter type styles that are available.

perforations. Lines are justified by a "Flash-O-Line" camera to extend or condense lines without changing the letter height. Corrections are typed on a separate roll, and the side perforations are used for alignment with the original. The machine photographs

Fig. 4-25. Intertype Fotosetter employs circulating "Fotomats" which allow letter-by-letter exposures from still images.

Fig. 4-26. Intertype Fotomatic is a single magazine cold type device operated by Teletypesetter tape.

eight lines a second. Coded punched holes indicate lines to be deleted.

Photographic Cold Type Composition (Justified). The Intertype Fotosetter, the first of the successful cold type devices, employs circulating "Fotomats" which allow letter-by-letter exposures from still images. See Figs. 4-25 and 4-26. Type sizes from 3 to 72 point are available from one font of Fotomats. Both straight matter and advertising display can be composed, as well as electrical and electronic diagrams. An Intertype "Fotomat" is illustrated in Fig. 4-27. The Fotosetter has full-kerning characters, as illustrated in Fig. 4-28. Figure 4-29 is a diagrammatic sketch showing how characters are photographed from the Fotomat. Figure 4-30 shows how type sizes are selected on the Fotosetter by merely turning dials which move a turret lens device. The lens turrets (see Fig. 4-31) of the Fotosetter allow sizes from 3

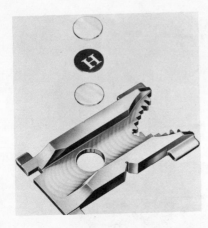

Fig. 4-27. Intertype Fotomat.

Fig. 4-28. Full kerning characters, like those in this book, are possible on the Fotosetter.

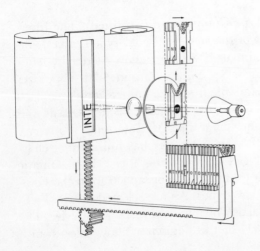

Fig. 4-29. This diagrammatic sketch shows how characters are photographed from the Fotomat.

Fig. 4-30. The Fotosetter film carriage; type sizes are selected on the Fotosetter by turning a dial.

Fig. 4-31. The Fotosetter lens turret allows type sizes from 3 to 72 points.

through 72 point. Figure 4-30 illustrates the Fotosetter film carriage and shows the film magazine and receiver. Figure 4-32 shows how the product of the Fotosetter is developed. Images can be right reading, or wrong (as seen in a mirror) reading to suit the process used in offset-lithography. Figure 4-33 (left) shows the

Fig. 4-32. Fotosetter film is being
developed.

Fig. 4-33. Paste-up (*left*) and stripping (*right*) of Fotosetter
materials is shown here.

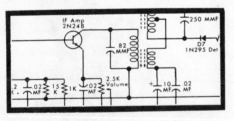

Fig. 4-34. Fotosetter composes
symbols, numerals and letters
for diagrams and charts.

pasting up of Fotosetter positive paper prints, and Fig. 4-33 (right)
how stripping is accomplished with Fotosetter positives.

The Fotosetter composes symbols, letters and numerals for
electrical, electronic, piping layouts, flow charts and the like, as
shown in Fig. 4-34.

The Intertype Fotomatic model is a one-magazine machine
using two-letter Fotomats. It is operated manually or by Teletypesetter tape. The Intertype Fotomatic produces more than

eight lines per minute for printing books, newspapers, and commercial work. Newspaper composition can be produced directly from wire services. An eight-lens turret provides eight type sizes from four point through 24 point. (See Fig. 4-26.)

The Intertype Electronic ("Fototronic") Photographic Typesetting System. In this device, the operator keyboards copy on a standard electric typewriter connected with a computor which calculates word spacing to achieve justification automatically. The computor produces a paper tape. The tape is then fed into the print-out

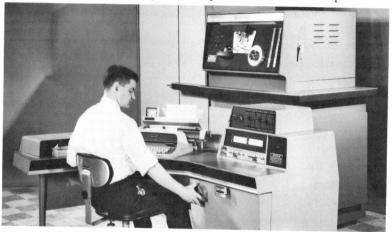

HARRIS-INTERTYPE ELECTRONIC PHOTOGRAPHIC TYPESETTING SYSTEM

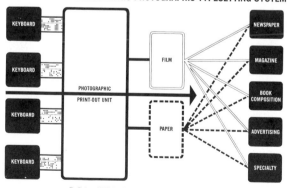

The Photographic Print-out Unit is the heart of the System. With an exposure rate of up to 20 type characters per second it is capable of processing the output of four or more Keyboard Consoles. It automatically produces type on film or photographic paper in 19 sizes from 5 pt. through 72 pt.

Fig. 4-35. (*Top*) The Intertype electronic photographic typesetting system (*Fototronic*) is shown here. (*Bottom*) A diagram of the Fototronic system.

unit, which provides lines on film or paper for making printing plates. See Fig. 4-35.

Any one of 480 different characters can be exposed in 19 different sizes from 5 point to 72 point. The print-out unit features a light source that flashes on and off in one-millionth of a second, and exposes characters inscribed on a glass disc as they spin past the camera at 2,400 revolutions per minute, or 70 miles an hour.

The Fototype Compositor. The lens system of the Fototype Compositor allows the projection of up to 100 different type sizes from 10 point to 84 point from one font called a carousel. Extra fonts allow sizes from 12 to 96 point.

Automatic horizontal spacing on paper or film feed is accomplished with a photo-electric cell. Each 35 mm. letterslide contains one character and a coding mark that is detected by the cell. As the beam of light passes through the code of the slide, it strikes the photo-electric cell in an exact pre-determined position, so placement of the character is automatically controlled by the advance of the paper or film.

A single dial controls the size of the type, and type style changes can be made in five seconds. Carousels have 70 positions for type characters, plus 30 additional positions for any special characters. After each line is composed, the operator tears off the film or paper and inserts it into an automatic developer for a five second processing. The Fototype Compositor is shown in Fig. 4-36.

The Berger system for composing difficult formulas is illustrated in Fig. 4-36A. Based on photography, it requires the erection of a visual image for the camera, made by five basic negatives which give proportional alphabets, and Greek and other symbols. The images are placed on a grid to proportion fractions, radicals, square roots, and the like.

Fig. 4-36. Lens adjustments on the Fototype Compositor permit more than 100 sizes from each type font.

$$\therefore\ T_1 = \frac{2d_1}{\cos i_{12}\, V_1} + \frac{X}{V_2} - \frac{2d_1 \sin^2 i_2}{\cos i_{12}\, V_1} = \frac{X}{V_2}$$

$$+ \frac{2d_1}{\cos i_{12}\, V_1}\,(1 - \sin^2 i_{12}) = \frac{X}{V_2} + \frac{2d_1}{V_1}\cos i_{12}$$

$$\therefore\ d_1 = \left(T_1 - \frac{X}{V_2}\right)\frac{V_1}{2\cos i_{12}} \quad \text{when}\ \ X = 0,\ T_1 = I_1$$

(intercept time); from the figure $d_1 = D_1$; $t_1 = \dfrac{D_1}{V_1}$

Fig. 4-36A. The Berger system can be used to set difficult formulas like the one shown here.

Corrections on Typewriter and VariTyper Cold Type Composition. Corrections may be made in several ways on "typed" cold type composition:

1. The corrected line may be "reset" and pasted over the line on which the error was made. This is accomplished by cutting out the line with scissors and pasting it carefully over the line in which the error occurred. A T-square is used for obtaining perfect alignment. Corrections may be typed on the new-style gummed paper which needs only moistening for application over the words to be corrected, but repositioning is not always possible. Or, a "waxing" device may be used on common paper to achieve the needed adhesion.

2. The line is retyped and the correction is made. Then the original "galley" is laid on a light table, and the correction is placed in register over the line in which the error was made. A sharp razor-like knife is used to cut through *both* the correction and the line below it. The line containing the error is thrown away, and the corrected line is placed in the cut out section, and secured with "Scotch" tape on the bottom of the sheet.

3. Corrections may be made over a fluid applied on the error when the typist catches an error. The fluid, called "Snopake," dries to a white color in a few moments, and will "take" the carbon from the ribbon of the machine.

Factors in Strike-on Cold Type Recognition. Students, offset printers, and layout men often need to know what type of device or machine has been used in previously-printed work they receive for production by offset. These factors will help them. Characteristics of Strike-on Cold Type are listed below:

1. Almost always printed offset.
2. Uneven "character fit" of letters. Widely spaced at times, perhaps overlapping in instances.
3. Periods and commas heavy for type design.
4. Vertical alignment of letters sometimes off.
5. No kerning letters.
6. Ligatures missing or rare (fi, ff, fl, ffi, ffl). VariTyper 660 (DSJ) has only fi, fl, and ff, and they are seldom used.

VariTyper 660 (DSJ). Differential Spacing

1. Based on three widths of characters; hence, wide letters are thinned, narrow letters are widened.
    Capitol "M" and "W" of narrow design;
    Lower-case "i" and "s" of wider design;
    Periods and apostrophes heavy.
2. Underscoring rare.
3. Varying styles of type faces common, bold, italic, etc.
4. Varying sizes of type common, 6, 7, 8, 9, 10, 12 point.

VariTyper 120. No differential spacing—characters of one width. Underscoring is rare. Varying styles of type faces on one page are common. Different sizes (6 through 12 point) are common.

Justowriter

1. Based on five widths of characters.
2. Usually one face design.
3. Generally no italics.
4. Usually one face size, but different reductions possible in parts of work.
5. Hyphens wider than hot type.
6. Quotes similar to hot type.
7. Underscoring of words may be prevalent.

ATF Typesetter, Fotosetter, Photon and Monophoto. Work done by these devices is difficult to distinguish from hot type.

Display Cold Type Devices

1. Look for "fit" of letters—sometimes variations not found in hand or machine set type; thinner or wider letterspacing.
2. Look for "bounce" in vertical alignment.

Photographic Typesetting

ATF Photographic Typesetting. The Keyboard Unit of the Model B ATF Photographic Typesetter is designed for high-speed production of text and tabular type composition. See Fig. 4-37. The operator can see what he is setting, so errors can be corrected or lines on which mistakes are made can be "killed." One control switch automatically justifies the line of type and also returns the carriage. The typed copy can be proofread. As the typing is done, a tape is punched with a character code. The tape then actuates the Photographic Unit.

Fig. 4-37. The ATF Typesetter keyboard unit punches a coded tape while typing the copy.

Fig. 4-38. The character code chart for the ATF Typesetter.

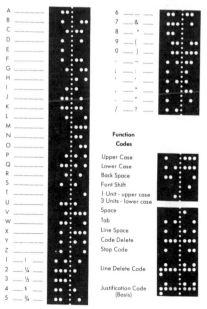

The character code chart of the ATF Typesetter B-8 model (Fig. 4-38) shows holes punched in tape which indicate characters of a 176-character type font. Operators learn to read the tape readily. A sample of one of many fonts of type (see Fig. 4-39) on the ATF Typesetter. Two fonts are available on the disc, in this instance Spartan Medium and Italic. Figure 4-40 shows a font of "type" used on the ATF Typesetter. Two complete fonts are contained on one disc, and range from 5 to 14 point sizes.

Many different methods of type setting have been used during the past 500 years. With the growth of lithography and the expansion of photo-mechanical printing during the last two decades, there has been a constant demand for a more economical text composition system that would permit the printing industry to take full advantage of these newer printing processes.

ABCDEFGHIJKLMNOPQRSTUVWXYZ
abcdefghijklmnopqrstuvwxyz
1 2 3 4 5 6 7 8 9 0

Many different methods of type setting have been used during the past 500 years. With the growth of lithography and the expansion of photo-mechanical printing during the last two decades, there has been a constant demand for a more economical text composition system that would permit the printing industry to take full advantage of these newer printing processes.

ABCDEFGHIJKLMNOPQRSTUVWXYZ
abcdefghijklmnopqrstuvwxyz
1 2 3 4 5 6 7 8 9 0

Fig. 4-39. Two fonts of type are available on each ATF Typesetter disc. Spartan Medium and Spartan Medium Italic are shown here.

Fig. 4-40. The disc for the ATF Typesetter contains two complete fonts of type. Sizes from five point to 14 point can be set from the disc.

Fig. 4-41. The photographic unit of the ATF Photographic Typesetter.

The Photographic Unit (see Fig. 4-41) of the ATF Photographic Typesetter automatically reproduces, on film or on paper, justified type composition from 5 to 14 point sizes in widths up to 7⅜ inches. Two fonts of type are contained on a disc similar to a small phonograph record. The unit is actuated by the tape punched on the keyboard unit. Leading between lines can be accomplished in one-half point increments to 16 points. The film or paper, after the automatic exposure, is developed in the usual manner.

The ATF KD-84 Model is a headline and advertisement display photographic typesetting device capable of setting from 10-point through 84-point sizes in a wide variety of designs. Copy is keyboarded on the photographic unit. Hence, no tape processing is required.

Foto-Drafting. The ATF Foto-Draft System by-passes pen-and-ink drafting, and "draws" schematic diagrams directly on film from lightweight photo-matrix discs. The keyboard-operated, tape-controlled system uses the ATF photographic Typesetter for automated photomechanical drafting.

At the left in Fig. 4-42, a completed draft is shown. At right is a tape and photo-matrix containing 168 symbols which can provide characters for electric wiring, electronics, piping, architecture, construction, etc. The regular ATF keyboard keys are covered with removable identification caps. A tape is provided for the ATF photographic unit.

Linotype Linofilm. The Linotype Linofilm keyboard (Fig. 4-43) controls all functions of the system. Eighteen fonts are avail-

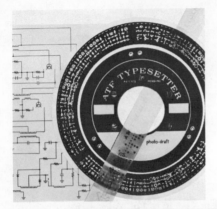

Fig. 4-42. The ATF Foto-Draft system is used to "set" schematic diagrams. This system is used with the ATF Typesetter.

Fig. 4-43. Linotype's Linofilm is a computerized photographic typesetting device. The keyboard is shown here.

able from 6 to 36 point. A recorded tape from the keyboard actuates the Photographic Unit. The push-button control (Fig. 4-44) of the Linofilm Keyboard controls spacing, quadding, line eraser, centering, flush-left and flush-right, justification, and the like. Figure 4-45 illustrates a Linofilm grid font of type.

The Linofilm photographic unit (see Fig. 4-46), actuated by the tape from the keyboard, automatically changes fonts of type, point sizes, leading, and line lengths. The unit contains 18 grid

Fig. 4-44. The push-button control panel of the Linofilm.

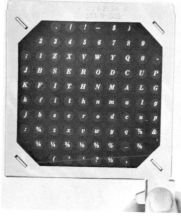

Fig. 4-45. A Linofilm grid font is shown here.

fonts, the equivalent of 72 magazines on the hot metal Linotype. The machine photographs six ems per second, the equivalent of 15 lines per minute of 12 point type 18 picas wide. Maximum line length is 42 picas. Right-reading positive type on film or paper is produced.

The Linofilm Quick device produces 5 to 18-point type on film or paper through two grids of two alphabets of 184 characters each. Output is up to 17 newspaper lines per minute.

Corrections and alterations are keyboarded and come to the

Fig. 4-46. The Linofilm photographic unit is actuated by a punched tape from the Linofilm keyboard.

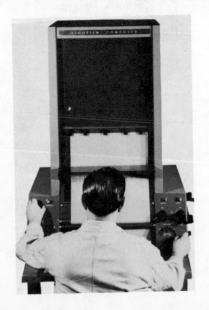

Fig. 4-47. The Linofilm Composer is used in make-up operation for offset-lithography.

Photo Unit as a "correction galley." A film corrector automatically cuts out lines containing errors and replaces them with a corrected film line.

The Linofilm Composer shown in Fig. 4-47, performs make-up of various sizes of type, and can enlarge or reduce type. The operator works from a layout on tracing paper placed over a screen. The operator can enlarge type up to 30 points, reduce it two-thirds, or enlarge it six times its original size, as well as angle lines up to 90 degrees.

Alphatype. The Alphatype is designed to produce all classes of quality composition. It utilizes a standard electric typewriter as its keyboard. The keyboard (left in Fig. 4-48) is electrically connected to the Alphatype recorder unit (right in Fig. 4-48) which transmits a ten-channel binary signal to magnetic tape. These signals identify each character and character width as it is composed. At the end of each line the carriage returns automatically and transmits the necessary justification information. After the job is recorded on the magnetic tape, the reel is fed into the exposure unit. The recorder-unit selector buttons provide finger-tip control. See Fig. 4-49.

The desired font is inserted into the Alphatype exposure unit (Fig. 4-50) and the leading between lines is selected. Sensitized

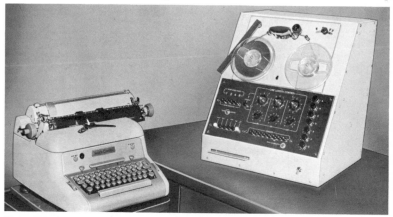

Fig. 4-48. The Alphatype uses a standard electric typewriter for its keyboard (*left*). The Alphatype Recorder Unit (*Right*) receives signals from the keyboard and records them on magnetic tape.

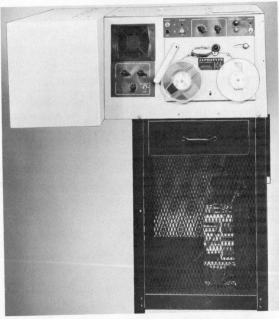

Fig. 4-49. The Recorder-Unit selector buttons are used to select line
length and type specifications.

Fig. 4-50. The Alphatype Exposure Unit photographically composes copy from
the Recorder unit tape.

paper or film is then mounted on the carrier and the exposure unit
"reads" the magnetic tape and composes photographically. Upon
completion a buzzer sounds. The sensitized paper or film is
removed and processed in the usual manner. The maximum line

Fig. 4-51. The Monophoto keyboard prepares a punched tape for
the Monophoto caster.

length is 60 picas, "galley" depth is 11½ inches. The Alphatype
recorder unit and *exposure unit* utilizes transistorized electronic cir-
cuitry for memory, computer and control functions.

Two Alphatype Fonts are contained on one film. Each alphabet
has 84 characters. Mixing of the fonts can be done; separate font
is provided for each size of type, from 6 to 18 point.

Monophoto. A cold type device operated by a tape like the
one used on the hot type Monotype casters. Justified lines of type
from 6 to 24 point are provided on film or on paper. See Figs. 4-51
and 4-52. The master negative case of the Monophoto area cold
type device contains 225 positions and characters for spacing. See
Fig. 4-53. Each character on the negative is approximately 8
points in size, and the characters are arranged in unit rows identical with the principle employed with cellular matrices used on
the hot metal Monotype caster.

Photon. The Photon, an electro-mechanical photocomposing
machine, produces lines of straight type matter, mixing any of 16

Fig. 4-52. The Monophoto caster accepts computer tapes from the keyboard and "casts" type in justified lines.

Fig. 4-53. A "font" of Monophoto "type" and the punched tape.

type designs. The Photon can also produce whole advertisements in one operation—all from the keyboard. The machine calculates the necessary spacing so each character is in correct position. Film or paper movement is controlled visually by the operator. The make-up guide shows just where the type is being placed, horizontally and vertically, at all times. The operator can make corrections at any point in the line before it is photographed. A memory unit holds information in intermediate storage until ready to be released. The Photon has automatic justification, centering and quadding right or left. Composition speed is from eight to ten characters per second. Type sizes to 72 point are available up to 54 picas wide. A simple keyboard commands 17,280 characters on light-weight matrix discs at typewriter speed. The Photon can be equipped to accept automatic input from any perforated tape or punched card system—Flexowriter, Justowriter, Teletypesetter, perforating typewriters, or news service tapes. See Fig. 4-54.

Figure 4-55 shows how the Photon area cold type system places characters on film. Note the matrix disc at the right which carries a selected font of type with 1,440 characters and symbols. These characters may be used in 12 different sizes—for a 17,280 total.

The Photon Zip model sets up to 500 letters per second from a grid of 264 characters, or about the speed of 160 newspaper lines

Fig. 4-54. The Photon keyboard (*Right*) and the Recorder Unit (*left*) are shown here.

Fig. 4-55. The Photon Cold type system works photographically as shown here.

per minute. Only one size of type is available at any one time, but changes in type sizes can be made by changing grids.

Lettering Devices

Letters are formed on the Varigraph Lettering Instrument (see Fig. 4-56) by moving a stylus along the letters in a grooved template, while a pen or pencil draws the letter on the work surface. The letters are outlined and filled with the same pen. Letters from 6 through 72 point may be produced from a single template.

Fig. 4-56. The Varigraph lettering instrument is operated with a stylus and grooved template.

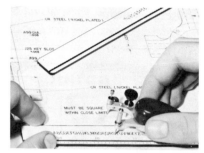

Fig. 4-57. The Leroy lettering device is a popular lettering guide.

Fig. 4-58. Another popular guide is the Wrico Lettering Guide.

Fig. 4-59. The parts of the Wrico pen.

The Leroy Lettering device (see Fig. 4-57) is used to prepare type lines for offset printing. Caps, lowercase and numbers are engraved in a template which serves as a guide for the pen. Characters are complete; no combinations of the template are needed. An adjustment on the scriber provides italic or oblique letters.

Figure 4-58 shows a Wrico Lettering Guide in use. This draftsman's tool can also be used for preparing display lines for offset printing. Various sizes, weights and type styles are available. Figure 4-59 illustrates the parts of the pen used to ink letters with a Wrico Lettering Guide.

Fig. 4-60. Senso lettering guides are used in preparing copy for offset printing.

Fig. 4-61. The Print-O-Stat device is shown here in use.

Fig. 4-62. A Print-O-Stat template is shown here.

Senso Lettering guides (see Fig. 4-60) are useful in the preparation of copy for offset printing.

The Print-O-Stat device creates type lines on artwork using special templates in 14 sizes, from 6 to 60 point. The template guides a pen below an ink reservoir as shown in Figs. 4-61 and 4-62.

Templates are not shifted to complete a letter or figure. Interchangeable pens allow 11 widths of strokes from about one-half point to 6 points.

Paper and Plastic Type

The Fototype system (Fig. 4-63) of display type composition consists of packs of characters on cards in many designs and sizes, and assembled letter-by-letter, as shown, in a composing stick. Scotch tape binds the characters together. Fonts are kept in cabinets.

Presto Paper Type is illustrated in Fig. 4-64. Characters are on light paper which can be assembled and overlapped. Letters have a fixed base line and an extra-large right-hand margin. Lines are anchored with "Scotch" tape.

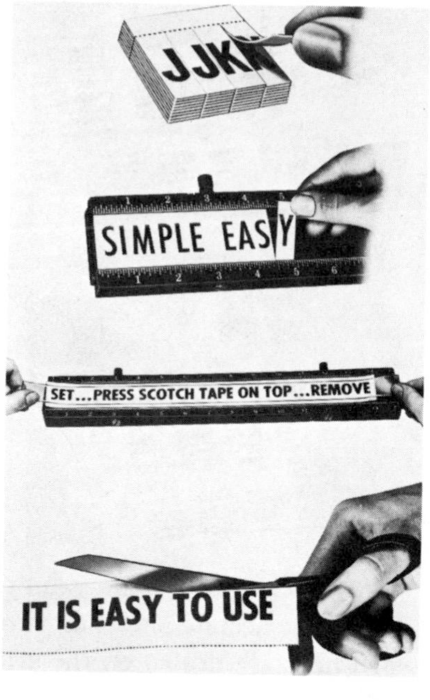

Fig. 4-63. The Fototype system uses pads of characters.

Fig. 4-64. Presto Paper Type is also assembled from pads of characters.

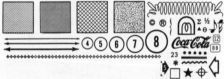

Fig. 4-65. Craftype is a paper "type" which uses a wax backing, making it self adhering.

Fig. 4-66. The first step in using Artype is to remove the backing sheet.

Fig. 4-67. A stylus is used to cut out the Artype character and to remove it from the sheet.

Craftype, from 10 to 96 point sizes, features a self-adhering wax back on the acetate letters or characters. See Fig. 4-65. Light blue pencil lines are drawn on the artwork, and each letter, including

Fig. 4-68. The Artype letter is registered to a guide-line on the layout sheet.

Fig. 4-69. The letter is then rubbed to keep it firmly in place.

its guideline, is cut out with a stylus. After lifting from the backing sheet, the letter is placed so that the guide line and blue pencilled lines coincide. The letter is then burnished to assure that it adheres to the artwork.

Artype (Trans-Art) pressure-sensitive transparent sheets of letters, symbols or shading media are laid face down, and the backing sheet is drawn away, as shown in Fig. 4-66.

A stylus is used on Artype (see Fig. 4-67) to cut around the letter or character. The letter or character is lifted from the sheet with the stylus. The Artype letter is placed in register with a light blue guide line drawn on the artwork, and pressed into place. (See Fig. 4-68). When the line is completed, Artype is burnished firmly to the artwork. Sample characters of Artype are shown in Fig. 4-69. Note the register lines below letters, as well as symbols and shading media.

Formatt sheets are printed in jet-black ink on the underside of matte acetate sheets which have a heat-resistant adhesive. The sheets feature a large collection of modern alphabets along with a

Fig. 4-70. Formatt sheets have a heat-resistant, adhesive backing.

Fig. 4-71. The Letraset Instant Lettering is a transfer system of cold type.

complete range of sizes in standard type styles. See Fig. 4-70. A variety of characters are available: arrows and numbers, rules, borders, dashes, symbols and other ornaments. The alphabets feature a precise representation of the most frequently used letters of the alphabet—E, A, I, N, O, R, S, T—in proper proportion to other characters to provide the user with more words per sheet. Characters are hand cut with a stylus and applied to art work.

Letraset Instant Lettering features sheets of alphabets and other characters which are applied to artwork by laying the needed letter in place after peeling off the backing sheet. See Fig. 4-71. The letter is gently rubbed with a ball-point pen, and the pigment of the letter is transferred to the artwork, as shown in Fig. 4-72.

Monsen Trans-Adhesive Map Type is printed to specifications

Fig. 4-72. The Letraset characters are rubbed with a ballpoint pen or blunt stylus to make the pigment adhere.

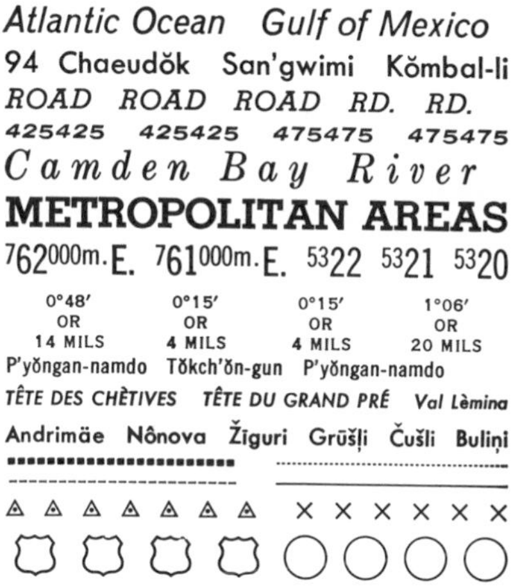

Fig. 4-73. Transparent acetate is used to make Monsen Trans-Adhesive map tape. Characters are made to order.

on transparent acetate having a self-adhesive backing. See Fig. 4-73.

Redi-Kut cold type display letters (see Fig. 4-74) eliminate the need for cutting characters apart. Printed on pressure-sensitive clear acetate sheets, letters are pulled up with fingers or a stylus, and aligned with a blue line previously drawn on the artwork. Type sizes from 16 to 48 point as well as borders and special characters are available.

"Transfer Type," illustrated in Fig. 4-75, places a jet black type image on artwork for offset printing. The "Cello-Tak" make shown here is aligned to a blue pencil line on the artwork (1), then the

Fig. 4-74. Redi-Kut display letters are pre-cut and have
a pressure-sensitive backing.

Fig. 4-75. Transfer Type is rubbed to make the pigment adhere
to the desired surface.

reversed letter is rubbed with a pencil (2), finally the sheet backing
is peeled off as shown.

Cello-Tak alphabets on pressure-sensitive transparent film are
applied to artwork in the following manner, as outlined in Fig.
4-76. The letter is cut out with a razor blade, taking care to include
the guide line at the bottom. The point of the razor blade is placed
under the edge of the cut letter, and the letter is peeled away from
the backing sheet. The letter is placed in position. It will not stick
to the artwork until pressure is applied. Note the blue line which
is used as a guide to insure alignment.

Fig. 4-76. Cello-Tak is another pressure-sensitive alphabet available on transparent film.

Fig. 4-77. **Optiset Photo Headliner.** This table top device allows setting of 14, 21, 28 and 42 point type lines in 10 colors. Individual negative letters are composed on the machine, and the entire line is re-produced in one exposure. No darkroom is needed

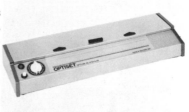

Fig. 4-78. The Optiskop is used to enlarge copy up to 20 times.

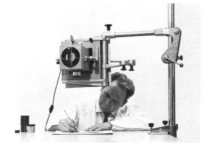

Display type faces in various sizes are available to the offset printer in printed sheets providing characters of the alphabet with numerals and points. They are merely cut out and pasted on art work for photography preparatory to making offset plates.

The Optiskop device (shown in Fig. 4-78.) enlarges up to 20 times actual size and reduces to .4, from non-transparent copy of

Fig. 4-79. Foto-Riter is a system which supplies negative of letters in a loose leaf notebook.

Fig. 4-80. Here a negative letter is being inserted in the Foto-Riter cold type device.

Fig. 4-81. The letter is exposed by pressing the lever as shown here.

any kind. The projection is copied by the operator to produce artwork for offset printing. Enlargements or reductions of any lettering or artwork may be made on photographic paper.

Photographic Line Composers

Many photographic devices are available to compose both small and large display lines for offset printing, thus bypassing the need for reproduction proofs furnished by hot type processes. This chapter presents many of them.

Negatives of letters are contained in a loose-leaf notebook for Foto-Riter reproduction for offset printing. See Fig. 4-79.

Fig. 4-82. The Foto-Riter is dialed to print the next letter on 35 mm. film.

Fig. 4-83. The VariTyper Headliner 840 uses discs and a photographic technique to produce multiple-line head-lines.

Figure 4-80 shows a negative of a letter being inserted in the *Foto-Riter* cold type display device. An exposure of the letter is made on the Foto-Riter as shown in Fig. 4-81. The Foto-Riter is "dialed" to "print" the next letter on the Foto-Riter on 35 mm film. See Fig. 4-82.

Figure 4-83 illustrates the *Headliner Model 840* on which characters are "dialed" to produce either film or reproduction proofs of large type sizes, usually from 10 to 72 point. Each type font is on a flat plastic disc. Discs are readily interchangeable. Multiple line headings can be composed. Model 820 provides single line headings.

The *Model 880 Headliner* by VariType allows area composition rather than in single lines. See Fig. 4-84. Type styles and sizes are instantly changeable from 6 to 84 point negatives in disc form.

Fig. 4-84. The 880 VariTyper Headliner allows area composition.

Fig. 4-85. The Friden Typro is another photographic process used in setting headlines for offset reproduction.

The *Friden Typro Photo-Composing Machine* (see Fig. 4-85) can set perfectly-aligned type up to 72-point. One reel of film holds 15 fonts to photograph onto paper or film. Other features are direct reverses, more than one line on a strip, interlaced words, screened backgrounds, centering or justifying of lines, characters with shadow or bounce. Over 1800 face designs are available. The operator dials a character at the right of the machine which brings

Fig. 4-86. Script type is one of the many styles available on the Friden Typro.

it into magnified view. Composing targets show the best spacing. A lever brings paper or film to view during the exposure. The copy comes out of the device automatically developed, fixed and dried, ready for paste-up. A few script style type faces available on the *Typro Phototype* composition machine are shown in Fig. 4-86.

The *Filmotype Photo-Compositor* machine (Fig. 4-87) produces headlines on film or on paper in over 1,000 type designs from 12 to 144 point, including special designs similar to handlettering. Fonts are on film reels, and the film is moved from letter to letter with two hand wheels and photographed by touching a foot lever. Film can be developed manually, or automatically on an attachment (far left in Fig. 4-87) which develops, fixes and washes the film or paper. A few Filmotype lettering styles unlike the usual type faces appear to be special handlettering, as shown in Fig. 4-88.

The *StripPrinter* (see Fig. 4-89) cold type display device photo-

FILMOTYPE Auto-Processor

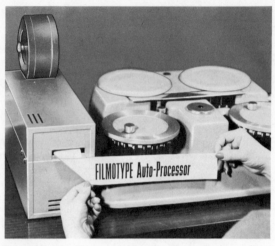

Fig. 4-87. The Filmotype headline device is shown here.

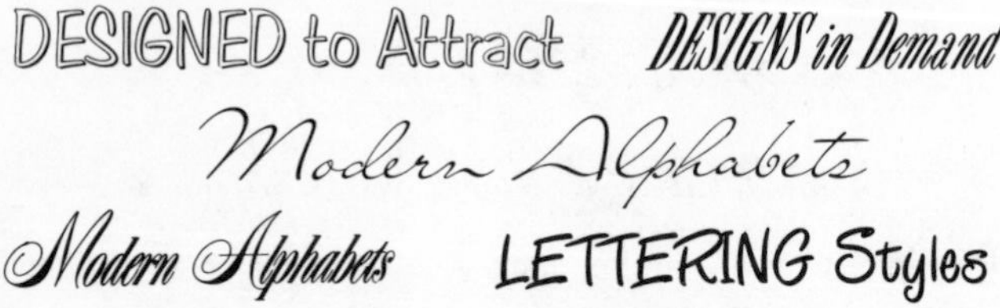

DESIGNED to Attract
DESIGNS in Demand
Modern Alphabets
Modern Alphabets
LETTERING Styles

Fig. 4-88. Some of the many type styles available on the Filmotype are shown here.

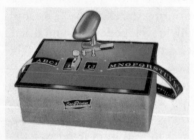

Fig. 4-89. StripPrinter is another cold type device which uses a photographic technique.

graphs characters on paper or 35 mm film. The operator moves the film font of type to the desired position and presses a lever, then proceeds to the next character. The film or paper is then developed. Positives, reverses, patterned type and brush styles are possible. The model 90 StripPrinter provides type sizes from one inch to two and one-half inches in height.

Fig. 4-90. Fotorex uses inexpensive letters in negative form.

AND SIZES of 𝒯ype That CAN be SET *on*
DEMONSTRATING *A* 𝕱ew *of* THE 𝒮𝓉𝓎𝓁𝑒𝓈

Fig. 4-91. A few of the Fotorex type styles are shown here.

The *Fotorex* cold type device (see Fig. 4-90) uses inexpensive letters in negative form which are inserted into the device, and exposed in two seconds. A dial is turned to the degree indicated on the film slide of the letter. After exposure on the Fotorex, the large dial is turned seven revolutions. After two minutes the positive film is developed and is removed for use. Type sizes from 6 to 84 point are available. A few designs of type on the Fotorex are illustrated in Fig. 4-91.

The Megatype Phototypesetter and Composer is a single, desk-type unit with keyboard, supplemental keyboard as well as controls for spacing, justifying, leading, font and size selector (54 type sizes from 6 to 200 point), and shifting controls for the

Fig. 4-92. Megatype is a cold type device which can do type setting and make-up in one operation.

Fig. 4-93. Protype is a cold type device which exposes copy to film letter by letter.

composer. See Fig. 4-92. Type is exposed according to a layout up to 18 × 24 inches. A master font carrier consists of four plastic grids, each containing up to 126 characters—or 504 carriers always in exposing position. No tape or magnetic tape is used. A new concept in memory units is used. Characters can be one of 22 increments wide. In display work, the operator types each line, justifies it, spots it on the layout and flips a switch. Memory units are cleared after a line is exposed.

The *Protype Photographic Composition Machine* features 25,000 type faces on film in sized from 6 to 90 point. See Fig. 4-93. The operator selects his font and places it in position in the device over sensitized paper fed from a roll. Exposure is made letter-by-letter, and spacing and alignment taken care of by a systematic movement of a character index spacer. The paper is then developed for pasting up, although this might not be necessary inasmuch as the entire job can be composed on one piece of paper 17 inches wide. No darkroom is needed. The machine has no moving parts. An ultraviolet lamp is used for making exposures. Characters can be "bounced" or staggered.

The *UD Phototypesetter* is a desk-top display type device, one inch high and 29 inches long. It spaces letters automatically and photographs them on paper from film fonts. Dry runs are possible to assure proper kerning and correct letterspacing. A developing pack is used with the device. See Fig. 4-94.

The *Hadego Phototypesetting Machine* (Fig. 4-95) is basically a camera which photographs, line for line, "matrices" which are hand-assembled similarly to those used on the hot-metal Ludlow machine. Letters are plastic "blocks" having a white image on a black background. Type sizes from 4 to 34 point are produced from a font of 20 point matrices. Type up to 82 point can be produced from a font of 48 point matrices. The camera controls type sizes, centering, flush-right and flush-left quadding is automatic. The device can produce areas of type matter up to 11 × 15 inches— hence, an entire newspaper advertisement can be produced. Lines can be set to overlap, or as closely together as wanted. Screened effects can be produced by placing film screens over the film in the film holder. A type storage cabinet and some type faces which are available on the Hadego machine are shown in Fig. 4-96 and 4-99B.

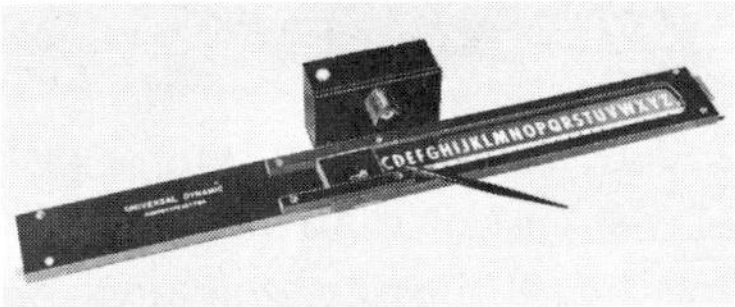

Fig. 4-94. The Universal Dynamic Phototypesetter is shown here.

Fig. 4-95. The ATF Hadego phototypesetting machine is based on a camera process. It is similar to Ludlow in the hot metal field.

Fig. 4-96. A cabinet like the one shown here holds the cases of the Hadego characters.

The Hadego cold type device features a cabinet in which cases of the plastic "matrices" are sorted, similarly to that of the Ludlow hot metal casting machine. See Fig. 4-96. The handwheel (see

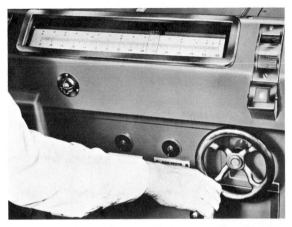

Fig. 4-97. The hand wheel shown here is used to adjust the Hadego for enlarging and reducing type faces.

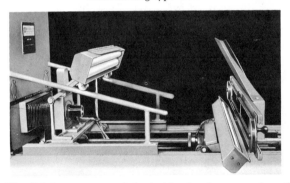

Fig. 4-98. The lighting system and the holder for the composing stick on the ATF Hadego are shown here.

Fig. 4-97) used for enlarging or reducing type faces on the Hadego device. It is linked with an "autofocussing" system. A side view of the Hadego device (see Fig. 4-98) shows the lighting system (see tubes) and the holder (right) for the composing stick. Figure 4-99A shows a few of the hand-assembled "matrices" used on the Hadego Phototypesetting Machine. The negative letters photograph positive. See Fig. 4-99B.

The *Kameratype* cold type display method uses hand-assembled white plastic characters on a black background. See Fig. 4-100. A special composing stick is used. The offset printer used his regular

Engravers Roman No. 43 - 20 pt.
TURNING SCRIPT INTO TYPE IS A PROBLEM WHICH TH

Evidés - 48 pt.
TURNING SCRIPT INTO TYPE IS A PROBLEM WHICH TH

•• Excelsior - 48 pt.
Turning Script Into Type is a Problem Which The Earliest Printers Solved With Great

Franklin Gothic - 20 pt. and 48 pt.
TURNING SCRIPT INTO TYPE is a problem which the earliest

Franklin Gothic Italic - 20 pt. and 48 pt.
TURNING SCRIPT INTO TYPE is a problem which the earliest

Franklin Gothic Condensed - 20 pt.
TURNING SCRIPT INTO TYPE is a problem which the earliest printers

Franklin Gothic Extra Condensed - 20 pt. and 48 pt.
TURNING SCRIPT INTO TYPE is a problem which the earliest printers solved with great

Garamond - 20 pt. and 48 pt.
TURNING SCRIPT INTO TYPE is a problem which the earliest printers solved with

Fig. 4-99. *Left*—A few Hadego "matrices." *Above*—Some of the type styles available on the ATF Hadego.

Fig. 4-100. Kameratype uses white on black letters which are assembled in a special composing stick.

camera to provide negatives with reductions or enlargements from a 96-point character size. A 48-point size is available for reductions to from 8 to 12-point.

Several photolettering devices are imports and include the *Diatype*, H. Berthold Messinglinenfabrik, West Berlin; *Letterphot*, Kowalsky & Company, Munich, Germany; *Magnascop*, Adolph

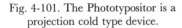
Fig. 4-101. The Phototypositor is a projection cold type device.

Wulff *Industrihuset,* Copenhagen, Denmark; and *Typofot,* Hoh & Hahne Hohlux, Offenback-Main, Germany.

The *Phototypositor* (see Fig. 4-101), a projection cold type device, uses one film to make enlargements to 144 point and reductions to 9 point sizes. Modification is possible to condense, expand, italicize, backslant, reproportion height and width, interlock letters, overlap, exaggerate, distort, angle, letter-space and drop-out shadows in Benday screens. The operator can observe what is taking place; script type can be perfectly connected visually. One or two-inch film fonts may be used. No dark room is needed to make lines of type in 175 different point sizes. A special attachment may be used to prepare type lines in arcs or circles.

A second machine, called the *Posteriter,* provides characters from 2¾ to 3¾ inches in height. No dark room is required and type composition is continuous on rolls of film or paper.

The *Letterphot* projection-type cold type photographic display device is a German import which uses one film font to produce type sizes from 4 point to letters 4 inches high on film or paper. The type disc used allows changes in type style and size, and screened backgrounds for special effects.

The *Optype* (Fig. 4-102) is used to justify (align the right-hand margin) typewriter composition with a ragged right-hand margin at a rate of five seconds per line. It produces a negative, ready for stripping into flats for offset printing. Copy can be reduced when aligned. The type face being photographed can also be condensed or italicized.

Fig. 4-102. The Optype is used to justify typewriter composition.

Fig. 4-103. The Starlettograph is a projection type cold type device imported from West Germany.

The *Starlettograph* is a West German import which produces type sizes from ³⁄₃₂ to 4 inches. See Fig. 4-103. Single letters are projected from negatives, letter-by-letter, in much the same manner as a photographic enlarger. A first exposure is made in red light for positioning the negative, then the final exposure is made with a white light.

The *Fairchild Morisawa Photo Composing Machine* provides 5 to 48 or 12 to 72 point type from one "letterplate" containing characters in negative form. Word and letterspacing are automatic. See Fig. 4-104. Type faces can be set at a 10, 20, or 30 degree angle, and condensed, expanded, or distorted. Lenses are changed to

Fig. 4-104. The Fairchild Morisawa Photocompositor is shown here.

Fig. 4-105. The Pasco copysetting uses magnetically attracted black letters.

provide the various type sizes, on film or paper 10 × 12 inches in size. Developing is a separate operation.

The *Pasco* cold type system uses magnetically-attracted black letters as shown in Fig. 4-105. The operator picks characters from

Fig. 4-106. The various parts of the Pasco system are shown here.

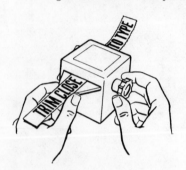

Fig. 4-107. Twisttype employs corrugated paper to produce curved lines and circles of type.

a type cabinet and aligns them with a special tool on a board with a non-photographable grid pattern which is permanently magnetized. See Fig. 4-106. The usual camera is used to make negatives for offset printing. The letters are returned to the cabinet for re-use. Type sizes range from 14 to 120 point in a variety of designs.

The Twisttype device allows straight lines of type on proofs or photographed on paper to be corrugated so that curved lines or circles may be cemented on the artwork. See Fig. 4-107.

Modification Devices

Employing prisms and lens, the *Modigraphic Fotomaster* camera can, from proofs of single lines, stretch or condense type, make type thicker or thinner, make outline letters from solid faces, make italics from roman, and can create from a straight line of type any kind of perspective or curve. It can change proportions of advertisements; i.e., wide advertisements can be made narrow and vice versa. Drawings and type can be made lighter or heavier in tone. Modification of copy is effected simply by liquid-filled cylindrical

Fig. 4-108. The Modigraphic system can produce effects like those shown above.

Fig. 4-109. Fotolist is a sequential card camera.

lenses or prisms in front of the copy or film. Considerable hand-lettering can be eliminated with the camera.

Samples of work done in the Modigraphic Fotomaster camera from proofs of type in straight lines shown in Fig. 4-108.

A camera which can "reproportion" is the Clydesdale which squeezes, expands, heightens, "squats," italicizes and backslants any type of artwork—photo or reproduction proof of type.

The *Fotolist* by VariTyper (See Fig. 4-109) features typed cards which cascade before a camera at a speed of 7,200 per hour. Each line is recorded on film. The resultant negative is used to print by offset-lithography. Cards can be prepared, proofread, put in the desired sequence, and catalogs, directories and like publications put to press much quicker than by conventional printing methods. The use of a card counter minimizes errors in card count.

The VariTyper Model 940F, a multiple line composer, is a machine in which IBM-type cards are typed for use in the Fotolist

OLD PART NO.	NEW PART NO.	DESCRIPTION	PRICE
HL-2420	50-2420-0	Knife Feed Bkt. & Bearing	10.50
HL-2430	50-2430-0	Selector Cam & Shift........	2.80
	50-2431-1	Clutch Selector Cam	1.15
	50-2432-1	Clutch Selector Cam Shaft.....	1.35
HL-3002	50-3002-0	Side Tank Guide	2.25
HL-3004	50-3004-0	Pressure Foot Act. Lever	.95
	50-3005-2	Back Frame	31.30
HL-3006	50-3006-0	Delay Switch	4.05
	50-3006-1	Developer Light Switch	4.05
HL-3007	50-3007-0	Delay Switch Bracket	1.70
	50-3007-1	Limit Switch Bracket	1.15
	50-3008-1	Cam Stop	.95
HL-3009	50-3009-0	Tank Drive Chain	2.90
HL-3010	50-3010-0	Coin Switch	2.65
	50-3011-1	Limit Switch	2.75
HL-3015	50-3015-0	Back Frame Cable Connector ..	4.85
HL-3018	50-3018-1	Paper Baffle Plate	1.65
	50-3018-1	Paper Baffle Plate	1.65
	50-3019-0	Paper Baffle Extension	.70
HL-3020A	50-3020-1	Contact Printer & Tank Guide..	6.15
HL-3025	50-3025-0	Limit Switch	8.90
	50-3025-1	Limit Switch	7.40
HL-3035	50-3035-0	Limit Switch Bracket	1.20
HL-3040A	50-3040-1	Foot Bearing Bkt.	3.35
HL-3050	50-3050-0	Drive Sprocket	7.85
HL-3051	50-3051-0	Sprocket Hub	1.90
HL-3052	50-3052-0	Sprocket Gear	.30
HL-3053	50-3053-0	Sprocket End Plate	.40
	50-3060-1	Feed Sprocket	9.00
	50-3063-1	Worm	5.00
HL-3065	50-3065-0	Spacing Sprocket............	50.95
HL-3075	50-3075-0	Tank Drive Gear Bkt.	2.85
HL-3078	50-3078-0	Motor Drive Sprocket Shaft ...	.15
HL-3080	50-3080-0	Tank Drive Gear & Shaft	4.75
HL-3083	50-3083-0	Idler Sprocket Bkt.	3.65
HL-3085	50-3085-0	Motor Drive Idler Sprocket.....	3.25
HL-3086	50-3086-0	Chain Drive Sprocket & Rivet..	3.50

Fig. 4-110. Here a sample negative from the Fotolist is shown.

Machine. Many type designs are available in sizes from 6 to 12 point. Lines can be keyboarded within a half-inch vertical space for photographing on the Fotolist Machine. Model 100 is used for single lines. Cards are placed on pins which insure correct positioning of the cards.

The compact Model 90 Fotolist (see Fig. 4-109) is a table-top sized sequential card camera which can process IBM-type cards at 3600 per hour, producing film negatives in galley or page form. Cards are "pinned" into exact position on a VariTyper Composing Machine, and lines are composed. The cards are then run through the Fotolist. Cards are kept in sequence and up-to-date for future runs. A sample of a negative produced on a Model 90 Fotolist is illustrated in Fig. 4-110.

The *Friden Compos-O-Line Sequential Card Camera* converts original source data from card records to film at 7200 per hour per line. See Fig. 4-111. Cards can be sub-divided into page and galley groups at 18,000 per hour. The camera can select one line from a group on a card. Its use eliminates proofreading in galley and page form (proofreading is done on the cards), and speed production of lists, directories, and the like. Other sequential card cameras

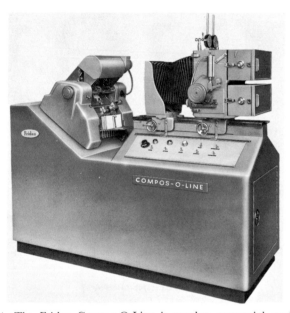

Fig. 4-111. The Friden Compos-O-Line is another sequential card camera.

are Cartoprint from Denmark, and the Flexoprint of Remington-Rand.

Tape-Operated Cold Type Devices

The Intertype Fotomatic and Photon cold type devices can be tape operated, which increases production considerably. With the use of the Teletypesetter keyboard units an operator prepares tape, which is then placed on machines which are activated automatically by the tape.

The ATF Computor 15 features a drum storage of 4,096 words and tape-in-and-out equipment and typewriter, and produces 60 lines a minute, which makes possible the production of tape at a speed of one newspaper column in three minutes. The device is applicable to both hot and cold type production. A monitor action is used for word division. Tape is "read" and information is stored on a magnetic drum. One computor can keep up with four linecasters producing 15 lines per minute.

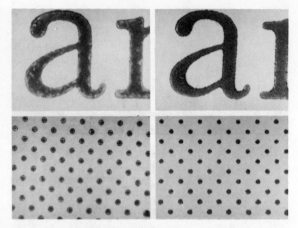

Fig. 4-112. (*Left*) A proof pulled from letterpress plates on regular paper. (*Right*) A proof pulled from an electrotype on Scotchprint for use as an offset reproduction proof.

Conversion Devices

Where letterpress hot type forms or plates already exist, and the printer wants to convert them to film, (by-passing the camera operation) for use in offset printing, several "conversion" methods may be employed.

Conversion systems from type or plate to offset are used to produce negatives, positives, paper, and offset plates as follows:

Negatives: Converkal, Cronapress, Instant Negative, Silvertype and chalked engravings.

Positives: Texoprint, Brightype and Verticon, produce positive film or paper prints; Scotchprint (Figs. 4-112 & 4-113), uses proofs pulled on transparent acetate.

Offset plates: D-I Offset, Double Offset Transfer, and direct offset masters printed usually on small offset presses.

The Brightype method, see Fig. 4-114, converts any kind of letterpress type and plate to film for use in offset or gravure printing. A form containing type of any description and plates is first sprayed with an opaque solution. The faces of the type and plates are then burnished with a rubber pad to remove the solution from the printing surfaces to give a reflective shine. Next, the printing form is raised, see Fig. 4-115 to a vertical position before

Fig. 4-113A. A proof is pulled from a letterpress form on Scotchprint.

Fig. 4-113B. The Scotchprint proof is placed face down on photographic film, ink to emulsion, in a printing frame, to make a negative.

Fig. 4-113C. The negative made in the Scotchprint system is developed, stripped into a flat with other negatives, and an offset plate is made.

a camera lens (center of electric lamps). The battery of lamps rotate about a fixed camera lens, and negatives are made for offset or gravure printing.

The Silvertype Transfer Process converts letterpress type forms for offset or other printing methods. The type form is inked with a special ink on a proof press. The impression is pulled on a plastic sheet, which is then held vertically while a wetting agent is applied to it. This is followed by a silver spray application as in electro-

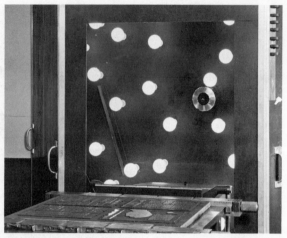

Fig. 4-114. The brightype system is used to convert letterpress plates to offset or gravure film.

Fig. 4-115. The plate is polished and then raised to face the light and camera where the plate is photographed.

typing. The silver adheres only to the plastic, and not to the ink. A solvent is used to wash away the ink, leaving only the image on the sheet.

d-i Offset Plates. An impression of type is made on a paper-backed aluminum foil offset plate on a letterpress which features a rubber blanket rather than the usual paper-draw-sheet. The impression is adjusted to emboss the plate about .003-inch. Then the plate is "debossed" to make it flat, and the plate is ready to print.

Double-Offset Transfer. An impression of the type form is made on a rubber blanket on a proof press. The form is removed from the press, and a type-high impression base with a laminated blanket top is placed in the press. Then the image is offset to the plate from the impression on the rubber blanket and used on an offset press.

Instant Negative. The type form is inked lightly on any paper, and the proof covered with a special film sheet. Under vacuum and heat, the chemicals are forced out of the ink and make an identical

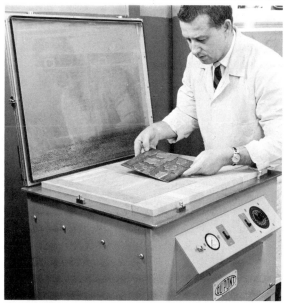

Fig. 4-116. The DuPont Cronapress converts letterpress plates to negatives for use in offset printing.

image on the film soluble of the special sheet. A solution cleans the image areas.

Converkal Process. A proof of a heated type form is pulled on an opaque resin coating on a dimensional-stable polyester sheet. The result is a negative-type film as the opacity is cleared. Infrared lamps heat the form from 260 to 270 degrees.

H-2 Acetate. A proof is pulled on a thin latex coating on transparent acetate. The density of the image is darkened with iron oxide powder, producing a positive. This is a German conversion.

Texoprint and Verticon. As in the Brightype process, the American Verticon and English Texoprint processes involve the photographing of the type form to produce a positive. The Verticon also makes negatives from copy.

Chalked Engravings. A letterpress engraving *plate* is first dusted with chalk, the excess is removed, and a proof pulled in black ink to make a white background and black image. The plate is then photographed to produce a negative.

The duPont Cronapress converts letterpress plates to negatives for use in offset printing. See Fig. 4-116. The letterpress form is placed on the machine, and conversion film is placed over it. The

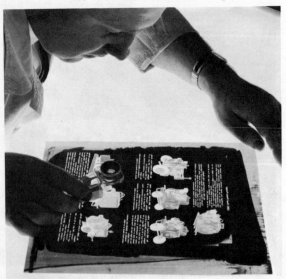

Fig. 4-117. Here a negative from the DuPont Cronapress is shown.

duPont Clarifier bounces hundreds of small lead balls against the film. Fig. 4-117 shows the resultant film negative.

Review Questions

1. All sizes of type are available in cold type. T or F?
2. All hot type designs are available in cold type. T or F?
3. Cold type methods will eventually eliminate hot type. T or F?
4. Generally speaking, cold type is as expensive as hot type. T or F?
5. Display cold type devices are limited to one size of type from each film font. T or F?
6. Storage of cold type negatives takes less space than type forms. T or F?
7. White space is not composed on cold type devices. T or F?
8. The VariTyper can be actuated by press wire tapes. T or F?
9. The Justowriter can be used to automate composition of phone directories with edge punch cards. T or F?
10. The Fotosetter has full-kerning characters. T or F?
11. Ribbons used on typewriter-like cold type devices should use silk ribbons. T or F?
12. The Typit device allows characters to be changed on cold type devices. T or F?
13. The Pasco uses magnetic characters. T or F?
14. The circulating matrix system is used on the Photon. T or F?
15. The ATF Typesetter utilizes a keyboard similar to that used on the Justowriter. T or F?
16. The Linofilm uses a circular grid font of type. T or F?
17. The StripPrinter utilizes negative characters on 35 mm. film. T or F?
18. The Brightype process converts type forms to offset plates. T or F?
19. The Marisawa Photo-Composing Machine will provide 5 to 144 point type on film from one negative alphabet. T or F?
20. The hot metal Monotype and the Monophoto use the same keyboard. T or F?
21. The Foto-Riter and Foto-Rex devices use hand-assembled negative characters. T or F?

22. The Headliner 880 allows dialing of characters on 35 mm. film. T or F?
23. The Headliner 840 allows area composition. T or F?
24. The Filmotype Photocompositor creates type from 12 to 144 point. T or F?
25. The following are desk-top devices: T or F?

a. VariTyper 610
b. Fotosetter
c. Linofilm
d. Monophoto
e. Justowriter
f. Varigraph
g. Optype

Match the character widths listed at the right with the devices on the left:

26. VariTyper 610 ——
27. VariTyper 230 ——
28. Justowriter ——
29. IBM Proportionally-spaced ——

a. One unit
b. Two units
c. Three units
d. Four units
e. Five units

30. The following are cold type devices which have proportionally-spaced characters: T or F?

a. VariTyper 230
b. VariTyper 610
c. Justowriter
d. IBM Selectric
e. Remington
f. Royal

31. The machines producing cold type which have changeable type faces are: (see a through f in question 30)
32. The following have type designs comparable in letter width to hot type: T or F?

a. Fotosetter
b. VariTyper 610
c. ATF Typesetter
d. IBM Selectric
e. Linofilm
f. VariTyper 230
g. Alphatype
h. Hermes
i. Monophoto
k. Photon

33. One font of characters can be used to set sizes from 3 to 72 point on the _____ .
34. An entire layout can be composed, up to 17 inches wide, from 6 to 90 point, on the _____ .
35. Plastic "matrices" are used in two systems, the _____ and the _____ .
36. One film is used to make characters from 9 point to 144 point on the _____ .
37. The device used to justify typewritten copy with an irregular right-hand margin is the _____ .
38. The device used to italicize, backslant, and made into a complete circle is called a _____ camera.
39. A device used to convert type forms only to offset negatives is called the _____ .

Sequential card cameras are

40. _____
41. _____
42. _____

The conversion systems which produce negatives from hot type are:

43. _____
44. _____
45. _____
46. _____
47. _____

The conversion systems which produce positives from hot type are:

48. _____
49. _____
50. _____
51. _____
52. _____
53. _____

The conversion systems which produce offset plates from hot type are:

54. _____

55. _____

The number of fonts of type instantly available on:

56. The Linofilm are _____ .
57. The ATF Typesetter are_____ .
58. The Justowriter are _____ .
59. VariTyper 610 are _____ .
60. The Alphatype are _____ .
61. The Photon are _____ .
62. Magnetic tape operates the _____ .
63. Two cold type devices which use templates of characters are the _____ and _____ .

Place the names of the correct device or devices on the answer sheet for the following:

64. Packs of characters on cards: _____ ,
_____ .

65. Dry Transfer of characters: _____ , _____ ,
_____ , _____ , _____ , _____ .

66. One reel of film holds 15 fonts on the _____ .

CHAPTER 5

Offset Photography

What is offset photography? What is a process camera? What is the function of the camera? What is the difference between line photography and halftone photography? How is a negative prepared for transferring the image to an offset plate?

The offset process can be divided into four major steps: copy preparation, photography, platemaking and presswork. In previous chapters the many devices available for setting and preparing copy were treated in detail. Photography is treated in this chapter and other operations are described in the chapters that follow. Photography is the link between the original copy and the printed page, because the lithographic plate is usually produced from a negative which is made with the process camera. Photography, then, is one of the many critical operations involved in the production of offset printing.

The basic principle of the process camera used for this work is the same as a snap-shot camera. However, the process camera is a much larger and very delicate piece of equipment on which many adjustments and settings are possible to obtain various results. The function of the camera is to hold the original copy and the film in position and reflect light from the copy to the film.

There are basically two types of images produced by the camera; line and halftone reproductions. Line reproductions are those where there is no gradation of dots, that is, an image that prints in a solid color of ink. An example of this is the type in this book. A halftone reproduction is an image containing a gradation of dots that enable the reproduction of various shades of a color.

After the film is developed, the negative is washed and dried. It is then "stripped" or placed in a predetermined position on a special type of paper for the plate maker who will expose the image onto the offset plate.

Photography is the process by which an image (copy) is transposed to a light sensitive material (film) by the action of reflected light and the camera is the means by which this process is accomplished. When the light sensitive material is developed, the image appears as a negative, which is then used to make the offset plate.

The first important step in reproducing good copy is done in the camera section. The negative must be such that when the offset plate is made and placed on the press, the printed product will be a quality reproduction.

Various kinds of copy require different handling. When the copy is good, the operating procedure is routine. Some copy will be weak (such as typewritten copy) and will necessitate readjusting the lights, exposure time, aperture setting, or developing. When the only available copy is poor, steps must be taken to improve it. Furthermore, the camera man is often called upon to reduce or enlarge the copy to fit into a specific area. A recently developed device, called "Modi-Graphic," actually permits the operator to change the copy to any desired size, shape and design.

The copy to be reproduced is placed on the *copyboard* of the camera and the film is placed in the back of the camera. During

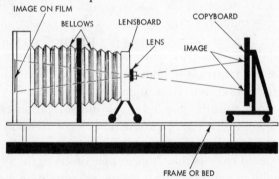

Fig. 5-1. The basic camera setup for photographing copy.

the exposure, the light reflected from the white areas of the copy goes through the lens to strike the emulsion of the film, causing a chemical change which produces a latent image on the film. This image cannot be seen until the film is developed.

If the copy is in the copyboard right side up, it will appear upside down and reversed from left to right when viewed in the ground glass of the camera. Most offset photographers prefer to place the copy on the copyboard upside down so that when it is being focused or centered the copy will appear right side up and readable.

Parts of the Camera

There are five basic parts of a process camera (Fig. 5-1): copyboard, lensboard, bellows, camera back, and light source.

The copyboard holds the copy to be reproduced. It is a flat board with a hinged glass cover. For use, the copyboard is turned to a horizontal position, the glass cover is opened and the copy is positioned. The glass cover is then closed and locked. The copyboard is replaced in a vertical position to face the lens. The copyboard may contain some packing to flatten the copy and hold it in place when the glass cover is closed and the board turned upright, or the copyboard may have a vacuum-type frame that will hold the copy in place.

The lensboard, located directly in front of the copyboard, houses the lens. The lens is the most delicate and perhaps the most expensive and critical part of the camera.

The diaphragm, which is a partition or disk, is attached to the lens of the camera. This device has adjustable stops with pre-calibrated openings and it permits only a specific amount of light to be reflected to the film. A small lever or knurled collar is used to adjust the diaphragm to the desired opening.

A series of *f*-numbers: (f 11, f 22) is found on the collar of the lens. They are used to indicate the diaphragm opening or *aperture setting*.

The lens barrel contains a slot, called the "Waterhouse Stop Slot." This slot is used to insert filters for color work or other special exposures. It has a built-in slide cover which should remain closed when the camera is not in use. The slide cover prevents dust and stray light from entering the camera.

Each lens has a definite focal length (*FL*) at which it operates best for particular types of copy.

Selection of a lens depends upon the following:

1. The amount of reduction and enlargement.
2. The type of lights to be used.
3. Line, halftone, or color reproductions.
4. The amount of bellows extension possible.

The focal length of a lens is the distance from the point in the lens where the light rays converge, to the point behind the lens where the image is first seen in focus. The focal length is given in inches; for the majority of lenses it is 16 to 20 inches. This information is usually found on the inner surface of the lens retaining ring.

If the lens is unmarked and you wish to know the focal length, place some copy in the copyboard and adjust the camera so that the image on the ground glass is in focus and the same size as the copy. Measure the distance from the copyboard to the image on the ground glass and divide by four. (Four is used because the focal length of a lens is one-fourth of the distance from the copyboard to the ground glass when the image is in focus and the same size as the copy in the copyboard.) The resulting number will be the focal length.

The bellows is the accordian-like structure between the lensboard and the camera back. This box-like structure keeps all light out of the camera except that which comes through the lens.

The camera back contains the ground glass, the film holder and controls. The ground glass is used for viewing the copy in the copyboard to make sure it is in focus, the right size, and positioned properly. (Any of these adjustments can be made within the darkroom on the darkroom type camera.) The ground glass may swing to the side on hinges or swing upward on a counterbalance.

The film holder may also swing to the side or be lowered to a horizontal position. It may be coated with a "stayflat" solution on a flat surface, or the camera may be equipped with a vacuum back which holds the film flat to the surface by means of a vacuum or suction generated by a vacuum pump.

The film holder on the gallery type camera is coated with a stay-flat solution because this holder must be loaded and unloaded only in the darkroom. A thin flat slide passes through a slot in the frame of the film holder to cover the film completely and protect it from light. This cover slide is removed only for the exposure of the film and is immediately replaced after the exposure is made.

Types of Cameras

Several types of cameras are used in offset photography, but basic operations are the same. The two principal types are the sheet-loaded camera and the roll film camera.

Sheet-loaded Cameras. The sheet-loaded camera may be either horizontal or vertical.

Horizontal cameras are divided into two types: The darkroom camera and the gallery camera. The darkroom camera is also divided into two types: The low bed camera (Fig. 5-2) and the overhead camera (Fig. 5-3).

Fig. 5-2. The low-bed camera is one of the two types of darkroom cameras. *Robertson Photo Mechanix.*

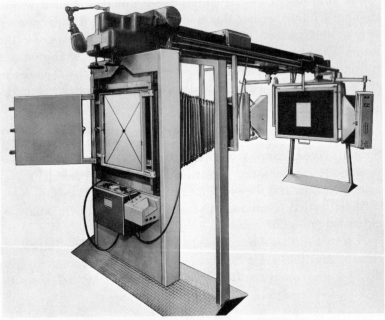

Fig. 5-3. The overhead camera is another darkroom camera.

The darkroom camera is constructed so the back of the camera (film holder and controls) extends through the wall of the darkroom sealed from light. After the copy is placed in the copyboard, the cameraman may operate the camera from inside the darkroom. The bellows, lensboard, and copyboard moves back and forth for scale reproductions and focusing.

Gallery type cameras (Fig. 5-4) are located either inside or outside the darkroom, depending on the relative sizes since a gallery camera is not connected to the darkroom wall. The film holder is removable and the film must be loaded and unloaded in the darkroom.

Vertical cameras (Fig. 5-5) are coming into wide use because they require less space than horizontal types. Although these cameras are designed primarily for line and halftone negatives, some models have an accessory that permits the camera to make color, black and white prints, or transparencies (enlarged, reduced, or same size).

Fig. 5-4. Film for the gallery type process camera is loaded in a detachable film holder. The film holder must be loaded and unloaded in the darkroom.

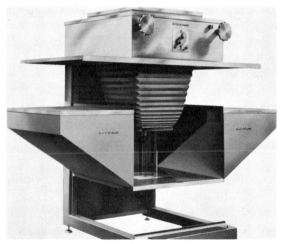

Fig. 5-5. Vertical cameras require less floor space than horizontal cameras.

Roll film cameras (Fig. 5-6) are constructed so that the back of the camera is mounted in the darkroom wall. These cameras are designed to handle either three rolls of film from six to twenty-four inches wide and up to two hundred feet long, or four rolls of film in various sizes up to thirty inches wide. The roll-film type contains

Fig. 5-6. The back of the roll film camera is mounted in the darkroom wall.

a feature which permits the contact screen to roll automatically into vacuum contact with the film, saving time and increasing the life of the screen by eliminating the handling which is necessary on the other cameras. This camera also contains screen-carrying mechanisms for rectangular and circular halftone screens made of glass.

Film

Many types of film, or emulsions, are used in the printing industry and new ones are always being introduced. These emulsions, identified by various trade names such as Cronar Polyester by DuPont and Kodalith by Eastman Kodak, are divided into three main classifications:

Orthochromatic, panchromatic and *monochromatic* (or color blind). Before these are described in detail something should be said about the composition and manufacture of film.

Photographic film is composed of a transparent base of cellulose nitrate or cellulose acetate with a very thin layer of a light sensitive substance called the "emulsion" spread over it. The reverse side of the film may or may not be coated with a colored substance, the purpose of which is to absorb unwanted light. This substance may be green, red, or some other color, depending upon the kind of emulsion. Film with this coating is called anti-halation film. (Halation is the blurring or spreading of the image caused by the light rays spreading between the emulsion and the base.) Halation may also occur when a film positive is made from a film negative. Film with an extremely thin base is used to prevent halation in this case. Uncoated film is known as clear back or clear base. Both kinds are used in the industry and their use depends on the nature of the work.

The light sensitive emulsion on all film is a mixture in which small particles of silver halides are suspended in gelatin.

In the manufacturing process, gelatin is dissolved in cold water and potassium bromide is added. (Sodium chloride is used for photographic *paper*.) Another gelatin solution containing silver nitrate is added which precipitates a light-sensitive silver salt. All emulsions are sensitive to blue and ultra-violet rays.

Types of Film

Orthochromatic film has a wide range for reproducing colored copy. In addition to being sensitive to blue and ultra-violet, it is also sensitive to green and yellow. Although it is insensitive to red, dyes can be added to make it red-sensitive. This film is used for making line and halftone negatives requiring high contrast and sharp reproduction.

Another type of commonly used film classified as orthochromatic is transparent stripping film or "thin base." This film is very thin and is used for making combination halftone and line negatives. The stripping layer on this film may be peeled off and turned over to reverse the image.

Panchromatic film is sensitive to all colors. This capability is achieved by the use of panchromatic sensitizing dyes. Panchromatic film is mainly used for preparing color separations. When used with certain filters, it may be used for photographing copy which is printed in any single color.

Monochromatic film (or color-blind) is sensitive only to blue and ultra-violet light. Blue photographs as white and all other colors as black. This film is suitable where all copy is to be reproduced as black and white. For example, red and yellow areas would reproduce as solid black; blue and white areas would reproduce as white. With this film, there is no gradation of tones.

Adjustments of the Camera

The camera is so designed that the distance from the film-holder to the lens and the distance from the lens to the copyboard may be varied. These variations of distances produce an image on the film or ground glass as an enlargement, reduction, or same size as the copy in the copyboard.

Most newly purchased cameras have an operating manual that gives the settings for reproduction sizes, which are automatically set. In some instances the best f-number of the lens and the best length of exposure are also available in the manufacturer's manual.

If none of this information is available, the following procedure may be used to determine this basic information. Even if such information is available, it is advisable to know how to determine and to adjust the settings.

1. Setting the camera for same size:

Adjust the bellows extension and the copyboard extension, Fig. 5-7, so that each one is equal to two focal lengths of the lens being used. Place the copy in the copyboard; then measure the height or width of the image on the ground glass. Compare this measurement with the same measurement on the copy in the copyboard; both should be the same. By using one of the controls provided, a slight adjustment may be necessary to make it the same size or bring it into focus.

2. Determining the basic aperture setting or f-number:

Place a piece of copy containing small type matter (preferably 6 point) in the copyboard of the camera. Set the camera for same size reproduction. Make a series of exposures on different parts of a fairly large piece of film using a different f-number for each

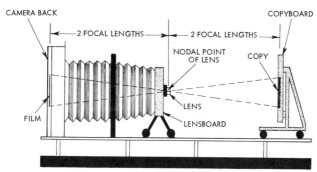

Fig. 5-7. When setting the camera for "same-size," the distance between the copy and the film should be four focal lengths. As shown here, the distance from the copy to the lens should be 2 focal lengths; the distance from the lens to the film should also be 2 focal lengths.

exposure. *Make sure the same exposure time is used for each of the f-stops.* Then develop the film. A close examination of the negative will indicate the image showing the sharpest result and consequently the best *f*-number for that particular lens. This *f*-number should be used for all future exposures with this lens.

3. Determining the length of exposure:

Set the camera for same-size reproduction and the lens at its best *f*-number. Using the same 6 point copy, make a series of exposures on a fairly large sheet of film. Vary the length of each exposure in seconds or minutes. After the film is developed the image showing the sharpest results will indicate the best exposure time to use for same-size reproductions.

The development for each of these series of tests should be as specified by the manufacturer of the film being used. Normally the development time is about two minutes with the developer at a temperature of 68° F.

Since not all cameras are equipped with automatic devices for the setting of enlargements and reductions, it is necessary to be able to make certain calculations without the aid of modern techniques. Three factors must be determined and set before the camera man can proceed with the actual exposure required when changing the size of the copy. These factors are: the scale of reproduction, the copyboard extension, and the bellows extension.

Before proceeding with these calculations, it will be necessary to become familiar with some commonly used abbreviations and formulas.

Commonly used abbreviations:
SR—Scale of reproduction
FL—Focal length of lens
CE—Copyboard extension
BE—Bellows extension
OET—Old exposure time
NET—New exposure time
$f_\#$—Basic aperture setting or f-number
N$f_\#$—New aperture setting or f-number
OD—Original distance of lights from copyboard
ND—New distance of lights from copyboard

The following procedure may be used and in the order stated below to set the camera for an enlargement or reduction with new exposure time.

Scale of reproduction: This is determined by dividing the copy size desired by the original size:

$$\text{SR} = \frac{\text{copy size desired}}{\text{original size}}$$

Copyboard extension: This is determined by adding the focal length of the lens to the quotient of the focal length divided by the scale of reproduction: CE = FL + (FL ÷ SR)

Bellows extension: The bellows extension is determined by adding the focal length of the lens to the product of the focal length multiplied by the scale of reproduction: BE = FL + (FL × SR).

After these three steps are completed, the image on the ground glass should be checked for focus. The copyboard may require a slight adjustment by moving it either towards or away from the lensboard to bring the image into perfect focus.

Upon completion of these settings the new exposure time must be determined. The new exposure time may be determined by two methods:

1. The scale of reproduction plus 1, this quantity squared, then divided by four.

$$\text{NET} = \frac{(\text{SR} + 1)^2}{4} \times \text{OET}$$

2. The scale of reproduction plus 1 divided by 2, this quantity squared, then multiplied by the old exposure time.

$$\text{NET} = \left[\frac{(\text{SR} + 1)}{2} \right]^2 \times \text{OET}$$

Let us solve a problem in setting the camera for a reduction and the new exposure time required. The following basic information must be known beforehand; for example:

1 Focal length of lens is 16 inches

2 Best lens opening is $f32$

3 Best exposure time is 40 seconds

4 Lights are at a 45° angle and 24 inches from the center of the copyboard.

The problem is to reduce to 6 inches in depth a photograph that measures 11 inches in depth.

Compute the SR, CE, BE, and NET.

$$\text{SR} = \frac{\text{Copy size desired}}{\text{Original size}}$$

$$= \frac{6}{11}$$

$$= .55$$

$$= 55\%$$

$$\text{CE} = \text{FL} + (\text{FL} \div \text{SR})$$

$$= 16 + (16 \div .55)$$

$$= 16 + 29.09$$

$$= 45.09 \text{ inches}$$

$$\text{BE} = \text{FL} + (\text{FL} \times \text{SR})$$

$$= 16 + (16 \times .55)$$

$$= 16 + 8.80$$

$$= 24.80 \text{ inches}$$

NET *by Method 1*

$$\text{NET} = \frac{(\text{SR} + 1)^2}{4} \times \text{OET}$$

$$= \frac{(.55 + 1)^2}{4} \times 40$$

$$= \frac{1.55^2}{4} \times 40$$

$$= \frac{2.40}{4} \times 40$$

NET = .60 or .6 $\times$ Old exposure time (40 seconds)
      .6 $\times$ 40 = 24 seconds = length of new exposure

Method 2

$$\text{NET} = \left(\frac{\text{SR} + 1}{2}\right)^2 \times \text{OET}$$

$$= \left(\frac{.55 + 1}{2}\right)^2 \times 40$$

$$= \left(\frac{1.55}{2}\right)^2 \times 40$$

$$= .78^2 \times 40$$

$$= .6084 \times 40$$

NET = .6 $\times$ 40 = 24.0 seconds—the length of new exposure

It is often necessary to change the aperture setting of the lens. To find the new aperture setting at any scale of reproduction when the exposure is held constant, multiply the basic *f*-number by two and divide by one plus the scale of reproduction:

$$\text{N}f_\# = \frac{f_\# \times 2}{1 + \text{SR}}$$

$$= \frac{32 \times 2}{1 + .55}$$

$$= \frac{64}{1.55} = 41 \text{ the new aperture setting}$$

Occasionally, it will be necessary to change the distance of the lights to avoid hot spots or to distribute equal lighting over the copy or to change the angle. This also requires a change in the exposure time.

To find the new exposure time when the light angle is changed but the distance of the lights and all other factors remain the same, divide .707 by the *sine** of the new light angle, multiplied by the old exposure time:

$$\text{NET} = \frac{.707}{\text{Sine new light angle}} \times \text{OET}$$

Example: The lights had to be moved to a 50° angle

$$\text{NET} = \frac{.707}{.766} \times 40$$

$$= .93 \times 40$$

$$= 37.20 \text{ or } 37 \text{ seconds}$$

The following are the sines of angles that are commonly used in lighting for camera work:

Sine 15° = .258   Sine 50° = .766
Sine 30° = .500   Sine 55° = .819
Sine 35° = .573   Sine 60° = .866
(.707 is the sine for a 45° angle.)

To find the new exposure time when the distance of the lights has been changed, use the following formula:

$$\frac{\text{OET}}{(\text{OD})^2} = \frac{\text{NET}}{(\text{ND})^2}$$

Example: The old exposure time was 40 seconds, and we want

---

*For our purposes, a *sine* may be defined as a value attached to an angle of a triangle which expresses a relationship between two sides of a right triangle. For a detailed discussion of trigonometric functions, see any standard trigonometry textbook.

to move the lights from the basic setting of 24 in. to 36 in. What is the new exposure time?

$$\frac{40}{576} = \frac{\text{NET}}{1296}$$

$$576 \text{ NET} = 40 \times 1296$$

$$\text{NET} = \frac{40 \times 1296}{576}$$

$$\text{NET} = 90 \text{ seconds, the new exposure time}$$

Lights

The light source, Fig. 5-8, for the camera may be carbon arc, photoflood, or fluorescent lamps. These lights may be purchased singly, doubly, or in multiples and are generally mounted on adjustable brackets which are attached to the camera frame. The lights can be positioned for distance and angle desired. The normal position for the lights is at a 45° angle to the copy and at a distance that will give equal lighting over the full image. Some carbon arcs are available on a heavy base separate from the camera.

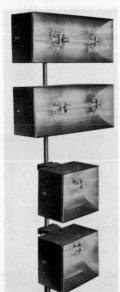

Fig. 5-8. Carbon arc lights are generally mounted on adjustable brackets which are attached to the camera frame.

Halftone Photography

Halftone photography makes the printing of continuous tone photographs possible. It is used in almost every phase of the graphic arts. The basic principles of the process are the same throughout the industry.

The halftone negative may be considered as a special type of line negative. It is made on the same type of film and developed in the same type of developer. There are, however, certain differences especially in the control of exposure and development. In halftone photography, these two states require great care and precision.

The continuous tone of the photograph is reproduced by means of an optical illusion. The halftone negative translates the copy into a "discontinuous tone" through the use of small closely spaced dots. When this is reproduced, it gives the optical illusion of a continuous tone at a distance from the eye.

The Halftone Screen. The series of dots in the negative are made by mounting a glass† halftone screen between the copy and the film.

This screen is made by ruling precise lines on two optically flat pieces of glass by means of a very accurate lining machine. These lines are then etched into the glass and filled with a black pigment. The two pieces of glass are cemented together so that the lines are at right angles to each other (Fig. 5-9). The glass is then bound around the edges with a metal band. When the screen is mounted on the camera, these ruled lines will form a 45° angle to the base of the camera. This angle causes the least amount of difficulty to secure continuous tone.

Halftone screens are classified according to the number of lines to the inch. For example, a 133-line screen will have 133 lines to the linear inch. Screens are available with 50, 60, 65, 80, 85, 100, 110, 120, 133, 150, 175, 200, 250, 300, and 400 lines per inch. The most common screens used for black and white reproductions are the 120, 133, and 150 line screens. Finer screens up to 300 and 400

---

†The contact screen is more commonly used now, but the glass screen is described here first because it provides the best approach to the halftone screen.

Fig. 5-9. A much enlarged screen is shown here. The screen is used to break down continuous tone photographs into discrete areas of black and white so that it can be printed with black ink and still give the appearance of having gray tones.

lines are used for a higher degree of workmanship. Coarser screens, such as the 65-line screen, are used in newspapers printed by letterpress. The 150-line screen is possible on newsprint by offset.

Screens are made either square, rectangular, or circular. Rectangular screens are the most commonly used in black and white reproduction. The circular screens are designed to turn in their mounting so the angle of screen rulings may be changed for making color halftone negatives.

The cost of a screen varies according to its size, shape and fineness. Circular screens are the most expensive and may cost as much as five times the price of a rectangular screen.

Mounting the Glass Halftone Screen. Before it is mounted in the camera, the screen must be cleaned because any speck of dirt or dust will become apparent in the halftone negative. Beware of finger prints on the screen. The screen must be handled on the extreme edges, preferably on the metal band around the screen. Experienced cameramen hold and mount the screen not by their fingers, but with their open hands. The screen is held on both sides by the palm of the hands with just enough pressure to insure that it will not fall.

The etched serial number of the screen is then located; it is found usually in the lower right hand corner. The side of the screen bearing the number is the cover glass and will face the film. The screen is then placed in the camera, making sure it is resting properly in the hangers provided for it. Springs hold it firmly in proper alignment.

Care of the Glass Halftone Screen. Cleaning of the halftone screen requires great care. To remove any dirt or grit that may scratch the screen, a camel's hair brush may be used. *Jewelry should never be worn by the person doing the cleaning because sharp edges or hard metal may scratch or mar the screen and ruin it.* Surgical cotton or lens tissue may be used to wipe the screen after it has been moistened with water, alcohol, or lens cleaner. Small areas may be cleaned by breathing on the screen and wiping it with lens tissue. Do not allow liquid to seep in along the binding because it may dissolve the cement and split the elements of the screen. If the screen is very dirty, it may be cleaned with optical rouge. A spot of rouge about the size of a silver dollar is poured in the center of the screen. Using a piece of very moist surgical cotton, spread the rouge evenly over the screen. Allow the rouge to dry and then polish the screen with another piece of surgical cotton.

To prevent warping, screens should be stored on edge in a cool, dry place at 55° to 75° F. Never store the screen in the sun or near a radiator or stove. Never allow the screen to be dropped, jarred, or submitted to rapid temperature changes. The screen will break if put under pressure.

Every time the screen is cleaned, the chance of damage is increased; therefore, care should be taken to keep the necessity of cleaning to a minimum.

Screen Distance or Separation. Halftone screens have a definite distance between the film and the lens at which they work best. Each of the transparent areas in the screen acts as a lens in transmitting the light from the lens of the camera to the film. Therefore, the halftone screen has a definite focal length. Figure 5-10 illustrates the different screen distances with constant lens apertures.

The most common and generally accepted method of determining the proper distance for each particular screen is the 1:64 ratio. The screen opening multiplied by 64 equals the screen distance. For example, to find the correct screen separation for a 133 line screen:

DIFFERENT SCREEN DISTANCES WITH CONSTANT LENS APERTURES

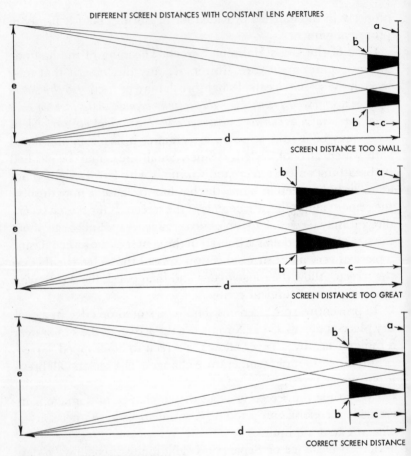

SCREEN DISTANCE TOO SMALL

SCREEN DISTANCE TOO GREAT

CORRECT SCREEN DISTANCE

A. PLANE OF FILM OR SENSITIVE MATERIAL

B. PLANE OR SCREEN RULINGS

C. DISTANCE FROM SCREEN RULINGS TO FILM OR SENSITIVE MATERIAL

D. LENS DISTANCE FROM FILM OR SENSITIVE MATERIAL

E. LENS APERTURE

Fig. 5-10. This diagram shows the effect of different screen distances with a constant lens aperature.

Screen opening $\frac{1}{266} \times 64$ equals $\frac{64}{266}$ inches or $\frac{1}{4}$ inch, the proper screen distance.

(The figure "266" is double the 133 line screen, for lines run horizontally and vertically. The screen opening for a 120 line screen is $\frac{1}{240}$; for a 150 line screen the opening is $\frac{1}{300}$, etc.).

Fig. 5-11. The process cameraman shown here is setting the diaphram to the proper opening. The lens and lensboard are shown.

Every camera equipped with a screen-carrying mechanism has a scale which indicates the average screen distances. A calibrated wedge marked in 64ths of an inch can be used to make sure the screen is set parallel to the copyboard, lensboard and film.

The proper screen distance is a key operation in halftone photography. Contrast may be changed by changing the screen separation. More contrast may be obtained by increasing the screen distance or less contrast by decreasing the screen distance.

Aperture setting. The proper lens aperture settings, Fig. 5-11, are determined in several ways: focusing by eye, by the 1 : 64 ratio, or by the use of mechanical cameras.

In focusing by eye, a magnifying glass is used over the clear spot in the ground glass. Begin with a very small aperture such that the screen will be noticeable; slowly enlarge the aperture until all the lines of the screen have disappeared, and only dots are visible. The dots will be scarcely touching or will appear to be joined by a hair line. This is the proper opening for the highlight exposure. The detail and flash settings are determined from this by "stopping" down the aperture (closing the lens opening) a given amount.

In the 1 : 64 ratio method, the distance from the center of the lens to the film is measured. This distance is then divided by 64. This is the diameter of the proper aperture setting for the detail exposure. The highlight as well as the flash is derived from this setting by opening the aperture one and a half full stops for the highlight exposure, and down two full stops for the flash exposure. Determining the detail and flash aperture settings in the focusing by eye method are the same, except that the calculations are made from the highlight aperture.

Cameras may be equipped with a mechanical attachment which determines the lens stop. The setting corresponds to the scale of reproduction.

The actual exposure times for the detail, highlight and middletone are of such duration as to give proper development when the developing has been carried out to the full recommended time at the proper temperature.

The flash exposure aperture may vary according to the photograph. A photograph may have very small solid black areas which should remain solid. This kind of work would require very little flash. For larger black areas, more flash is needed.

Exposures and aperture settings may vary to some degree because of the peculiarities of a photograph.

Exposure. After the proper screen distance and aperture settings have been determined, the next important consideration is the exposure.

Various exposure techniques are used and are commonly called the one-stop, two-stop, and three-stop methods. In addition to these, there is always a flash exposure to be made. The stop method means breaking up the exposure so that part of it is made with one, two, three, or four different aperture settings. (For line work, only one setting is used and the full exposure time is used at this particular setting.)

The stops used in halftone work are:

One stop: the detail exposure plus flash.

Two stop: the detail exposure and highlight exposure plus flash.

Three stop: the detail exposure, highlight exposure, and middletone exposure plus flash.

The two stop method seems to be the most popular with the "main" exposure being the detail exposure.

Highlight tones in the copy will appear in the negative as small transparent dots surrounded by large round opaque dots whose edges overlap. The highlight exposure requires the largest aperture setting.

Middletones are intermediate tones between shadows and highlights in halftone illustrations. Dots in the negative correspond to the amounts of light reflected by areas of the copy.

This is, light grays produce small transparent dots, and dark grays produce large transparent dots and smaller opaque dots. The middletone exposure requires the next to largest aperture setting.

The detail exposure is used to record detail and tone gradations. The detail exposure requires the next to smallest aperture setting.

The flash requires the smallest aperture setting, and is used because black areas of the original reflect no light. Therefore, silver in the emulsion of the film over that area is not exposed. By adding this flash exposure, these areas are exposed to reflected light. A *flash sheet* or *flash gun* may be used.

A white sheet of paper called a flash sheet is used to cover the original for this part of the exposure. This sheet may be placed directly on the glass of the copyboard with a piece of tape in the corners. This reflects light to the film.

A flash gun is a lamp which is fitted over the lens and light is thrown through the lens and screen to the film.

Magenta Contact Screen. The contact screen is now widely used to prepare black and white halftones. It considerably simplifies the process. As a result, more plants have been able to do halftone work at less cost.

The contact screen is made of flexible acetate plastic material and is used in direct contact with the film in the camera back. The emulsion or dull side of the screen lies against the emulsion side of the film. To insure proper contact between the screen and film, a soft rubber roller, a chamois, or a velvet cloth should be used to smooth the surfaces together. A camel's hair brush, if used, should be handled with care, since it may cause tiny scratches on the back of the screen. In time, the screen will become filled with dirt and dust and will become difficult to clean; eventually the screen must be discarded.

In addition to a magenta contact screen, a gray contact screen is also used. The magenta contact screen is the most popular and is used extensively both with black and white negatives and for making halftone positives from color separation negatives. Gray screens are used mainly for specialized direct color separation work.

Exposure and development may be different with each screen. Each contact screen will handle a given type or density range of copy most effectively. To make the best use of any particular screen, it is necessary to learn what its working density is under specific plant conditions. This is determined with a reflection gray scale.

Since density rates and exposure factors vary from screen to screen, and from manufacturer to manufacturer, for best results follow the instructions as given by the manufacturer for the particular screen in use. Obtain from him a reflection gray scale and exposure computer to determine the information needed to secure the desired halftone quality.

Care of the Magenta Screen. The magenta contact screen must be handled with great care. Clean the vacuum back of the camera before mounting the screen. The screen must be handled only by its corners. If the screen is splashed with chemicals, wash it first in a new acid fixing bath, then in running water, sponge with a good clean viscose sponge, and dry it in a cool, clean, dry room. Grease or other foreign matter may be removed with carbon tetrachloride or alcohol. The recommended cleaning solution is Xylol or Xylene. Since continuous cleaning tends to warp the screen, it is better to keep the screen clean by good care.

Advantages and Disadvantages. The contact screen has several advantages and disadvantages as compared to the glass halftone screen. The advantages of the contact screen are:

1. It is easier and faster to use.
2. There is no screen distance or separation to consider.
3. Any camera equipped with a vacuum back can be used.
4. Contrast control is relatively simple.
5. The initial cost of the screen is low.

The disadvantages are:

1. The screen is very fragile and must be handled carefully.
2. It can be easily scratched, wrinkled, torn, or kinked.
3. It will warp and shrink with changes in humidity and it is highly susceptible to chemical changes.
4. Density ranges and exposure factors vary from screen to screen and from manufacturer to manufacturer.

5. The dye density of the dot-forming pattern can change during the life of the screen.

Kodalith Autoscreen Ortho Film, when exposed to a continuous tone original, produces a dot pattern automatically just as if a halftone screen had been used in the camera. This film has several advantages. It can be used in any sheet film camera utilizing a filmholder. No vacuum back is necessary. The film is capable of greatly improved recording of detail because no screen is used. All of the image light reaches the film, which results in a higher effective speed. Much wider lens apertures can be used than are considered practical with the screen and film combination. No screen distance or separation is necessary, and only two exposures are required. Smaller shops that cannot afford the expense of halftone screens have found this film ideal for their operations.

The two exposures needed are a detail exposure based on the highlight density of the original, and a flash exposure to control the contrast. The basic detail and flash exposure may be determined by a trial and error method, but, by using the Kodal Graphic Arts Exposure Computer and Flash Table, time and material may be saved. If the computer and flash table are not available, the following exposures may be used as approximations from which other exposures may be determined. Under average shop conditions, for an average photograph at same-size reproduction, the exposure should be for about 30 sec. with the aperture setting at $f/22$ with two 500-watt 3200-K lamps (or two No. 2 Photoflood lamps) in reflectors at three feet. Exposure should be about 10 sec. at $f/22$ with two 35 ampere arc lamps at about 4 ft.

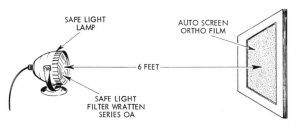

Fig. 5-12. Flash exposure is used to control the contrast and the size of the shadow dot. The safelight may be mounted for horizontal exposure as shown here, or it may be mounted for vertical exposure.

The exposure controls the size of the highlight dots. These dots should be slightly more open than with the screen and film combination.

The flash exposure is used to control the contrast and the size of the shadow dot. Using a safelight lamp at 6 ft. with a 25 watt bulb and a safelight filter, Wratten Series OA, a flash exposure of about 25 sec. will usually be required. The safelight lamp for the flash may be mounted so that the exposure is horizontal as shown in the illustration Fig. 5-12 or the lamp may be suspended from the ceiling and the film placed flat on a table 6 ft. below. The shadow dots should appear larger when using this process than normal.

The detail exposure will need to be varied in the usual manner according to the scale of reproduction and the lens aperture setting. The flash exposure should remain the same. The overall negative made from this film should appear flatter than usual, that is, grayer with less contrast between the blacks and whites. Two and one-fourth min. at 68° F in fresh developer is the normal development requirement. The developer should be agitated vigorously for a few seconds before the film is immersed and the agitation should be continued for 1½ min. The film is then allowed to lie perfectly still in the bottom of the tray until the total time of 2¼ min. has elapsed. The film may be developed by the time-and-temperature method, or by inspection.

Agitation must be equally vigorous in both methods. In the time-and-temperature method, a tray of fresh developer must be used for each negative and the temperature must be controlled within a +½ or −½° F range.

For development by inspection, the negative may be examined by reflecting the safelight from the bottom of a white enameled tray. This safelight should not be turned on until the film has been in the developer for one and a half minutes.

The film is then placed in the stop bath solution for about 10 sec. and then fixed for at least 3 min. or twice the time it requires for the film to clear.

The film should be agitated frequently when placed in the stop and fixing bath.

Screened Snapshots

A new method in the printing of halftones is the development of screened snapshots. By inserting a special halftone screen in a snapshot camera at the time of loading, every picture taken on a roll will have a halftone dot which may then be rephotographed along with type composition as a "line shot." The screen may be removed by opening the camera in a darkroom before the roll is finished to allow other non-screened photos to be taken.

The screen slightly reduces the amount of light reaching the film; therefore, a larger lens opening should be used while the screen and filter, if any, are in the camera.

The screens are available in 65, 85, and 100 lines to the inch. Although this may appear to be a coarse reproduction, a reduction of the photograph will reduce the size of the dot pattern, giving the appearance of a finer screen.

Although no claim is made that the use of this screen will improve the quality of the picture, this new technique will reduce the cost of prescreening the photographs and then stripping the halftone negative into the flat. Firms preparing catalogs, flyers, manuals, etc. when an undetermined or large number of photographs are desirable, will find that this development is advantageous. This method also makes it economically possible for schools and churches to produce offset printing containing more photographs.

Cameras using regular black and white negative film are suitable for making screened negatives. These screened negatives may be stripped into the flat with other line negatives and burned (exposed) directly into the plate. A variation in exposure may be necessary but this may be compensated for by placing a piece of masking paper over the area that will need less exposure. The masking paper is taped to the outside of the glass of the exposure frame with transparent tape and may be removed without interfering with the exposure.

Rescreening

Until recently a moire pattern was apparent in the negative when a printed halftone was photographed and rescreened. A device called the Canon Re-Screener now permits direct screening of halftone copy that removes the screen dots and reduces the graininess from enlargements.

The Canon Re-Screener, contained in a case, consists of five transparent filters, a lens mounting, an adapter ring, a compensating glass, a selector chart and instruction book. The filters are flat glass discs about 2.2 in. in diameter and coated on one side with a random pattern of circles. The coating is less than one-millionth of an inch thick. This makes an optical path of about a half wave length for the reflected light from an individual dot in the copy. When the light waves pass through the filter, they reinforce each other, producing a smoothing over or continuous tone pattern in the reproduction.

In use, a computer is used to select a proper filter, depending on the screen of the copy, the percentage of enlargement or reduction desired, and the focal length of the lens used. The adapter ring is fastened on the camera lens, and the filter is inserted into the ring. The usual procedure for halftone photography is then used; that is, the copy is placed in the copyboard and the film and screen are placed in the camera. The exposures are made in the same manner as when screening a photograph, except that the main exposure time is 15 percent to 25 percent higher than normal. The flash exposure for the control of the shadow dot is reduced or eliminated. The film is then developed as usual with constant agitation. The Canon Re-Screener is used with contact screens or glass screens.

If a Re-Screener is not available when it is necessary to re-screen a previously printed halftone, several methods are used to reduce the moire pattern. Motor-driven lenses, or hit-or-miss methods involving tricky out-of-focus photographic and lighting techniques are used.

If the copy was printed with a coarse screen, satisfactory results may be achieved by photographing the printed halftone as line copy. No halftone screen is necessary. The copy is placed in the copyboard, exposed and developed in the same manner as line copy except that the exposure and the development are very critical and must be watched carefully to prevent over- or under-exposure and over- or under-development. It is advisable to use this method only when the printed halftone does not contain much detail and when screening of the printed halftone is not very fine.

When the use of a halftone screen is necessary to photograph the printed halftone, the following may be used:

If the copy is a: 50-, 85-, 100-, 120-line screen, use a: 100, 133, 150, 175 line screen or vice-versa.

For example: If the printed halftone contains a 85 line screen, a 133 line screen is used for rescreening. If the printed halftone contains a 133 line screen, an 85 line screen is used for rescreening. A 100-line screen may be re-screened with either a 50- or 150-line screen.

Without the use of the Canon Re-Screener, elimination of the moire pattern is almost impossible.

Color Separation

Full-color process printing requires four separate printing plates and press impressions. A halftone negative must be made for each

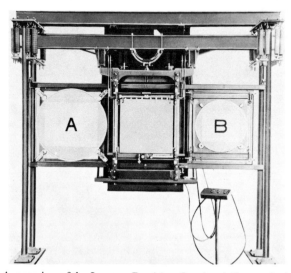

Fig. 5-13. A rear view of the Lanston Precision Overhead Camera is shown here. "A" is the oversize circular screen; "B" is the standard circular screen.

color plate. In making the separation from a colored original or transparency, the circular glass halftone screen (Fig. 5-13) is used. The screen is changed to a different angle for each color to prevent the dots of one color from printing on top of the dots of another color. The usual screen angles used are: 90° for the yellow, 75° for the red, 15° for the blue and 45° for the black (Fig. 5-14).

The colors of ink required in process color printing are the primary colors—yellow, red, and blue, more properly termed as yellow, magenta, and cyan (blue-violet). Black is added to these colors. Combination of these colors produce the secondary colors and combination of these produce tertiary colors. Secondary colors are formed by mixing two primary colors, and tertiary colors are the result of mixing two secondary colors, or of mixing the three primary colors in certain proportions.

In exposing process color negatives, the colored original is photographed through filters (Fig. 5-15) which allow only certain colors to register on the film. The cyan filter is used to obtain the image for the yellow plate, the green filter is used to obtain the image for the red plate, the red filter is used to obtain the image for the blue plate and the yellow filter is used to obtain the image for the black plate.

The exact exposure necessary for the separation negatives is a matter of experience, ingenuity, and practical judgment on the

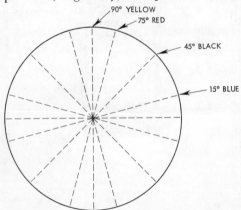

Fig. 5-14. The proper screen angles for color separations using a circular screen is shown here.

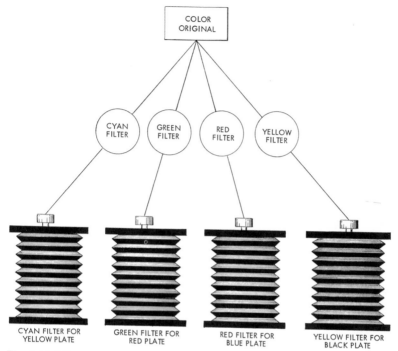

Fig. 5-15. Filters are used to make color separations. The proper filter for each color is shown here.

part of the cameraman. The exposure depends on several factors: the type of original being reproduced, the scale of reproduction, the position and intensity of the lighting, and the nature and sensitivity of the film. In addition to these factors is the problem of filter selection. Each filter has its own factor and this varies with each type of emulsion. To make it even more complicated, the filter factors recommended by the manufacturers of films being used are only guides and must be adjusted to individual plant conditions and requirements.

Filters. Filters are used to absorb or suppress certain colors and transmit other colors to the light-sensitive material. The filters commonly used are films of dyed gelatin. They are inserted before or behind the lens so that when the light is reflected from the copy, it will pass through the filter before it reaches the film.

Additional exposure time is needed to compensate for the absorbing powers of the filter. The time by which the exposure must be increased is called the "factor" of the filter. This factor, or number, must be multiplied by the normal exposure time to obtain the same effect that one would get if no filter were used.

Filters are used mostly in color photography. When using filters for any type of color work, one may consider it a form of separation, because it actually involves eliminating certain colors while retaining others. Some camera work requires the use of filters not only for separation of colors but also to intensify a certain color so that it can be recorded on the film.

Manufacturers will furnish the filter factors for their products. This information should serve only as a guide. Exact factors will vary under different working conditions and assignments; the actual factors are achieved only by trial.

The aim of the camera man is to record a color as "white" (opaque area) or as "black" (transparent or image area) in the negative. To be able to record these colors, the proper filters and sensitive materials must be used.

The following charts will serve as a guide for the proper selection of the film and filter for a particular problem. The color filters mentioned are of the Wratten (Kodak) type. Abbreviations of the types of film being recommended are: "Pan" for Panchromatic, "Ortho" for Orthochromatic and "CB" for Color Blind or Monochromatic.

Color to Photograph	Film	Color of Filter
Red as black	Pan	Green
Red as black	Ortho	None or green
Red as white	CB	None
Red as white	Pan	Red or orange
Orange as black	Pan	Green or blue
Orange as black	Ortho	Green or blue
Orange as black	CB	None
Orange as white	Pan	Red or orange
Yellow as black	Pan	Blue
Yellow as black	Ortho	None or blue
Yellow as black	CB	None

Yellow as white	Pan	Red
Yellow as white	Ortho	Yellow or orange
Yellow-green as black	Pan	Blue
Yellow-green as black	Ortho	Blue
Yellow-green as black	CB	None
Yellow-green as white	Ortho	Green or yellow
Yellow-green as white	Pan	Green
Green as black	Pan	Red
Green as black	Ortho	None
Green as white	Pan	Red
Green as white	Ortho	Green or yellow
Blue-green as black	Pan	Red
Blue-green as white	Pan	Blue or green
Blue-green as white	Ortho	Blue or green
Blue as black	Pan	Red or orange
Blue as black	Ortho	Yellow or orange
Blue as white	Pan	Blue
Blue as white	Ortho	None or blue
Blue as white	CB	None
Violet as black	Pan	Green
Violet as black	Ortho	Deep yellow or light green
Violet as white	Pan	Blue
Violet as white	Ortho	None or blue
Violet as white	CB	None

Filters To Use To Photograph As Black on Film When Using Colored Originals

Color of Original	Ortho	CB	Pan
Magenta	Yellow or Green	Not recommended	Green
Red	None or Green	None	Green or blue
Yellow	Blue or Magenta	None	Blue
Green	Blue or Magenta	None	Red or blue

	Ortho	CB	Pan
Cyan	Not recommended Yellow	Not recommended	Red
Blue-violet	Orange or Green	Not recommended	Green or Red

Filters To Use To Photograph As White On Film When Using Colored Originals

Color of Original	Ortho	CB	Pan
Magenta	Blue or Magenta	None	Red or Magenta
Red	Not recommended	Not recommended	Red
Yellow	Green	Not recommended	Green or Red
Green	Blue or Magenta	None	Green or Blue
Blue-violet	Blue or Magenta	None	Blue

Duotones

Some confusion exists in the printing industry in differentiating between duotones, duographs, and duotypes. The three are similar only in that two colors are used for a reproduction. They are different in procedure of reproduction and the final printed copy will show the difference.

A true *duotone* is a two color reproduction (Fig. 5-16) made by two halftone negatives at two different screen angles, with the halftone plates printed in complementary colors. Popular combinations are yellow and blue, red and green, and red or green and blue. Today printers have begun to print duotones using black with one color. Although black is not commonly called a color, these combinations are still usually called duotones.

When making the halftone negative for duotone reproduction, the screen angles for colors are usually placed 30° apart with the

Fig. 5-16. The duotone is printed with two colors—black and one other here.

strongest color placed on the 45° angle. This rule prevails whether the negatives have been made from monochrome or colored originals. When using a monochrome original, no color filters are needed. The cameraman can make a normal halftone negative for the keyplate and a flat negative for the second plate, provided that this second plate will be printed in a light color or tint.

When using a colored original, it is almost necessary to have a set of six different pairs of Wratten filters. These filters are suited for originals made in colors complementary to each other, the various pairs of filters are also of complementary hue or tint.

A duograph differs from a duotone in that the key-plate is made from one of the angled halftone negatives and printed in a dark color. The plate from the other negative is printed in a lighter

Fig. 5-17. The duotype is a two color halftone made from one negative.

tint of hue of the same color. These are sometimes referred to as duoplex halftones.

A duotype (Fig. 5-17) is a two color halftone made from one halftone negative. The keyplate is etched for detail and also printed in a dark color and the other plate is subjected to flat etching and printed in a light tint. The pressman printing this type of halftone must exercise great care, since both plates are made from the same screen angle and any slight misregister between the plates or the press may result in a moire pattern.

Two color combinations are not restricted to halftone reproduction but can be used for line and Ben Day characters, rotogravure, and collotype. Care in the selection of colors will improve the final result. Not only the harmony of the colors used must be taken into account but also the suitability of the colors to the subject matter.

Combination Halftone and Line

The use of line work on a printed halftone picture is known as a

Fig. 5-18. A combination halftone and line illustration is shown here.

"combination" (Fig. 5-18). This combination may appear in several ways:

1. Black type matter on the halftone picture.

2. Open lettering or reversed type matter shown as white letters on the halftone picture.

3. Arrowheads, lines and nomenclature (names of parts) on a halftone picture of a machine, building, etc.

These lines, arrowheads, type composition, etc. cannot be placed directly on the original photograph because they will produce as halftone dots. A border will be apparent around the type matter and the photograph itself could be made unfit for future use. To avoid this, a combination plate is made by two methods.

A. Make a transparent overlay with the desired line or type composition in correct position and registered to the original photograph. In making this overlay, it would be advantageous first to reduce or enlarge the original to size, then tape the acetate or cellophane overlay and register it into the exact position.

Fig. 5-19. The drop-out halftone can be made by painting out the illustration or by "bumping."

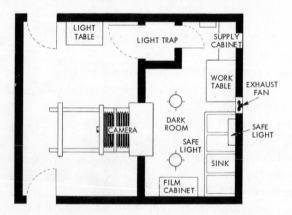

Fig. 5-20. The darkroom should be light proof and equipped with an exhaust fan.

B. Make a separate line and halftone negative and combine the two images by stripping them into single flats, or strip them in registered position on two separate flats and expose each flat separately on the same sensitized plate.

Drop Out Halftone

The drop-out halftone (Fig. 5-19) is made where it is desirable to eliminate the highlight background of an illustration. The most effective way of producing such an illustration is to oqaque out the background by painting in the unwanted areas on the negative. However, in order to save costs, another way is to eliminate the dots during the exposure of the film. After the basic exposure is made, a highlight "bump" or additional exposure is made to burn out the dots of the background.

The Darkroom

The darkroom where the negative is developed should provide for efficient processing of the film and insure safety precautions.

The room itself (Fig. 5-20) should be large enough to allow easy movement. It should be so constructed that light cannot seep into the room. A light trap should be built to allow entrance without letting in light from outside. An exhaust or ventilating fan is necessary for removing fumes and odors. The solutions used in developing contain posionous chemicals which may cause serious injury. If no fan is available, mixing or weighing chemicals should not be done in the darkroom. Doors should be left open, for ventilation, when the room is not in use.

Fig. 5-21. Two necessary features for any developing sink are a corrosion resistant lining and hot and cold running water.

The developing sink (Fig. 5-21) should be equipped with controls to maintain the proper developing temperature of the film. The sink should be made of extra heavy stainless steel with all fittings rust and acid resistant to prevent costly maintenance and repairs. The bottom of the sink may have a storage area.

If a commercial sink is not available, a homemade one can be designed and built. Two necessary features for such a sink are a corrosion resistant lining and hot and cold running water. The water is necessary for mixing formulas and washing the solutions down the drain. Water can also be used to help maintain the developing temperature by filling the sink while checking the temperature by a thermometer, and allowing the water to stay in the sink by plugging the drain. The trays containing solutions are placed in the water and soon reach the same temperature as the water. This type of control is makeshift, but will suffice if better equipment is not obtainable.

Shelves should be provided above and below the sink, and there should be worktables for handling graduates, trays, and other accessories. Bottled chemicals should be placed on the lowest shelves for safety. A cabinet with drawers for storing boxes of film should also be available as an extra precaution to prevent chemicals and light from reaching the film.

Because film is sensitive to normal light, the darkroom must be equipped with safe lights, which are special lights to which film is not sensitive. The room should contain a normal light to be used when film is not being handled or negatives being developed. When film is handled or being developed, safe lights are used. One safe light should be provided above the developing tray for inspection of the negatives as the developing progresses and one or two more should be placed in other positions to allow efficient processing. The type or color of safe lights used will depend upon the type of film being developed. Check the manufacturer's direction for each kind of film. For general work, the following safe lights will be suitable:

Orthochromatic film may be developed when using a Wratten Series 1A (light red) filter in a safe light with a 15 watt bulb at a distance of about four feet.

Panchromatic film is developed in total darkness except for only a few seconds when a Wratten Series 3 (dark green) filter in a safe light with a 15 watt bulb can be used to examine the negative during development. This safe light should not be turned on until the developing is more than half completed.

Monochromatic film may be developed when using a Wratten Series OA yellow or O orange filter in a safe light with a 15 watt bulb at a distance of about four feet.

Development, Fixing, and Washing

During the exposure, the copy in the copyboard reflected the light to the film. The white areas or nearly white areas reflect the light while the black areas reflect little or no light. A latent image is formed on the film by this reflected light, but this image cannot be seen until the film is developed.

After the film is exposed, it is immersed in the developing solution, so that the image becomes visible. The developing solution is composed of a reducing agent, an accelerating agent, a governor, and a preservative.

The reducing agent is a chemical that reduces the silver salt to metallic silver in the exposed areas. Many chemicals have the ability to do this, but only a few have the selectivity necessary to be used in a developing solution. Selectivity as it is used here means the ability of a chemical to confine its activity to the portions of silver that have been struck by light. If the reducing agent did not possess the necessary selectivity, the entire negative would be black or opaque. Hydroquinone is the most popular reducing agent used in developing solutions.

The accelerator is a chemical that makes the developing solution alkaline. A water soluble alkali, such as sodium hydroxide, is generally used. Paraformaldehyde, another chemical that can be used, is itself neither base or acid, but forms sodium hydroxide when used in the developing solution. Paraformaldehyde gives more density or contrast in the negative and for this reason is the most popular accelerating agent.

The accelerator activates the reducing agent and opens the gelatin of the emulsion in which the silver crystals are suspended, allowing the reducing agent to penetrate the emulsion and reduce the exposed silver salt in the image area.

The governor, potassium bromide, is a chemical used to keep fog to a minimum. It increases the selectivity of the reducing agent. Fog is the cloudiness noticed in the image area. This area should be absolutely transparent when properly developed and fixed.

Boric acid, potassium metabisulphite, or both, are usually found in developing formulas. These are weak acids and are used to control the activity of the alkali.

The preservative is a chemical that combines with the reducing agent to form a more stable compound. The reducing agent alone is susceptible to oxidation, but combined with the preservative, the solution may be stored for a longer period. Sodium sulphite is the most common chemical used as a preservative.

By varying the amounts of the principal agents, many developing formulas are possible, which may be used with different types of film. Various types of film are necessary because of varying copy and different methods of reproduction.

The length of development will depend upon the film and developer used. It is carried on to completion, i.e., until the black areas of the negative are as dense as possible, without filling or fogging either the transparent or the image areas. It is best to follow the directions of the manufacturer of the film used. Normally the development time is approximately two minutes with the developer at a temperature of 68° F.

Many factors will present problems during developing, which will vary the time factor. A few of these are changing from a developer that has been used to freshly mixed developer, an oxidized developer, and a rapid change in the temperature.

The best known method for developing is the "time and inspection method." When using this method, carefully observe the time it takes to bring the initial appearance of the image into view, then *continue* development for about four times this interval. For example, if the image appeared in thirty seconds then development should be completed in about 2½ minutes. If it took forty-five seconds, then development should be about 3 minutes + 45 seconds.

When about three quarters of the time has elapsed, the negative may be placed in front of a safe light for a quick inspection. In most instances, it will be necessary to replace the negative in the developer a little longer and then inspect it again a little later. The second inspection time should indicate the time for the negative to be completely developed.

To insure even development over the entire area of the negative, turn the film face down. Then grip a corner of the film between the thumb and forefinger and immerse the edge of the film using a steady motion, gradually sliding the film through the developer. Repeat this three or four times. At the end of about fifteen seconds turn the film face upward and place it in the developer. Agitate the film only enough to keep it in motion.

The short stop bath is used to prolong the life of the fixing agent. After the negative has been completely developed, it is placed in this bath for approximately fifteen seconds. The short stop bath is simply acetic acid and water, and its purpose is to partially neutralize the alkali in the emulsion brought from the developing solution.

The function of the fixation process or the fixing bath is to stop development. Because the parts of the copy that were black did not reflect any light, the silver salts in the emulsion in that area are not reduced to metallic silver. If this development were to continue however, over-development would result, reducing all of the silver salt in the emulsion. With proper development, the silver salt crystals will remain on the portions not struck with light.

To neutralize the alkali in the emulsion brought over from the developing solution, the fixing bath must be an acid. When the accelerator becomes neutralized, the reducing agent no longer works with proficiency; therefore, the reduction of the silver stops.

Sodium thiosulphate, better known as "hypo" is an ingredient of the fixing bath. The purpose of the "hypo" is to remove the unexposed emulsion, leaving only the transparent film base.

Alum is another ingredient and is used to harden the emulsion for future handling.

All of these solutions should be kept and used at the same temperature. Most developers work best at 68° F. If the solution is used at a much higher or lower temperature, poor negatives will result.

After fixation, the negative must be thoroughly washed in running water to remove all traces of the fixing bath solution from the negative.

CAUTION: All film should be handled at the extreme corners or edges. Anywhere the finger tips are placed on the film a spot will show up during development. If these smudges show over the image, especially on a halftone, the negative will be completely ruined.

Precautions should always be taken when using chemicals. Avoid inhaling the fumes for an extended period of time and prevent splashing. The fixing bath should be kept in a deep pan placed in the sink to prevent any of the bath from falling on the floor. If the fixing bath should fall on the floor, the floor should be immediately washed, mopped, and oiled. If this is not done, the water will evaporate, leaving the sodium thiosulfate, which crystallizes. Eventually it will be stirred up by the feet or sweeping and float in the air. These particles will eventually fall into the developing solution. Wherever they touch the film, they will remove the emulsion. This will produce pin holes in a negative. These pin holes must be painted or opaqued before the negative can be used.

If these precautions are not taken, the condition will eventually become such that everything in the darkroom must be removed and the floor, walls, and ceiling either repainted or oiled and everything well dusted.

Development and Fixation of Halftone Negatives. After the film is exposed, it is placed in the developing solution and developed in the same manner as line work. Constant agitation is necessary, and all solutions should be at 68° F. Full development time for a halftone should be between 2 and 2½ min. when the developing solution is at the proper temperature and all other factors are correct.

The negative is then placed in the short stop bath for approximately 15 sec. and then transferred to the fixing bath. After the negative has been fixed and washed it may be placed on a light top table and examined through a magnifying glass to determine if the gradation of dots are of proper size and density required in a good halftone negative.

If the dots in certain areas are not correct it will be necessary to re-photograph the copy, making the correction in the lens aperture setting, screen distance, light intensity, or exposure time (whichever is determined to be the contributing factor). Sometimes more than one factor will cause the fault. Practical exercise will yield experience in accurately controlling all the contributing factors in obtaining a good halftone negative.

Formulas. There are various developing, short stop bath, and fixing solutions available today, pre-mixed by manufacturers. The instructions for these are stated on the containers. For those who wish to mix their own, the following formulas have been accepted and widely used.

Developing Solution:

	Avoirdupois	Metric
Water 90° F.	64 ozs.	2.0 liter
Sodium Sulfite (Anhydrous)	4 ozs.	120 grams
Paraformaldehyde	1 oz.	30 grams
Potassium Meta-Bisulphite	150 grains	10 grams
Acid Boric Photo (Granular)	1 oz.	30 grams
Hydroquinone	3 ozs.	90 grams
Potassium Bromide	90 grains	6 grams
Water to make	1 gallon	4.0 liter

Dissolve the chemicals in the order given. For best results develop at a temperature of 68° F. for about 2½ min. Do not allow the temperature to go below 65° or higher than 70° F. Develop for 3 minutes at 65° or 2 min. at 70° F.

Developer (Stock Solution)

	Avoirdupois	Metric
Water, about 125° F.	96 ozs.	3.0 liters
Sodium Sulfite, Desiccated (E. K. Co.)	12 ozs.	360.0 grams

Hydroquinone	6 ozs.	180.0 grams
Sodium Hydroxide	5 ozs.	150.0 grams
Potassium Bromide	4 ozs.	120.0 grams
Water to make	1 gallon	4.0 liters

Dissolve the chemicals in the order given. For use, mix two parts of the stock solution to one part of water. Development time should not exceed 2½ minutes at 65° F.

Short Stop Bath

	Avoirdupois	Metric
Water	1 gallon	4.0 liters
Acetic Acid 28%	16 ozs.	500 cc.

To make 28 percent acetic acid from glacial acid 99 percent, dilute 3 parts (ounces) of glacial acetic acid with 8 parts (ounces) of water.

Fixing Bath

	Avoirdupois	Metric
Water, about 125° F.	20 ozs.	600 cc.
Sodium Thiosulfate (Hypo)	8 ozs.	240 grams
Sodium Sulfite, desiccated	½ oz.	15.0 grams
Acetic Acid, 28%	1½ fluid ozs.	48.0 cc.
Boric Acid, crystals	¼ oz.	7.5 grams
Potassium Alum	½ oz.	15.0 grams
Cold water to make	32 ozs.	1.0 liter

Dissolve chemicals in the order given.

Stock Solution for Preparing Fixing Bath

	Avoirdupois	Metric
Water, about 125° F.	20 ozs.	600 cc.
Sodium Sulfite, desiccated	2½ ozs.	75.0 grams
Acetic Acid 28%	7½ ozs.	235 cc.
Boric Acid, crystals	1¼ ozs.	37.5 grams

| Potassium Alum | 2½ ozs. | 75.0 grams |
| Cold water to make | 32 ozs. | 1.0 liter |

Dissolve chemicals in the order given. Add one part of the cool stock solution to 4 parts of cool 30% hypo solution (2½ lb. per gallon of solution), while stirring the hypo rapidly.

Projects

1. Become acquainted with the parts of the camera and its controls.
2. Place copy in the copyboard.
3. Find the focal length of the lens of the camera.
    a. Find where it is stamped on the lens.
    b. Determine the focal length, assuming the lens is unmarked.
4. Set the camera for same size reproduction.
5. Mix the chemicals and place them in the trays.
6. Determine the best aperture setting (f-number).
7. Determine the best exposure time using the aperture setting determined above.
8. Compute the SR, CE, BE, and NET for the following:
    a. Copy 10 inches high to be reduced to 8 inches high.
    b. Copy 10 inches wide to be reduced to 7 inches wide.
    c. Copy 8 inches high to be enlarged to 10 inches high.
    d. Change the light angle to 30° and compute the NET.
    e. Move the lights 6 inches farther away from the OD and compute the NET. Then move the lights 5 inches closer from the OD and compute the NET.
9. Make an outline stating the procedure for shooting line copy.

Analysis of a Halftone Negative. The following are helpful hints on the causes and corrections of faulty negatives:

Causes of fog:
1. Poor storage of film
2. Out-dated film
3. Incomplete fixation

4. Wrong safe lights
5. Over and underexposure
6. Over and underdevelopment

Brown negative obtained:
1. Developing solution too hot or caustic
2. Exhausted fixing bath

Highlight:
1. White appearing dots too large—decrease highlight exposure
2. White appearing dots too small—increase highlight exposure

Flash:
1. Black dots too large—decrease flash exposure
2. Black dots too small—increase flash exposure

To change contrast:
1. Longer highlight exposure
2. Larger highlight aperture
3. Shorter detail exposure
4. Smaller detail aperture
5. Smaller aperture and shorter flash exposure

Common faults of halftone negatives:
1. Overexposure
2. Underexposure
3. Overdevelopment
4. Underdevelopment
5. Careless alignment
6. Not enough contrast
7. Too much contrast
8. Wrong aperture setting
9. Improper screen distance or separation
10. Any combination of two or more of the above

Since it is almost impossible to describe accurately the many common defects found in the halftone negative, an attempt will be made to convey these errors by illustrations. The defects are from improper exposure, development, screen separation, or any

Fig. 5-22. Correct exposure and screen separation, but *overdevelopment*. A grainy halo will be noticeable, outlining the dots throughout the image. The highlight dots may be filled in and the shadow dots may appear square.

Fig. 5-23. Correct exposure and screen separation, but *underdevelopment*. The highlight dots will be sufficiently large and clear. The shadow dots will be of insufficient size and opacity.

Fig. 5-24. Correct development and screen separation, but *overexposure*. The dots will appear too great in size throughout the tonal range.

Fig. 5-25. Correct development and screen separation, but *underexposure*. The highlight dots will be slightly large and appear to be square. The shadow dots will be small and not opaque.

Fig. 5-26. Correct screen separation, but *underexposure* and *underdevelopment*. The highlight dots will be separated and no shadow dots will appear.

Fig. 5-27. Correct screen separation, but *overexposure* and *overdevelopment*. The highlight dots will appear to be completely filled in. The shadow dots will be too large and may appear to be square rather than round.

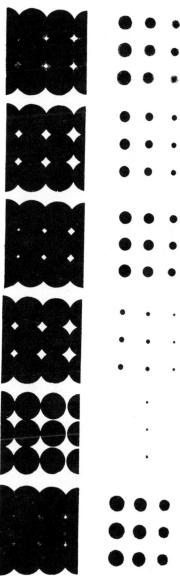

combination of these operations. Figures 5-22 through 5-35 illustrate these faults with descriptions.

Each dot on the negative represents a minute area of the origi-

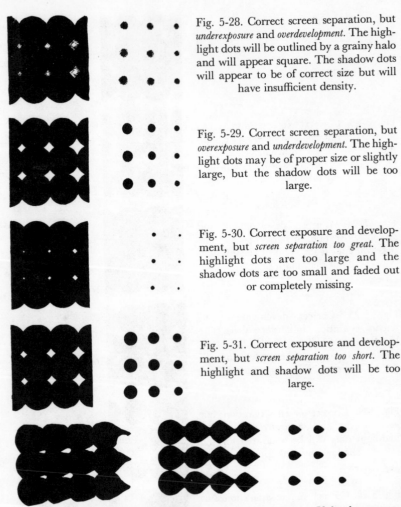

Fig. 5-28. Correct screen separation, but *underexposure* and *overdevelopment*. The highlight dots will be outlined by a grainy halo and will appear square. The shadow dots will appear to be of correct size but will have insufficient density.

Fig. 5-29. Correct screen separation, but *overexposure* and *underdevelopment*. The highlight dots may be of proper size or slightly large, but the shadow dots will be too large.

Fig. 5-30. Correct exposure and development, but *screen separation too great*. The highlight dots are too large and the shadow dots are too small and faded out or completely missing.

Fig. 5-31. Correct exposure and development, but *screen separation too short*. The highlight and shadow dots will be too large.

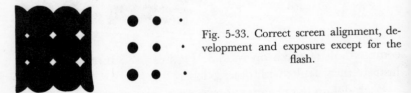

Fig. 5-32. *Careless screen alignment* results in dots of odd shapes. If the dots appear odd in a small area instead of the entire area, the cause may be a bulge in the film or reflection.

Fig. 5-33. Correct screen alignment, development and exposure except for the flash.

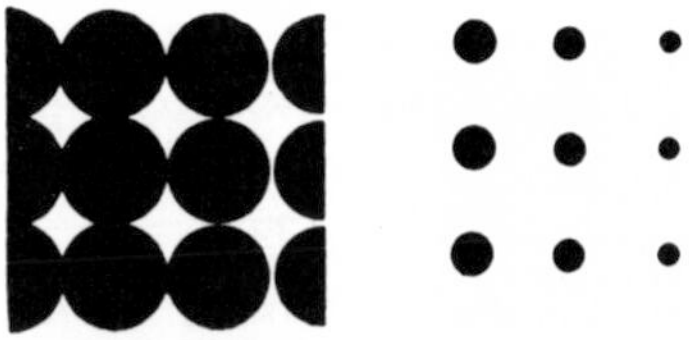

Fig. 5-34. Correct screen alignment, development and exposure in the shadow and detail dots but not enough highlight exposure.

Fig. 5-35. This enlargement shows the extremes of the detail, highlight, and shadow dots in the halftone negative. This is the effect of *correct exposure, correct development* and *correct screen alignment.*

nal. Every opaque dot in the negative must be dense and sharp and the transparent area clear. To achieve the reproduction desired, every dot must be of the size and shape necessary to make it an actual representation of the original.

A very effective and accurate way to determine whether the halftone negative accurately reproduces the original is to use a gray scale beside the original (Fig. 5-36). Check the dot formation on the gray scale during development. The scale must have the same type of finish as the original, that is, glossy, semimatte, etc.

Fig. 5-36. The gray scale is used to check the accuracy of halftone reproduction.

Sometimes the original itself may not have good reproductive qualities. Some photographs may have been over- or under-exposed, or over- or underdeveloped. Other photographs may become discolored from age. The camera man in this instance must use his own judgment to improve the original in the reproduction.

For any portion of a tone to be emphasized, additional exposure in that area of the tone may be used. If a spread of contrast is desired, additional exposure in an area and a decrease in exposure in another area is usually required.

Stripping the Flat

Negative Preparation. Once a plate has been exposed and developed, the image is in a fixed position, and any changes will require a new plate. Therefore, it is important that the negatives be placed accurately when stripping the flat. The paper usually used for a flat is 80 lb. double-coated goldenrod stock. This paper is translucent enough to allow sufficient light to work by, but will not allow any actinic light from the arc lamps to penetrate and affect the sensitized coating on the plate during the exposure. This goldenrod paper with the taped on negatives is called a "flat." The term "stripping" refers to the arrangement and mounting of the negatives on the goldenrod sheet.

Supplies and Equipment. Certain supplies and equipment are necessary when stripping a flat. Below is a basic list of items. Other material may be added from time to time as the need arises.

1. Layout table (Fig. 5-37) with frosted glass, lighted from below.
2. Goldenrod paper stock cut to press plate sizes in the plant.
3. T-Square.
4. Steel ruler with beveled edges.
5. Triangles (30–60° and 45°).
6. Set of scribing tools.
7. Scissors.
8. Various sizes of artists' brushes.
9. Magnifying glass.
10. Draftmen's set.
11. Black India drafting ink.

12. Opaque solution.
13. Transparent tape with dispenser.
14. Red photographic tape with dispenser.
15. Stripping knife or single-edge razor blades.

Laying Out the Flat. All traces of tape should be removed from the glass top with a razor blade. Wash the glass top with a glass cleaner and dry thoroughly. If more than one T-square is available, select one for use and use the same one for all work on the same flat. Work from only one edge of the table using the triangles to draw lines at angles to the T-square.

Place a sheet of goldenrod paper on the table (Fig. 5-38A) cut to press plate size. One long end of the sheet, which will be called the gripper or lead edge (Fig. 5-38B) must be lined up parallel with T-square. On small duplicators, the gripper edge or lead edge will be the short edge of the sheet. It is a matter of choice whether to use the top edge or bottom edge of the sheet to lay out the flat.

Fig. 5-37. The layout table is a basic piece of equipment used in stripping a flat. This is a Craftsman Photo-Lith layout table used for making layouts, lining up press sheets, register color work, etc. The table is equipped with two straight edges that may be raised or lowered to the glass level by means of a raising lever or both may be placed outside the work area when not being used. Each straight-edge is also equipped with a special marker which rules on any surface. Side guides, sheet stops, grippers, and scales in 16ths are provided for faster and easier processing of layout flats and other work.

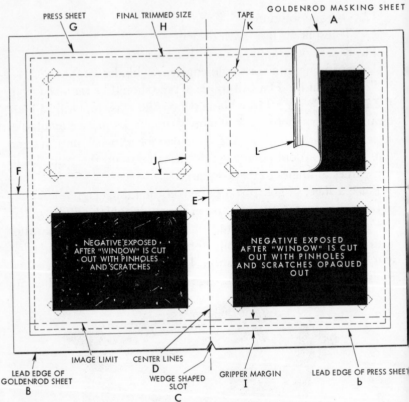

PRESS SHEET
G

FINAL TRIMMED SIZE
H

TAPE
K

GOLDENROD MASKING SHEET
A

F

J

L

E

NEGATIVE EXPOSED
AFTER "WINDOW" IS CUT
OUT WITH PINHOLES
AND SCRATCHES

NEGATIVE EXPOSED
AFTER "WINDOW" IS CUT
OUT WITH PINHOLES
AND SCRATCHES OPAQUED
OUT

IMAGE LIMIT

CENTER LINES
D

LEAD EDGE OF
GOLDENROD SHEET
B

WEDGE SHAPED
SLOT
C

GRIPPER MARGIN
I

LEAD EDGE OF PRESS SHEET
b

Fig. 5-38. This illustration shows various stages of placing a negative in a flat. No. 1 position shows negative in back of or under the goldenrod masking sheet. No. 2 position shows the masking sheet being cut away. No. 3 position shows the "window" in which the masking sheet is cut away exposing the negative with pinholes. No. 4 position shows the negative completed after the pinholes and scratches are opaqued out.

In this case the bottom or lower edge of the goldenrod sheet will be used as the gripper edge. This edge of the sheet will correspond to the edge of the plate which will print on the leading edge of the paper as it is fed into the press. A wedge-shaped slot (Fig. 5-38C) is cut out of the edge of the flat to enable the platemaker and pressman to identify the gripper edge.

1. Line up the gripper edge of paper (Fig. 5-38B) with upper part of the T-square and fasten it to the table with tape.
2. Work from diagonal corners and smooth the sheet before fastening it.

3. Cut the wedge shape out of the sheet.
   (Offset presses have an under-cut on the cylinders where the plate and blanket are clamped. This under-cut of the cylinders and the portion of the press sheet which is gripped by the press grippers cannot receive an impression during the printing, therefore the image must be placed back off the lead edge to the point where it can actually print and still be in a position to keep the pressman's work of adjusting the press to a minimum).

4. Locate the center of the flat (Fig. 5-38D) and draw a line (Fig. 5-38E) from top to bottom and from left to right (Fig. 5-38F).

5. Measure and draw in the size of the press sheet (Fig. 5-38G) and final trimmed size of the job (Fig. 5-38H) if any, allowing the distance needed for the under-cut of the plate cylinder and the gripper margin (Fig. 5-38I).

6. Measure and draw in the lines (Fig. 5-38J) where the image is to be positioned for the final reproduction. Make all measurements from the center lines on the sheet.

7. Place the negatives on the flat in the reversed position (emulsion side up or negative in "unreadable" position). The image is lined up evenly, using the T-square or guide lines, and the negative is taped (Fig. 5-38K) on all four corners.

8. Turn the flat over so that the negative is "readable" and cut "windows" (Fig. 5-38L) through the goldenrod paper exposing the negative. Cut around the image as closely as possible, usually about a quarter inch. This is done to eliminate the need of additional opaquing.

9. Turn the flat over again to the "unreadable" position and examine the negative for pinholes and scratches.

10. Paint out these holes and scratches (Fig. 5-39) with an opaquing solution only in the areas where the negative is exposed.

NOTE: The specifications of the press being used will determine the distance necessary for the gripper margin required. Some specifications also will state the distance required for the under-

Fig. 5-39. The negative must be opaqued in order to remove pinholes and unwanted lines from the negative, before it is stripped into a flat.

cut of the plate cylinder. If this information is not available, locate the maximum printing area given in the specifications, subtract this from the plate size and divide by two. This will center the image on the plate. From this center, measurements for the flat may be made. The margin across the lead edge will give the distance from the lead edge to the point where the image will start to print. This distance will also include the gripper margin space needed.

Example:

The press size is 14½ × 20½ in. The 14½ in. measurement is the distance from top to bottom or depth. The 20½ in. measurement is the distance across the lead edge of the plate or the distance from left to right.

The plate size (A in Fig. 5-40) is 16⅜ × 20½ in. The 16⅜ in. is the distance from top to bottom or depth. The 20½ in. is the distance across the lead edge.

The maximum printing area (B Fig. 5-40) is 14⅛ × 20 in. — the 14⅛ in. is the depth and the 20 in. is the lead edge.

	16⅜″	20½″
minus	14⅛″	20
	2⅜ or 2¼″	½″

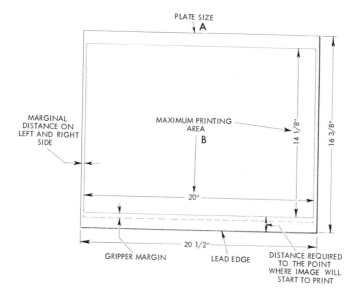

Fig. 5-40. The maximum printing area on a 14½ × 20½ plate is shown here.

2¼ in. divided by 2 equals 1⅛ in., the distance across the lead edge required before the image begins to print.

½ in. divided by 2 equals the distance or margin required on the left and right side.

Reference or Guide Marks. Reference or guide marks (Fig. 5-41 A,B, and C) may be used to line up the negative with the marked-out position on the flat. This may be done by the following procedure:

1. Place the negative in the "unreadable" position. Line up the bottom part of the image with the upper part of the T-square.
2. Measure the distance needed for margins on the final printed sheet on all four sides. If more than one negative is being stripped into the flat then the distance between the negatives must also be measured.
3. Scribe a line into the negative (Fig. 5-41E) where the measurements were made for the margins (Fig. 5-41B).
4. Place the negative on the flat so that these scribed lines on the negative will line up with the final trimmed size as outlined on the goldenrod masking sheet.

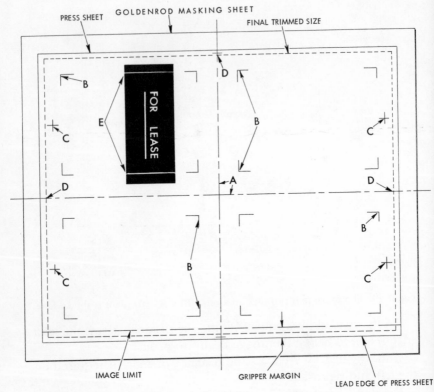

Fig. 5-41. Use of guide lines and reference marks are shown here:

A. Center lines from which forms are measured for equal spacing and position.
B. Guide lines for placing forms into position.
C. Center lines for folio position when used for books.
D. Register marks for use in color work or critical positioning of a second form or more.
E. Register lines for use to insert negative in position.

    5. Tape the negative into position with tape on all four corners and proceed to complete the flat by cutting out the "windows" and opaquing as required.

Scribing Lines on Negatives: Sometimes printed work will require lines that did not appear on the original copy or reproduction proof that was photographed. These lines may be scribed into the negatives (Fig. 5-42) using film scribing tools. Each tool head

Fig. 5-42. Lines which do not appear on the original copy or "repro" proof may be scribed directly on the negative.

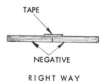

Fig. 5-43. Negatives should never be overlapped when splicing.

has two cutting edges. A complete set will enable one to scribe single or parallel lines of various thickness. A lithographer's needle, sharpened to a chisel-shaped end of the desired width may be used if the scribing tools are not available.

Splicing Negatives. When splicing (joining) two negatives (Fig. 5-43) do not allow them to overlap. If they do, complete contact with the plate is made impossible; and the light rays will creep underneath the film and spread or blur the image being formed on the plate.

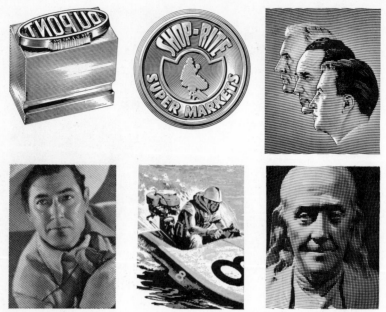

Fig. 5-44. The Weber Process uses continuous tone photographs to make a printed product that appears in one of the many line patterns shown here.

To splice two negatives together proceed as follows:

1. Cut away the opaque part of the negatives as close as possible to the image of both negatives. Use a straight edge as a guide for cutting, so that when the negatives are "bumped" together, the image on both negatives will be parallel and lined up evenly.

2. Tape the negatives together with a piece of transparent tape. This tape may go over the image because there will be no noticeable effect on the plate since the tape is transparent.

NOTE: Splicing should be done with the negatives in the readable position and *only* when working with *line copy*.

Weber Process

The Weber Process reproduces continuous tone black and white originals by means of various patterns of lines. This process permits a halftone effect with the simplicity of line work (Fig. 5-44).

Care and Cleaning of the Camera

Proper care and cleaning of the camera will not only save on costly repairs but also insure ease and quality in processing the film. The following hints will help to prevent unnecessary problems and delays.

1. Keep the lens capped at all times when it is not in use.
2. Keep fingers off the lens.
3. Clean the lens only when necessary and only under the direction of a supervisor.
4. Never take the lens apart.
5. Keep the glass cover on the copyboard clean at all times.
6. Sprinkle some water on the floor before sweeping around the camera. This will prevent most of the dirt and dust from circulating and filtering into the lens and camera.
7. When the camera is not in use cover it completely with a large piece of plastic or cloth.

Projects
(Keep a Record)

1. Using the gray scale, determine the tonal range of a photograph and place the scale and photograph in the copyboard.
2. Set the camera for same size reproduction.
3. Determine and set the proper screen distance of the glass halftone screen being used.
4. Clean and mount the glass halftone screen in the camera.
5. Determine the proper lens aperture settings by the:
   a. Focusing-by-eye method
   b. 1:64 ratio method
6. Expose the copy using the two-stop-plus flash method and develop the negative. Analyze the negative, determine any faults and determine the reasons for them. Practice until a good halftone negative has been determined by the instructor.
7. Expose the copy using the magenta contact screen and develop the negative. Analyze the negative, determine any

faults and the reasons for them. Practice until a good half-tone has been approved by the instructor.

8. Expose the copy using the autoscreen Ortho Film and develop the negative. Analyze and determine any faults and the reasons for them. Practice until a good halftone negative has been approved by the instructor.

9. Expose a screened or printed halftone until a negative is produced showing the least moire pattern. (Use the methods described.)

10. Reduce the photograph 10 per cent, compute and set the CE, BE, and NET.

11. Determine and set the $Nf_{\#}$ when the OET remains the same.

12. Expose and develop a negative for both problems until a good halftone has been made.

13. Make an outline stating the proper procedure for making a halftone negative.

Review Questions

1. Copy is seen on the ground glass of a camera rightside up when placed right-side up on the copyboard. True or False:

2. The image cannot be seen until a film is developed. True or False:

3. Film base is opaque. True or False:

4. Antihalation film eliminates blurring of the image. True or False:

5. The short stop bath is used to prolong the life of the fixing bath. True or False:

6. The fixing bath also stops development. True or False:

7. A halftone print is made up of a multitude of infinitesimal dots. True or False:

8. The magenta contact screen is made of glass. True or False:

9. No screen distance or separation is required of contact screens. True or False:

10. Screens should be stored flat to prevent warping. True or False:

11. A moire pattern results when a previously printed halftone is re-photographed. True or False:

12. The Canon Re-Screener permits direct photographing of previously printed halftones. True or False:
13. Pre-screened film is available. True or False:
14. Spliced negatives should overlap slightly. True or False:

Match the characteristic of the film listed at the right with the type listed at the left.

15. Panchromatic ____   a. Sensitive to all colors
                         b. Blue photographs as white
16. Monochromatic ____   c. Thin base
                         d. Color blind
17. Orthochromatic ____ e. For line and halftone negatives

Match the developing process listed at the right with the films listed at the left.

18. Orthochromatic ____ a. Total darkness
19. Panchromatic ____   b. Wratten series OA yellow or
                            O orange
20. Monochromatic ____   c. Wratten series 1A red light

Match the statements at the left with the statements at the right.

21. Duotone ____   a. 2-color reproduction of a
                            halftone made from one half-
                            tone negative.
22. Duograph ____   b. 2-color reproduction made
                            from a keyplate made from
                            an angled halftone negative.
23. Duotype ____   c. 2-color reproduction made
                            by two halftone negatives at
                            two different screen angles.
24. Yellow screen angle ____ d. 75 degrees
25. Red screen angle ____   e. 15 degrees
26. Blue screen angle ____   f. 90 degrees
27. Black screen angle ____   g. 45 degrees
28. One stop ____   h. The detail, highlight and
                                 middletone exposure plus
                                 flash

29. Two stop
30. Three stop

i. Detail exposure plus flash
j. Detail and highlight exposure plus flash

31. The normal position of lights is at an angle of:

a. 35 degrees
b. 40 degrees

c. 45 degrees
d. 50 degrees

32. Halftone screens are available in these sizes:

a. 100-110-133-150
b. 95-100-120-160
c. 100-120-133-155
d. 85-100-115-133

Cameras may be of eight types:

33. _____
34. _____
35. _____
36. _____
37. _____
38. _____
39. _____
40. _____

Name the five basic parts of a camera:

41. _____
42. _____
43. _____
44. _____
45. _____

The dark room should have at least three physical necessities:

46. _____
47. _____
48. _____

The developing sink should have at least three physical characteristics:

49. _____

50. _____

51. _____

The dark room should have at least two lighting systems:

52. _____

53. _____

Selection of a lens includes:

54. _____

55. _____

56. _____

57. _____

58. _____

Light sources on cameras include:

59. _____

60. _____

61. _____

Emulsions may be divided into three types:

62. _____

63. _____

64. _____

A flat consists of:

65. _____

66. _____

67. _____

68. _____

69. The job of the camera is to make a _____ .

70. The use of _____ allows good negatives to be made of colored backgrounds on copy.

71. Filters are inserted in the _____ .
72. Developing solutions should be _____ degrees F.
73. Thilosulfate is known as _____ .
74. After fixation, a negative must be _____ .
75. Emulsions consist of a coating of _____ on transparent acetate.
76. A negative that contains line and halftone elements will produce a _____ plate.
77. To eliminate opaquing, a _____ _____ halftone negative may be made.
78. Operative settings are referred to as _____ numbers.
79. The common method to determine proper distance for a screen is the _____ ratio.
80. A halftone is made from a _____ tone photograph.
81. The term used to place lines on the emulsion of a film is _____ .
82. Light entering the camera is controlled by the _____ .
83. When photographing red as black, use a _____ filter with pan film.
84. When photographing red as black, use a _____ filter with ortho film.

CHAPTER 6

Offset Platemaking

What is an offset plate? What is the plate made of? How many types of plates are there? What are the most popular plates?

After the negative is stripped into position on a sheet of goldenrod paper, the "flat" is forwarded to the platemaking section where the platemaker will expose the image to an offset plate.

The offset plate is usually a flat sheet of rolled metal or combination of metals. Some plates, however, are made of paper and plastics.

In large offset plants, the platemaking department is a separate section in which the personnel are highly specialized. However, in small offset plants where only one or a few offset presses are installed, it is common practice to combine camera and press activities with platemaking.

Cameramen and pressmen should understand platemaking thoroughly because it is the intermediate step or link that combines their work. Platemaking is as important as any other operation in the plant in obtaining a high quality of work.

The Offset Plate

Plates can be divided into six general classifications: multi-metal, direct-image, deep-etch, surface-coated, xerography, and dry-offset.

The surface-coated plate has a thin layer of undissolved albumin or other coating solution over its entire area. After the image has been exposed on the plate, developing ink is placed on the plate and then washed off, leaving an image on the plate. This is the most popular plate in the plants utilizing small offset presses.

The deep-etch plate which employs a positive instead of a negative has the printing area etched slightly below the non-printing area. This type of plate permits the image to carry more ink and also has a longer press life.

The dry-offset plate is a metal plate that has the non-printing area slightly etched below the image area and deeper than the multi-metal plates. This plate is used on the offset press without the use of a dampening system.

The xerography plate is made by a photographic-electrostatic process. Xerography is employed for making paper (masters) and metal offset plates. An image is first electro-statically produced on a xerox plate. This image is transferred again electrostatically to either the paper or metal plate, and fused for permanency. This operation does not involve liquids or film negatives.

The multi-metal plate consists of either two or three layers of different metals. The top layer of metal is usually copper but may be some other metal that attracts ink. The bottom layer consists of a hard metal such as stainless steel to carry the water. The top layer is etched away in the non-printing area, leaving the image slightly above the non-printing area, but not enough to do away with the fountain solution.

The direct-image plate does not use a photographic process. The image may be placed on these plates by typewriting, printing, drawing by hand or using a greasy substance, such as crayon or a special type pencil containing a greasy substance.

General Steps of Making a Plate

Before explaining in detail the operational sequence of making three of the most commonly used plates, it will be best to acquaint the student in brief with the few general steps required in making an offset plate from the beginning until it is ready for the press.

These steps are:

1. Graining
2. Counter-etching
3. Coating
4. Exposing
5. Developing

6. Applying caustic solution
7. Desensitizing
8. Applying gum arabic
9. Applying asphaltum

Depending upon the type of plate, some of these steps are eliminated. The steps that are not used will become apparent when we describe the operations of making the plates in detail. The steps stated above are in the sequence that must be followed in making these plates.

NOTE: When applying counter-etch, caustic solution, desensitizer, gum arabic, and asphaltum, a sufficient amount of solution to cover the plate should be poured in the center of the plate and spread using a circular motion until the entire plate is covered. A separate applicator (piece of cotton or soft cloth) must be used for each solution. The developing ink is also applied in the same manner but need not cover the entire plate. However, be sure that the entire image area is covered, otherwise the plate may have to be discarded.

Plate Graining

Plates are grained for two reasons:
1. To roughen the surface area so it will hold the image, and
2. To allow the blank areas to carry water in a satisfactory manner.

The grain of a plate has countless high and low spots, hills and valleys or peaks and pits, which act as reservoirs and carry water during the printing.

The plate can be processed to produce a coarse, medium, or fine grain. The nature of the work determines the proper grain.

Plates are grained by placing them in a machine called a grainer, (Fig. 6-1) clamping them to the bed and rotating marbles and a cutting agent over them. (The marbles are usually made of steel and the most common cutting agents are sand and crushed

Fig. 6-1. Offset plates are usually grained. Steel marbles and a cutting agent are used in the graining process.

quartz.) Water is added, the machine is started, brought to the desired speed, and allowed to run for a predetermined time. Then the machine is stopped and the bed is tilted to allow the water, cutting agent and marbles to run off into a trap. The plates are rinsed off and removed to a sink where they are cleaned and dried with a fan. They are then marked with the type of grain on the reverse side and stored for use.

The different kinds of grain are generally referred to and classified by number: 00, 1, 2, 3, etc. The lower numbers indicate fine and become coarser as the numbers get larger.

Many arguments revolve around the question of proper grain among pressmen and between pressmen and platemakers.

The platemaker prefers a fine-grain plate for all classes of work because he can produce a sharper image and a better looking plate. The pressmen would rather have a coarse grain because it will carry the water better, thus keeping his troubles to a minimum.

There is no doubt that certain types of work are more critical than others and one grain is preferable over others, but for the general commercial work, the medium grain is accepted in most shops. The average shop will carry the three grains; namely, fine, medium and coarse, to provide for a wide range of work.

Fine grain plates are considered best for halftones and other fine sharp work.

If not handled properly on the press, this kind of plate will cause many problems. The grain is so shallow that the water is barely carried on the surface of the plate. The ink rollers and blanket, instead of rolling over the water, will squeeze (or squeegee) it to the end or tail of the cylinder. Even though an excessive amount of water seems to be going on the plate, the plate will tend to scum because the grain is so shallow the plate cannot hold the water properly. The rollers and blanket squeeze out and absorb the water which should be held on the plate.

Under these conditions, other problems will arise. The water will have a tendency to mix with the ink causing the ink to emulsify; the rollers will become stripped and drying problems will prevail resulting in a poor image. Eventually the plate will break down or lose the image.

Coated or enamel paper is very troublesome to run when using a fine-grained plate. The water, being squeegeed toward the tail of the plate, will pile up and gradually flip or throw drops of water on to the paper. No matter how small the drops may be, they will cause the sheets to stick together in the pile. This water, stained or discolored by the ink, will leave dirty spots on the paper.

The fine grain is obtained by using small, light marbles and a very fine cutting agent such as pumice stone, emery dust, or very fine crushed flint, quartz. The graining time may also need to be extended due to the lightness and fineness of the materials being used.

Medium grain has been found the most suitable for a wide range from fine linework to halftone to rather heavy solid linework. The average shop will use this for the general run of work. An occasional exception is made for extremely fine or extremely heavy solids.

This grain may be obtained by using as cutting agents No. 1 or 0 flint sand or their equivalent. The graining period may be extended slightly beyond the normal time for the coarse grain.

Coarse grain is best suited for solids, heavy type, lines, and reversals (printed material in which the background is in the color being printed and the image is in white). This work requires a great amount of ink; the coarse grain will enable the pressman to carry enough water to keep the blank areas clean, prevent the image from spreading, and the plate from scumming.

An extremely coarse grain definitely is not suitable for fine lines and halftones because the dots or parts of the fine lines may fall into the low areas of the grain and be so low they will not print.

Not all plates can be grained. Plates with a soft metal surface, like zinc, can be grained and regrained for use another time.

Counter Etch

Counter-etching is a chemical treatment given to a plate after graining. Its primary purpose is to make the plate more "friendly" or sensitive to grease, but it also helps to remove surface dirt which loosens during the process.

The counter-etch solution is composed of an acid mixed with water. The acid used depends upon the type of plate used. Acetic acid may be used for aluminum plates. For zinc plates, hydrochloric, acetic, or nitric acid may be used. The simplest, safest all-purpose counter-etch solution is a 5 percent solution of acetic acid.

After the plate is counter-etched and the solution is washed off, it is placed in a whirler where the coating solution is put on.

Coating Solution

The coating solution placed on the plate makes it sensitive to lights. This coating can be washed away with plain water. When it is exposed to sunlight or white light, a chemical change takes place, and the coating becomes insoluble in water. Since sunlight is impractical, arc lights are used. (The arc light is the artificial light which most closely resembles sunlight.)

When the printing frame containing the plate and flat is turned to an upright position and exposed, the light goes through the transparent areas (image) of the negative and strikes the coating on the plate, changing it to a substance that is not soluble in water.

The opaque or black areas of the negative prevent light from reaching blank parts of the plate. Where there should be no printing, the coating remains soluble and will wash away during the development.

The coating solution is composed of egg albumin flakes (dissolved), ammonium-bichromate (or dichromate), ammonium hydroxide (28 percent) and water.

Once the plate is coated and dried, it is ready to be placed in the vacuum printing frame or photo-composing machine to have the image exposed.

Vacuum Printing Frame and Exposure Time

The vacuum printing frame, Fig. 6-2, holds the sensitized plate and negative together while they are exposed to light to obtain the photographic image on the plate.

The bed of the frame is mounted on a pedestal or other base and has a heavy rubber and fiber blanket on which the plate is placed. A hinged glass cover is provided, similar to the copyboard of a camera, to help bring the negative and plate into contact. The glass also holds the plate in position when the frame is turned to a vertical position for exposure.

A motor driven suction pump is connected by a rubber hose to a valve in the blanket. After the negative is placed in position on the plate and the glass cover is clamped shut, the pump is turned on to suck air out of the closed frame creating a vacuum. This vacuum guarantees complete contact between the negative and plate. The glass frame is then turned to the vertical or upright position to face the light squarely.

Two factors play an important part in the proper exposure of an offset plate:

1. The relative humidity in the room where the plate is being made.
2. The distance between the lights and the frame.

Relative humidity plays an important part in the offset plant. Extreme variations in humidity will cause inconsistencies in plate-making (especially when exposing the plate), press operation,

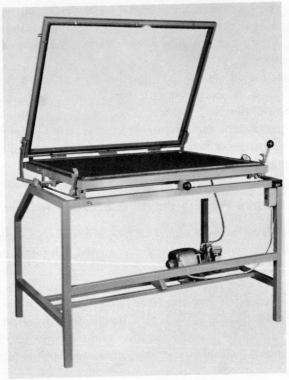

Fig. 6-2. The vacuum printing frame holds the plate and the negative together so that they may be exposed to light and the image transferred to the plate.

drying of inks, static-electricity, as well as stretching and shrinking of paper stock.

Humidity is moisture in the air. When the humidity is low, the air is dry and will absorb moisture from any surrounding exposed materials that contain more moisture than the air itself. When the humidity is high, the air is damp and it will give off moisture, which will be absorbed by any surrounding exposed materials that contain less moisture than the air.

One hundred percent relative humidity is achieved when the air contains all the moisture it can absorb. This is called the saturation point. At 100 per cent relative humidity, the amount of water contained in a cubic foot of air will vary according to the temperature. The warmer the air, the more water it can contain per cubic foot. Should the air contain 70 percent of the total amount it could hold, whatever the temperature, the relative humidity is said to be 70 percent.

Various indicators and thermometers for measuring the relative humidity, such as the hygrometer, are available and one should be on hand at all times.

The sensitivity of the bichromated sensitizers used in platemaking procedures will increase or decrease according to the relative humidity and temperature of the workroom atmosphere. These coatings, when in their dry unexposed state, will absorb the moisture in the air which will cause variations in the sensitivity.

As stated, when the humidity is high, any surrounding exposed materials will absorb moisture. To prevent this, the heat from the lights during exposure must be controlled to such a degree that proper developing of the plate will result. As the humidity increases the exposure must be shorter. The ideal atmospheric condition for platemaking is about 50 percent relative humidity with the temperature at about 70° F. If the humidity varies more than 5 percent, a change in exposure will be necessary.

To obtain the proper basic exposure, place a 24-step gray scale negative beside the image in the flat. (Make sure the flat is cut out so the gray scale negative will be exposed.) Make a test exposure anywhere from two or four minutes, remove the plate from the frame and spread developing ink over it. Place the plate in the sink and wash away the ink. The darker areas which did not receive enough exposure will wash away during the development of the plate. Those areas not so dark will produce the image on the plate.

Beginning with the darkest area of the gray scale, if the gray scale image develops up to the sixth step, the plate is properly exposed and satisfactorily developed. If the steps on the gray scale over the ninth step are retained during the development, the plate is overexposed and any halftones on the plate will be a little "plugged up" or filled in. If the plate doesn't contain any halftones, but only linework, then the scale may be developed up to about the eighth step without any noticeable filling in.

After the basic exposure has been determined, a chart should be made recording this particular exposure and the relative humidity. Every exposure after that should be recorded along with the relative humidity, until a complete chart has been made. These readings will be helpful for all future exposures.

Light distance. In general, the distance from the arc lights to the frame should equal the diagonal measurement of the printing frame being used.

Just as it may become necessary to change the distance of the lights on the camera, the same holds true for changing the distance on the vacuum frames to concentrate the light over a larger or smaller image area. This new exposure time may be determined by the following formula:

$$\frac{(ND)^2}{(OD)^2} \times OET = NET$$

ND equals New Distance
OD equals Original Distance
OET equals Original Exposure Time

A sample problem:

Exposure time for plates was 2 min. at 4 ft. and the lights had to be moved to a new distance of 6 ft. What would the new exposure time be?

Solution:

ND^2 equals 6 $\times$ 6 equals 36
OD^2 equals 4 $\times$ 4 equals 16
36 $\div$ 16 equals 2¼
2 (OET) $\times$ 2¼ equals 4½ min. —New Exposure time.

The Photo-Composing (Step and Repeat) Machine

The photo-composing machine, or step and repeat machine (Fig. 6-3) is slowly replacing the vacuum printing frame. In addition to being able to expose a single negative, the plate-maker can expose as many images as desired on the same plate (Fig. 6-4) utilizing a single negative with more ease than the printing frame. Also when making color plates for four color process, the accuracy

Fig. 6-3. The photocomposing machine, used to make offset plates, is slowly replacing the vacuum printing frame.

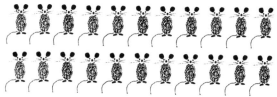

Fig. 6-4. The illustrative material shown here was reproduced on the offset plate from a single negative with a single mouse on it through the use of a step-and-repeat photocomposing machine. *The Baughman Company.*

necessary to register the negatives into position is a valuable feature of this machine.

Generally there are two types of photo-composing machines, the horizontal and vertical. The vertical is the most popular. These machines differ in construction, plate holders, and mechanical devices for holding and registering the negatives. Both have a bed on which to place the plate. A device holds and registers the negative, and by mechanical means the negative can be moved in both directions, (in the case of the vertical type the negative is moved vertically and horizontally) to any predetermined position on the plate.

The machines are equipped with a means of obtaining a vacuum between the negative and plate the same as on the vacuum printing frame.

Some of the smaller machines are scaled and can be moved to ⅟₃₂ in. while the larger machines are also scaled and can be moved to one .001 in. This accuracy makes these machines invaluable, especially in close critical work required when making four color process plates. Figure 6-5 shows the front view of a large photo-composing machine.

For instance: when the first plate is made, the negative is registered very accurately into the negative holder, then a recording of the machine settings is made. On the succeeding negatives, each negative is registered into the same position in the negative holder and the machine is set to the same readings recorded from the first plate.

The final result will be four plates (one for each color) with the image being registered into an identical position on each plate.

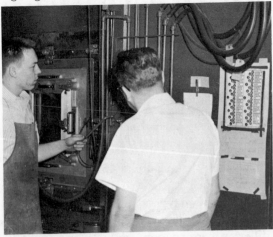

Fig. 6-5. Large photocomposing machines allow greater accuracy in platemaking. This accuracy is especially important in process color work. *Rutherford Company, Division of Sun Chemical.*

Misomex (Step and Repeat) Photo Composing Machine

The Misomex step and repeat photo composing machine (Fig. 6-3) is a fully automatic machine used for exposing more than one of an identical image on a plate. The operator loads the film or metal plate and original negative, then sets a control panel. This panel automatically establishes and governs all further operations. Push buttons regulate the exposure time and automatic gauges set the vacuum air pressure. A hold button makes it possible for the operator to interrupt and make changes any time during the automatic sequence. At the completion of the exposure, a bell alerts the operator.

This machine is capable of 350 repeat steps per hour with photographic materials, or 70 steps per hour with metal plates.

For multicolor work, cross-hair register marks sight the original material in precision-notched and pre-registered frames. A vernier position control with micrometer dial makes it possible to set the finest settings to .001 in.

After being exposed, the plate is ready for the developing ink which will bring out the image.

Developing Ink

The developing ink used on plates after exposure is a volatile, quick-drying ink made especially for photographic plates. This ink has three main purposes:

1. It provides the greasy foundation or image necessary in offset.
2. It makes the printing image visible on the plate.
3. It serves as an acid resistant against the action of offset etching solutions.

Ink which is too stiff or tacky will make development difficult. The plate should be developed immediately after the ink is applied. If left on a plate longer than 30 min., it will dry hard and may be difficult or even impossible to wash away. Turpentine or other volatile evaporating substance may be mixed with the developing ink if it becomes too thick, but *this should not be done unnecessarily.* Developing ink works better if the container in which it comes is kept tightly closed to prevent evaporation. Ink should be used directly from the container.

When the ink is placed on the plate, it is not necessary to spread the ink over the entire surface of the plate. One should, however, make sure that all the printing areas are covered.

Various developing inks are available, but in an emergency the ink may be mixed in the shop. (See the formula section of this chapter.)

After the ink is rubbed on the plate, the plate is placed in the sink and washed with water.

Caustic Solution

Some of the plate coating will not wash away under water: therefore, a caustic solution is used for cleaning plates after developing. If the plate is not thoroughly clean when it is placed on the press, it will show very fine dirt on the blank areas of the paper. The caustic solution will destroy grease. Caution must be exercised when using it, because the developing ink is a greasy substance and if the caustic solution is too strong or kept on the plate too long, it can weaken the image or remove it entirely.

The caustic solution contains ammonium hydroxide (28 percent and water, or bicarbonate of soda (baking soda) and water.

Desensitizer

As the plate was initially sensitized to light, it now must be desensitized to light. In spite of the thorough washing given to the plate, first with water and then with the caustic solution, tiny particles of coating solution may still cling to the plate. Desensitizing (etching) action removes these traces from the non-printing areas of the plate and cleans out the image area, particularly where there are halftones.

The desensitizing solution consists of a gum arabic solution 14 degrees Baume, ammonium dichromate stock solution, and phosphoric acid.

After the plate is desensitized and washed clean, care must be taken to prevent the plate from becoming oxidized or pitted from the reaction of moisture and air on the metal.

Gum Arabic

Gum Arabic has wide use in the printing industry. As previously explained, when mixed with other ingredients, it acts as a desensitizer.

Another use is the prevention of oxidation of the metal. Oxidation takes place when the press is stopped or when the plate is stored. To prevent this, gum is spread over the plate with a moistened sponge or cloth, and dried. When the plate is ready for use, it is simply washed with water.

Other uses of gum arabic, which will be further explained, are:
1. As coating solution of deep etch plates.
2. As press fountain solutions.

Asphaltum

If the plate is to be stored for a while before being placed on the press, or if the plate has already been used and is ready to be stored away for a time, then the application of asphaltum is necessary.

Asphaltum is a substance applied to the plate image area when the plate is to be stored. If the developing ink or press ink (after the plate was run on the press) is allowed to stay on the plate, it will harden and will not take ink again. To maintain an ink-receptive image, the ink is washed away and asphaltum is applied. Asphaltum forms a non-drying film over the image area.

If the plate is to be printed using a color other than black, it is advisable to gum the plate, then wash out the ink, and apply asphaltum. When the plate is ready for use, the gum and asphaltum will wash off easily with a sponge and water, leaving the clean image to accept the colored ink.

The Zinc Plate

The zinc plate is a surface-coated plate and was *the most commonly used* for albumin and deep-etch plates. This plate has advantages and disadvantages.

Advantages:
1. The plate can be grained or roughened easily and regrained a number of times for other work.
2. The initial cost is lower.
3. It has a more natural affinity for grease.

Disadvantages:
1. The metal is soft, therefore, the grain wears faster.
2. The dark color makes the contrast between the blank areas of the plate and very fine line or halftone dots less distinct.

Making A Zinc (Albumin) Plate. The following procedure may be used to make the zinc albumin plate.

1. Select the plate containing the proper grain for the specific type of work that is being reproduced.

2. Place the plate in the sink and wet with running water to prevent streaks that will otherwise occur from the chemical reaction that is about to take place.

3. Raise the plate by one edge to allow the excess water to flow off and place the plate again in the sink.

4. Pour on a liberal amount of counter-etch solution (Fig. 6-6).

5. Pick up the plate by opposite edges, forming a round trough, and roll it rapidly from side to side, allowing the counter-etch to flow over the entire plate. Lay the plate down and apply another amount of counter-etch and repeat the rolling operation. The plate may be scrubbed slightly with a bristle brush, if preferred, but not hard enough to scratch the grain.

6. Wash the plate well and thoroughly under running water, using a wad of clean absorbent cotton.

7. Pick up the plate by one edge and drain off the excess water.

8. Place the plate in the whirler. The whirler (Fig. 6-7) is a device in which the plates are placed and rotated while the coating solution is poured over them. This rotation continues for a pre-determined time to allow the coating solution to dry. Start the whirler, allowing the plate to rotate slowly.

9. Allow water to flow on the plate until the albumin coating solution is prepared.

Fig. 6-6. When making a zinc plate, a liberal amount of counter-etch solution is poured on the plate.

Fig. 6-7. The plate is sensitized with a coating solution while it is whirling.

10. Prepare albumin solution by measuring about four ounces into a small graduated container. Cover the mouth of the container with a couple of layers of cheesecloth to act as a filter.

11. Turn off the water and allow excess water to run off.

12. While plate is still wet and whirling, pour the coating solution on the plate (Fig. 6-7). Hold the container close to the plate to avoid splattering and causing air bubbles. Start pouring in the center of the plate and slowly work from the center to the outside of the plate.

13. Allow the plate to rotate slowly until the centrifugal motion causes the solution to cover the plate.

14. Speed up the whirler and allow the plate to whirl for a couple of minutes. Then turn on the fan or heater to speed drying.

15. After the plate is completely dried, remove it from the whirler and place the plate on the exposure frame. (The reverse side of the plate should be wiped off because some water and coating solution usually seep under it during the whirling. Another person may be needed to wipe off the plate while one holds the plate by its edges.)

16. Place the layout sheet (flat) containing the negative or negatives on the plate. Tape the flat to the plate, making sure it is placed in the proper position, squarely or evenly across the gripper or lead edge.

17. Inspect the glass cover to make sure it is clean. Clean it if necessary. (A good practice is to clean the glass cover while the plate is still in the whirling machine.)

18. Close the hinged glass cover and clamp it shut.

19. Turn on the suction pump to obtain the vacuum.

20. When the vacuum is obtained, tilt the frame to face the arc lights.

21. Place the lights directly at the area showing through the negative. Turn on the lights and expose for the desired length of time (Fig. 6-8).

22. After the plate has been exposed, cut off the arc light, bring

Fig. 6-8. The negative and plate are placed in the vacuum frame for exposure.

Fig. 6-9. After the plate has been exposed, a small amount of developing ink is poured in the center of the plate.

Fig. 6-10. Developing ink is rubbed over the entire image area of the plate. A circular motion is recommended.

the printing frame back to the original position, turn off the suction pump, unlock clamps, raise glass cover, and move plate from the frame to the work table.

23. Remove the flat from the plate and lay it aside until the plate is developed. (It may take some time to file the flat properly, and the plate should be developed immediately after being exposed.)

24. Pour a small amount of developing ink (Fig. 6-9) on the center of the plate. With a clean soft pad of cloth or absorbent cotton, rub the developing ink in a circular motion (Fig. 6-10) over the entire image area of the plate. (Keep rubbing until the pad has taken up all the surplus ink.)

25. Place the plate in the sink and allow lukewarm running water to flow over the plate for a few seconds (Fig. 6-11).

26. Rub the plate surface very gently with a clean pad of cloth or cotton while still under running water. Remove all traces of the

Fig. 6-11. After the plate has been covered with developing ink, it is placed in the sink; lukewarm water is run over the plate.

developing ink from the clear or non-printing areas of the plate. (Avoid continued use of a dirty pad. Turn the pad around often so that a clean portion is always used. This prevents rubbing the ink into areas which would cause problems.)

27. After the plate has been wiped clean, turn off the water and allow the excess water to flow off. Pour on a sufficient amount of a caustic soda solution and wash all blank areas of the plate, paying particular attention to spots that are dirty or ragged. This solution will remove the small amount of albumin egg coating which plain water does not take off.

28. Wash off the solution and tilt the plate to allow the excess to flow off.

29. Desensitize the plate by pouring on desensitizing solution. This removes any tiny traces of dirt or ink still clinging to the plate except the ink or developing ink on the image areas. Allow this solution to remain on the plate for a few minutes, then flush off thoroughly with water. Allow the excess water to flow off, but do not dry.

30. Remove the plate from the sink and place it on a clean area of the work table. Pour on a sufficient amount of gum arabic solution and spread it over the entire plate with a clean sponge. Rub the gum briskly and evenly up, down, and across the plate with a clean pad of cheese cloth, (Fig. 6-12) until a thin, hard finish, free of streaks, is obtained. Fan the plate dry.

The plate is now ready to be mounted on the press. However, if the plate is to be stored for any length of time before it is placed on

Fig. 6-12. The plate is removed from the sink and rubbed with gum arabic solution.

the press, the developing ink on the image area may dry and may not take ink.

To maintain this ink-receptive image on the plate, asphaltum is applied to the image area. This is applied as follows:

1. While the plate is still gummed, remove the developing ink from the image with a little turpentine or press cleaning solvent.

2. Apply a coating of asphaltum and rub it down to a thin coating, and dry.

3. Until it is ready for the press, store the plate in an area where it will not be damaged.

Repairing plates is a task that very few pressmen enjoy, because repair causes many lost production hours. Eventually a new plate is needed as well. Only zinc plates can be repaired. Repairing plates is justified in most cases when a relatively few more impressions are needed to complete the run.

Plates are repaired:

1. By using compounds to prolong the life of a plate.

2. By "fill in"—to repair broken lines and letters or small holes.

3. By "take out"—to remove dirty spots, register marks or other parts of the plate or image prints.

4. By "rub up"—to bring back or strengthen spots or areas that may become weak from an unknown cause.

5. By adding to an image after the plate has been made.

Several compounds or plate bases are on the market and may be used to prolong the life of a plate. However, to obtain the best results, directions furnished by the manufacturer for their use should be followed closely.

Broken lines and letters or small holes in solids may be repaired by "scratching in." More harm than good is usually accomplished on halftones or very fine work. It is only through experience that a pressman learns what he can repair and what he should leave alone.

To make a repair of this nature, the following procedure may be used:

1. Gum plate, smooth it down carefully and dry.

2. Fold a clean sheet of paper two or three times and place it on the plate so the hand can rest upon it, to prevent getting perspiration from the hands on the plate. Moisture will cut through the gum.

3. Using a sharp knife point or a pen or needle, scratch the gum from the place to be filled in, being careful not to scratch too deeply. The purpose is to remove only the gum and to lightly scratch the surface of the plate that the etch has desensitized. If the plate is scratched too deeply, it may not take ink.

4. Rub ink or grease into the spots "scratched in."

Repairing can be completed while the plate is on the press or directly after the plate has been made. The plate should be etched and gummed before proceeding.

It is often desirable to fill in larger areas of the image by hand. This is usually done while making the plate when possible, and very seldom tried while the plate is on the press.

This repair may be done as follows:

1. After the plate has been exposed and developed, counter etch the plate again.

2. Wash, rinse well, and if possible stand the plate on edge against a wall or rack and dry it with a fan.

3. The image is then painted by using one of two agents:
   a. Tusche is generally used, but because it tends to be water solvent it sometimes causes other trouble.
   b. Asphaltum (thinned down with a little turpentine) may be used.

This will repel the water during the other operations.

NOTE: When working with asphaltum, use extreme care because it will run into the grain of the plate and also cause additional trouble.

4. Paint on a thin film of asphaltum or tusche using a small camel's hair brush.

5. Allow the plate to dry completely.

6. Gum plate and dry.

7. Roll the plate up and finish as usual.

To remove dirty spots, register marks, or any other unwanted areas, a "snake slip" is generally used. (Snake slip or snake stone is usually powdered pumice stone, gum water and etch worked into a stiff paste, molded into small sticks and dried.)

To take out these areas, proceed as follows:

1. Wet the area with a water sponge and polish the area with the snake slip.

2. Sponge down the area and repeat until all trace of the work is gone. Caution: Polish as little as necessary in removing the unwanted areas, because polishing with the snake slip also removes the grain from the plate. This will only add to the trouble.

3. Etch the polished areas with weak etch if this repair is being done while the plate is on the press. If not, it should be done immediately before etching the plate.

After the plate is developed and certain areas appear to be weak, or if certain areas become weak on the press, it can sometimes be saved or brought back by "rubbing up." Usually, when the image becomes weak during the press run, it can only be brought back temporarily and if this operation is repeated more than once or twice, it will be noted that it comes back a little less each time. On a sizable press run, another plate will be necessary. To do this operation on halftones usually proves more disastrous than helpful.

To rub-up, the following procedure may be used:

1. Use a clean, soft cotton rag. Form it into a neat compact wad that can be held in the hand.

2. Put a little ink that is in use on one end of an ink slab or work table and a little asphaltum on the other end. *Do not mix.*

3. Dab the rag in the asphaltum, then in the ink, and rub out well on a clean area of the slab.

4. Repeat until rag is well soaked. Use short circular motions in rubbing.

5. Rub a gum sponge over the plate where it is to be done, then sponge with water.

6. Rub the inked rag over spot to be strengthened. (Caution: Stop rubbing before the plate becomes dry.) Sponge off the plate and examine. Repeat if necessary, renewing the ink on the rag if necessary.

Experience will teach how much ink and asphaltum to use, and in what proportions.

Sometimes it is necessary or desirable to add a line or other work to the image after the plate has been made. Rather than remake another plate, the following procedure may be used:

1. Prepare a layout sheet or flat containing the negative of the work to be added and position so that it can be registered into the proper place on the plate.

2. Cover the first image on the plate well with ink.

3. Counter-etch, coat, expose, and finish the plate as if making an entirely new plate.

There are other ways to "doctor" a plate, but in general, when a plate goes bad on the press, it will continue to go bad in spite of everything that can be done. Sometimes a second plate will also go bad before the run is completed. If this happens, then it is advisable to check the press for proper adjustments, ink, water, etc. to determine the cause. Only through experience can one hope to accomplish the operations that will obtain the desired results.

Making a Pre-Sensitized Plate

Pre-sensitized plates are surface coated by the manufacturer and ready for exposure when removed from the original package. This eliminates the processes of washing, counter-etching, and coating as is done to zinc plates.

When a plate is removed from its package, the plates remaining in the package should be resealed for protection against light.

Only four steps are necessary in the preparation of a pre-sensitized plate, and all four are practically done the same way as a zinc plate. They are: (1) Exposing, (2) Developing, (3) Desensitizing, (4) Gumming.

Each manufacturer of pre-sensitized plates has a complete line of prepared solutions for their plates. It is advisable to follow the instructions and use the solutions of each plate manufacturer.

The face side of the plate contains the sensitive coating. This face side is placed "up" as the package is opened. It is further identified by the trademark usually found in one of the corners of the plate.

Making a Deep-Etch Plate

Deep-etch plates are made by several methods, one of which will be explained here. Only slight variations in procedures are used in other methods.

The deep-etch process requires the use of positives instead of negatives. The positives are made from the negative, either by contact in the darkroom, or by photographing the negative with the camera.

The solutions and chemicals used in making the deep etch differ from those used for making a zinc or pre-sensitized plate. These will be explained.

Once the flat containing the positive is prepared (same as using a negative) proceed as follows:

1. Select the proper grain for the type of work to be done, wash and counter-etch as in zinc platemaking.

2. A positive deep-etch coating solution is used to coat the plate. Set the whirler at a speed of 40 to 50 R.P.M. and pour the coating solution on to the center of the plate through a wad of cheese cloth, beginning in the center and slowly working to the outside edges, exactly as in coating a zinc albumin plate. Be careful not to cause any bubbles.

3. Increase the speed of the whirler to about 80 R.P.M. and apply a little heat. Too much heat will cause difficulty in developing.

4. When the plate is thoroughly dry, remove it from the whirler and dry the reverse side and edges.

5. Place the plate on the printing frame and proceed with placing the flat on the plate and expose it in the same manner as a zinc albumin plate. However, the exposure time should be 25 percent to 50 percent longer.

6. After exposure is completed, remove the plate from the printing frame to the work table.

7. All the blank areas are now "stopped out," that is, they are painted over with a "stop-out solution" using an artist's brush. This solution is generally a form of shellac.

8. Fan dry.

9. Pour on the positive-developing solution and spread with a developing pad over the entire surface of the plate, using a circular motion. During this development, the coating on the plate which has not been affected by light is removed. This is the image itself, just the opposite of the albumin plate. Continue the circular motion until the bare printing areas are exposed and a foaming action begins. Remove with a squeegee and coat again with developer. Squeegee again. When the coating has been removed down to the metal, development is complete.

10. Pour on a quantity of etching solution and spread it over the entire surface with a pad. Allow this solution to penetrate for about 1½ min. on that portion of the image which has not taken the exposure (bare metal). Then squeegee off.

11. Pour on a little more developing solution over the plate. This is to guard against corrosion. Work this solution in with the developing pad to neutralize the etching solution. Squeegee the plate.

12. Wipe off the plate with a clean pad saturated with anhydrous alcohol. Repeat three or four times making sure the plate is clean. Dry thoroughly with a fan.

13. Pour on a quantity of deep-etch lacquer and spread it over the entire surface of the plate with a clean cloth pad. This lacquer will form the first base of the image. Dry out the lacquer thoroughly with a fan.

One can vary the procedure in the next step: apply the developing ink next, or apply the asphaltum to form a more stable greasy base, and then apply the developing ink.

14. Once the developing ink is applied, smooth it out with a cloth pad, rubbing it down until it is dry. Use fan to dry thoroughly.

15. Place the plate in the sink and wash with warm water.

16. Finish the plate using the same procedure as for the zinc albumin plates:

a. Desensitize.
b. Rinse with running water.
c. Allow excess water to flow off and squeegee.
d. Gum the plate.

When the plate is complete, the image should be etched slightly below the surface of the plate. This is usually about one and one-half thousandths of an inch.

As previously stated, several variations exist in making a deep etch plate, and different supplies may be purchased for making these plates. Before beginning a deep-etch plate, it is advisable to purchase the supplies from a manufacturer and follow his directions exactly. With a little time and experience, the average plate maker can successfully make a deep-etch plate.

Materials and Qualities of Offset Plates

Offset plates are made from several metals, combinations of metals, plastics, and paper, all of which will give satisfactory results if used properly and if used for specific types of work. Because of the many types of plates in use, only the most commonly used have been described in this chapter.

The Aluminum Plate. The aluminum pre-sensitized plate is also a surface-coated plate. It is harder than zinc, allowing a finer grain without too much depth which provides longer life. The finish is very bright (silvery gray), and this gives more contrast between the blank areas of the plate and the image.

This plate has gained tremendous popularity in recent years and is now the most commonly used plate, especially in small and medium size plants.

The Bi-Metal Plate. The bi-metal plate has a base metal of either zinc, copper, aluminum, or other metals, and undergoes a nickel plating process after it has been grained.

When used for deep-etch, the albumin or surface plate is made in the same manner up to the point of being fully developed and cleaned. Then it is placed in the plating device and nickeled over the entire surface, after which it is processed in the same way as other deep-etch plates.

The nickel does not adhere over the image area, but only to the blank areas. The printing area, or image, will be directly on whatever the base metal is, thus producing a plate similar to the deep-etch plate.

This plate no doubt has desirable qualities, but just as the tri-metal plate, the initial cost is greater than the ordinary zinc or aluminum plates, making it economical only on long press runs.

Tri-Metal Plates. The tri-metal plate consists of three layers of separate and distinct metals, and is intended primarily for deep-etch plates.

The base or body metal may be either steel or zinc. The second layer is very thin copper and the third or surface layer is chromium.

Since this plate was intended for deep-etch process and long press runs, the best known metals were included. Chromium is noted not only for its hardness and wear-resistance, but also for its anti-oxidant qualities. Copper has a great affinity for grease; therefore, it is used to take and hold the image. The chromium is eaten through by the deep-etching process.

The tri-metal plate with the chromium is less sensitive to grease than most other metals, hence less water is required to keep the image clean and open, securing sharper and cleaner impressions. This also helps to improve drying conditions and makes stronger colors possible. The long life of these plates provides fewer interrupted runs without costly shut-downs.

The disadvantages of this plate are:

1. It cannot be regrained. This would be impracticable, because the chronium would have to be replated.

2. The initial cost is high; therefore, this plate is economical only when used for long press runs.

The Aller plate is believed to have been developed in Europe and although it has not come into wide use, it is still available in this country. It is a stainless steel plate electrotyped or coated with copper.

The plate is made in the usual manner, but after development the copper is etched away in the blank areas. This leaves a copper base for the image, slightly above the blank areas and the stainless steel on the blank areas to carry the water.

This plate would also seem to be ideal for offset work, but once again, the cost is too great for short press runs.

Monel Metal and Stainless Steel Plates. These plates are very hard and will enable the pressman to obtain many thousands of impressions before they show signs of wear. They are light silver in color and are naturally impervious to oxidation. These plates have less tendency to scum; the pressman adjusts the press to reduce the flow of water and still maintain the same quality of work.

However, this hardness results in several disadvantages; it is practically impossible to obtain anything but a fine or shallow grain on them. Another problem is trying to get these plates to lie flat after graining. The graining of one side creates a surface tension which causes the plate to bow or form into a half cylinder. This is counteracted to some extent by graining the reverse side also. When this is done, it is found to be still almost impossible after graining to make these plates lie flat enough to coat and process in the plate making department.

The high initial cost of these metals is another factor to be considered since they are only economical for long press runs.

Plastic and Paper Plates. Plastic and paper plates have an appearance much like an oiled tympan sheet on a letterpress which is a special type paper used on the platen or bed of the press on which the paper stock being printed is fed.

The plastic plate is chemically treated or presensitized by the manufacturer so that it can be exposed through the use of negatives, then developed and finished similarly to that of an albumin plate.

Halftones and line work can be produced on this plate and first class work can be done with it. This plate will not hold up for exceptionally long runs as will a metal plate.

The paper plate is also treated by the manufacturer so that the image can be placed on it by typewriter and then placed on the offset press. Other means of placing an image on this plate are by pencil, crayon, brush and ink, pen and ink, or any other greasy substance which permits the picking up of the ink on the offset press. This paper plate, often referred to as a "master," is classified as a direct image plate.

Both the plastic and paper plates are used extensively by the

Armed Services and government. Their weight and storage space, the fact that one is pre-sensitized, and that countless numbers of reproductions which call for only a few to a few hundred copies when the highest possible speed is necessary, make these plates invaluable.

Other Plates. A few plates have recently come into the printing industry. Others are still in the experimental stage.

The plate with the hydrophilic or "water loving" surface is pre-treated by the offset grainer in the rolling operation at the zinc mill. This pre-treatment is a lubricant coating which produces zinc sheets with a high luster and gives the greatest oxidation resistance possible.

The Alum-O-Lith offset plate, made of aluminum, is a "wipe-on" plate that can be sensitized with one chemical and is suitable for web or sheet-fed offset presses.

The type "E" offset plate is a one-sided paper-plastic laminate designed for fast application. After the plate is exposed, it can be developed by one application of 3M-brand developer which is a combination of desensitizer, developing ink, and gum solution.

Experiments are being conducted on other plates, both metal and plastic. As a result, more new plates will be introduced claiming improved applications and more advantages.

Other Methods of Platemaking

Xerography. Paper and metal plates for the offset press may be made by Xerography, previously explained in Chapter Four. Almost any type of original may be copied by Xerography, including forms, reports, articles, pages of books, notices, bulletins, etc. No darkroom, film negatives, solutions, chemicals, or sensitized plates are required. The fused Xerographic image which is bonded to the surface of the offset plate actually strengthens the plate and will produce copies to the point where the plate wears out at the ends attached to the press. The entire process from the camera to the fusing takes approximately three minutes.

Only three pieces of equipment (Fig. 6-13) are actually needed in making plates by this process.

Fig. 6-13. Three pieces of equipment are necessary for making plates by Xerography: The camera, the processor and the heat fuser.

1. Camera No. 1 or No. 4 which permit the copying of the original. Camera No. 1 has a fixed focus with an extremely wide angle lens which permits 1:1 copying up to 8½ × 13 in.

2. Processor D unit houses all the equipment necessary for the charging and developing of the xerographic plates after they are exposed in either of the cameras.

The lower section of the Processor is used for charging, processing and cleaning of xerographic plates. It is in this section that the image is transferred from the xerographic plate onto ordinary paper or offset masters for duplicating.

3. The Heat Fuser unit fuses the image for permanency. In this unit the transferred copy is placed between two heated platens for fusing. The image will not rub or smear and will last as long as the material on which it is made.

The following procedure may be used in making a paper offset master by Xerography.

1. Place the copy to be duplicated face down on the glass platen of Camera No. 1 (Fig. 6-14). (If Camera No. 4 (Fig. 6-15) is used the original is mounted on an easel or copyboard.)

2. Charge the Xerographic plate in the Processor D (Fig. 6-16) and then place in the camera. The original is then exposed directly

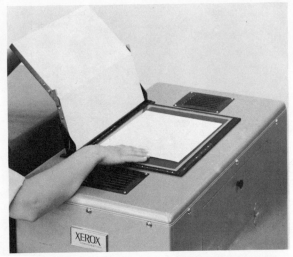

Fig. 6-14. To make a Xerox paper offset master, first place the copy face down on the glass platen of the camera.

Fig. 6-15. If Camera No. 4 is used, the copy is placed on the copy board.

Fig. 6-16. After the copy has been appropriately placed, the Xerox plate is charged in the processor.

Fig. 6-17. The copy is transferred to the Xerox plate by electrical charges.

Fig. 6-18. After the Xerographic plate has been made, the paper offset master is placed face down on the plate and inserted into the processor.

to the charged plate. After the exposure, a latent image remains on the areas unexposed on the plate.

3. Develop the plate by cascading oppositely charged black powder over it. Figure 6-17 illustrates the original material that has been copied directly onto the xerographic plate and then developed.

4. Place a paper master over the plate and insert into the lower section of the Processor D unit (Fig. 6-18).

5. Remove the paper offset master from the Processor D upon completion of the transfer.

6. Place the master into the Heat Fuser (Fig. 6-19) for a few seconds to make the print permanent.

7. The processed master is then attached to the offset press (Fig. 6-20) for running of multiple copies.

To make a metal offset plate by Xerography, the following procedure may be used:

Fig. 6-19. When the paper offset master has been removed from the processor, it is placed in the heat fuser for a few seconds.

Fig. 6-20. The completed paper master is then ready to be placed on the press.

Fig. 6-21. To make a metal offset plate, the plate and copy are treated in the same manner as the paper offset master to transfer the copy to the plate. Once the Xerographic plate has the copy transferred, it is placed in the processor to be charged.

Fig. 6-22. When the plate has been charged, insert the light shield and remove the plate from the processor.

1. Prepare the powder image on the plate in the same manner as stated for the paper master.

2. Slide the plate into the Processor D unit (Fig. 6-21) and press the charge button.

3. Insert the light shield (Fig. 6-22) remove the plate from Processor D and place it on the developer tray with the light shield up.

4. Place the metal master face down on the light shield (Fig. 6-23), then withdraw the shield until one-half inch of xerographic plate border is visible.

5. Position the tab end of the metal master against the inner portion of the xerographic plate frame (Fig. 6-24). Hold the end of the master firmly against the visible half-inch of plate and withdraw the light shield completely.

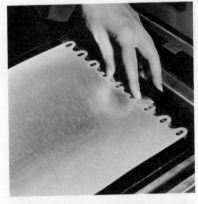

Fig. 6-23. Place the metal master on the light shield and withdraw the light shield until one-half inch of the plate border is visible.

Fig. 6-24. Now, remove the light shield so that the metal master contacts the Xerographic plate.

6. While still holding the end of the metal master, gently swab the entire back of the master with a cotton ball (Fig. 6-25) lengthwise and in one direction only.

7. Continue to hold the same end of the master to prevent shifting as it is peeled from the Xerographic plate (Fig. 6-26).

8. Place the metal master in the Heat Fuser for approximately 1½ min. to make the print permanent.

9. Place the metal master on the offset press and run off multiple copies.

The Electro-Rex Platemaker (Fig. 6-27) is based on a photoelectric principle.

The original or finished layout is inserted under an acetate cover of the right hand cylinder. This is called the manuscript

Fig. 6-25. Hold the metal master at one end and gently swab the metal master with a large ball of absorbent cotton. Be sure to rub lengthwise and in only one direction.

Fig. 6-26. Continue to hold one end of the metal master and peel it from the plate.

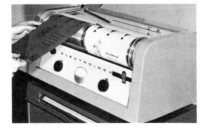

Fig. 6-27. The Electro-Rex platemaker uses a photo-electric process.

cylinder. Within a few minutes a phototube will scan and transfer all details to a mimeo-stencil or offset plate. The scanning can be adjusted to any degree between 125 to 750 lines per inch therefore greatly reducing or eliminating moire pattern from any photographs already printed.

Fig. 6-28. The Copy-Cat platemaker can make a negative and plate in three minutes.

The electronic stencil or offset plate up to 10 in. in width is automatically locked into the stencil drum and the device is started. Every detail of the original scanned by the phototube is transformed into high frequency current and conducted to a stylus which automatically "etches" a perfect copy into the stencil or offset plate. The Electro-Rex automatically stops when the stencil or plate is finished.

The stencil or plate is then removed and placed on the duplicating machine. Maximum copying area is 8½ × 12½ in.

The Copycat Platemaker (Fig. 6-28) is a compact unit capable of making a negative and plate in three minutes, and also making photocopies.

The original copy is exposed to the negative contact paper in the light box section on top. An automatic vacuum pump insures complete contact between the copy and negative during the exposure. The negative and aluminum plate (a surface coated plate) are developed by passing them through the automatic developing section on the bottom. The plate is then fixed with a fixing solution.

The plates can be made for simple printing jobs such as office forms, two and three color work, and jobs requiring a great number of press impressions. The plates can be stored for future use.

Units are available to expose an area 14 × 17 in. with a 15 inch developing section. Another model has a 17 × 24 in. exposure area with an 18 inch developing section.

The Itek Platemaster (Fig. 6-29) is an up-to-date unit that makes offset plates without the use of a negative. This unit exposes and processes plates automatically at the rate of two plates per minute at the touch of a button. The platemaster is equipped to also reduce or enlarge originals on the plate from 50% to 110%. This

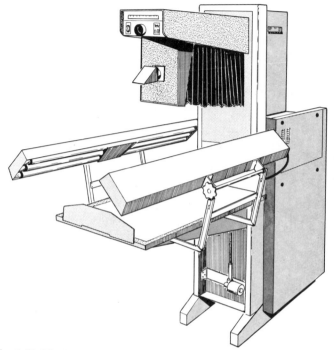

Fig. 6-29. The Itek Platemaster can make offset plates from positives—
no negative is required.

unit is ideal for printed material such as letters, instruction
manuals, circulars, charts, parts lists, etc.

Care and Cleaning (Storage)

Offset plates, as well as film, screen and other photographic supplies, must be properly cared for to insure good work. Listed below
are a few hints:

1. Carry small plates by holding the corners with the thumbs
and index fingers.

2. Carry large plates by the opposite corners (Fig. 6-30).

3. Avoid finger prints on the surface of the plate, especially
when the surface is sensitized.

4. Keep plates in a cool, dry place.

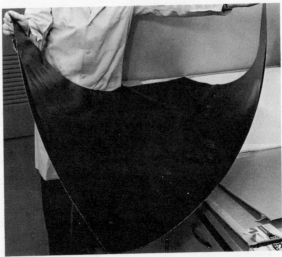

Fig. 6-30. Large offset plates should be carried by opposite corners.

Fig. 6-31. If possible, plates should be hung in storage, rather than stacked.

5. Avoid damp basements, sinks, sink counters and areas near radiators; hang plates (Fig. 6-31) if possible.

6. Pre-sensitized plates have an expiration date. Store plates so that the oldest ones are used first.

7. Protect plates from light, moisture and dirt.

8. Plates stored flat should be slip-sheeted.

9. A plate taken off the top of a pile of plates should be lifted by the diagonal corners to avoid damage.

10. Do not slide plates.

11. When using pre-sensitized plates, open the package carefully; close completely immediately after removing each plate.

12. When processing plates once they are sensitized, use subdued lighting or no lighting at all.

Formulas

Gum Arabic Solution. Gum Arabic crystals must be dissolved before they can be used in etches and fountain solutions. Most of the formulas require the gum solution to read 14 degrees Baume. The Baume reading can be lowered by adding water.

Dissolve one pound of granulated gum in approximately 36 ounces of water. After the gum crystals have dissolved, strain the solution through cheese cloth and add water to bring the solution to 14 degrees Baume.

Counter Etch "A"
For zinc albumin, Deep Etch or Aluminum Plates

Glacial Acetic Acid (99%) . . . . .6 ounces
Water to make . . . . .1 gallon

"B"
For Zinc Plates

Hydrochloric Acid . . . . .1 ounce
Water to make . . . . .1 gallon

"C"
For Zinc Plates

Nitric Acid . . . . .1 ounce
Water to make . . . . .1 gallon

"D"
For Zinc Plates

Nitric Acid . . . . .2 ounces
Powdered Alum . . . . .2 ounces
Water to make . . . . .1 gallon

When mixing solution "A," "B" or "C" it is advisable to use a one gallon, narrow-mouthed bottle. Fill the bottle half full of water, then add the acid after which more water to fill the bottle.

Albumin Coating Solution. The albumin coating solution consists of two parts:

1. The ammonium-dichromate or ammonium-bichromate (both essentially are the same).
2. The albumin solution

These solutions are prepared separately approximately 24 hours before the plates are to be coated. They are combined later into one solution when the plates are ready to be made.

Bichromate stock solution:
Ammonium Bichromate . . . . .16 ounces
Distilled water . . . . .24 ounces

Albumin Solution:
Egg albumin flakes . . . . .5 ounces
Water . . . . .24 ounces

Fold a cheesecloth into several thicknesses to make a pad about 9 or 10 in. in diameter. Place the egg albumin flakes in the center of the pad and tie up the ends forming a "sack." Suspend this sack in the graduate of water below the surface of the water so that it is fully submerged, but not touching the bottom or the sides.

Mixing the Coating Solution. After the albumin solution and ammonium dichromate solution have been allowed to stand over night, the two solutions must then be combined to make the coating solution.

Stir the dichromate solution and filter it through a wet pad of cheesecloth into a hydrometer jar. Take a hydrometer reading and add water if necessary until the solution has a density of 14.2 degrees Baume. Pour this solution into a jar marked "Ammonium Dichromate Stock Solution."

Remove the sack of albumin scales from the water and allow it to drain. *Do not squeeze it.* Either discard the sack or wash it for future use. Take a hydrometer reading to the closest .1 degree Baume. Refer to the "Albumin Density Table," and using the left hand column, locate this reading. Then read directly across to the right hand column where a figure will indicate how many ounces of the albumin solution is needed for the coating solution. Measure the indicated quantity, pour into a bottle marked "Coating Solution," and discard the balance of the albumin solution.

Measure out approximately 2½ oz. of the ammonium dichromate stock solution and add it to the albumin solution marked "Coating Solution." Add sufficient water to bring the coating solution to about 20 liquid oz.

The coating solution is now ready for use. If any ammonium dichromate stock solution is left over, it may be stored away out of the direct light for future use.

BICHROMATE STOCK SOLUTION

Ammonium Bichromate ....16 ounces
Distilled Water ....64 ounces
(Filter through cotton or cheesecloth and add distilled water slowly until the solution tests 14.2 degrees Baume.)

DEEP ETCH FORMULAS
(Zinc Plates)
Coating Solution

Gum Arabic (14 degrees Baume) ....24 ounces
Ammonium Bichromate (Stock Solution) ....8½ ounces
Ammonium Hydroxide (28%).....................1¼ ounces

Developing Solution

Hydrochloric Acid ....1½ ounces
Lactic Acid (85%)................................3 ounces
Calcium Chloride (Stock Solution 40 degrees Baume) to make 1 gallon

Deep Etching Solution

Hydrochloric Acid...............................1¼ ounces
Ferric Chloride Lumps ....1½ ounces
Calcium Chloride (Stock Solution, 40 degrees Baume) 64 ounces

Stock Solution of Calcium Chloride

Calcium Chloride (Commercial)..................75 ounces
Water ....64 ounces

(This mixture should be approximately 40 degrees Baume.)

CAUSTIC SOLUTION

(For cleaning Albumin Plates after development)

"A"

Bicarbonate of Soda ....1 ounce
Water to make ....1 gallon

"B"

Ammonium Hydroxide (28%) ....1 ounce
Water to make ....1 gallon

DESENSITIZING ETCHES
"A"
Bichromate Etch
(Zinc Plates)

Gum Arabic (14 degrees Baume) ....32 ounces
Ammonium Bichromate (Stock Solution)...........1½ ounces
Phosphoric Acid ....¾ ounces

(Keep in dark brown bottle. It must be used freshly mixed.)

"B"
Blue Etch
(Zinc Plates)

Gum Solution (14 degrees Baume) ....32 ounces
Tannic Acid ....2 ounces
Potassium Chrome Alum ....1½ ounces
Phosphoric Acid ....1½ ounces
Water to make ....1 gallon

"C"
For Aluminum Plates

Phosphoric Acid ....1 ounce
Gum Arabic (14 degrees Baume) ....25 ounces

ALBUMIN DENSITY TABLE

Density of Albumin solution at 77° F. Degrees Baume—or	Specific Gravity	Degrees—Eastman Tested Hydrometer	Volume of Solution Containing 3 Avoir. oz. of Albumin
5.1	1.0365	24	23⅛
5.2	1.0372	25	22¾
5.3	1.0379	25	22⅜
5.4	1.0387	26	21⅞
5.5	1.0394	26	21½
5.6	1.0402	27	21⅛
5.7	1.0409	27	20⅝
5.8	1.0417	28	20¼
5.9	1.0424	28	19⅞
6.0	1.0432	29	19⅝
6.1	1.0439	29	19¼
6.2	1.0447	30	18⅞
6.3	1.0454	30	18⅝
6.4	1.0462	31	18¼
6.5	1.0469	31	18
6.6	1.0477	32	17¾
6.7	1.0484	32	17½
6.8	1.0492	33	17¼
6.9	1.0500	33	16⅞
7.0	1.0507	34	16⅝
7.1	1.0515	34	16⅜
7.2	1.0522	35	16⅛
7.3	1.0530	35	15⅞
7.4	1.0538	36	15¾
7.5	1.0545	36	15½

Reprinted by permission from Lithographic Technical Foundation.

DEVELOPING INK

Oil of turpentine . . . . 16 ounces
Photoengravers etching ink . . . . ½ pound
Litho transfer ink . . . . 4 ounces
Black printing ink . . . . 4 ounces
Oil of lavender . . . . 20 drops

The inks are ground into the turpentine and then the oil of lavender is added. The mixture may be thinned to the consistency desired with distilled turpentine.

Projects

1. Prepare some Gum Arabic solution.
2. Prepare some counter etch solution.
3. Prepare the albumin coating solution.
4. Mix some coating solution.
5. Prepare the bichromate stock solution.
6. If deep etch plates are contemplated, prepare the deep etch solutions.
7. Prepare the caustic solution.
8. Prepare a direct image paper master plate by either typewriter, crayon, or greasy pencil.
9. Prepare a zinc albumin plate; coat, expose, develop and get it ready for press.
10. If deep etch plates are to be used, prepare, coat, expose, develop, and get it ready for press.
11. Expose, develop and prepare a pre-sensitized plate for press.
12. When the opportunity presents itself, repair plates by:
    a. Filling in
    b. Taking out
    c. Rubbing up
    d. Adding to image
13. Make an outline step by step of how to make a zinc albumin plate.
14. Make an outline step by step of how to make a deep etch plate.

Review Questions

Instructions

1. Do not write in the book, but on the test sheets provided.
2. Questions are in several forms: multiple choice, true or false, one or a few words, or matching.
3. Place T in the space provided if the statement is true; F if it is false.
4. Select from the list of statements or words the most correct answer.
5. Use one or a few words in the one-word answers.
6. In the matching questions, select the correct letter of the alphabet.

1. Both cameramen and platemakers should understand plate-making. True or false.
2. Plastic plates can have a typewritten image. True or false.
3. Plastic plates are pre-sensitized. True or false.
4. A "wipe on" plate is sensitized with two chemicals. True or false.
5. Higher humidity results in shorter exposures. True or false.
6. The deep etch process uses positive film. True or false.
7. Aluminum plates are slightly intaglio. True or false.
8. The device which will expose a single negative once or many times is called a _____ .
9. A device to determine proper exposures is the _____ .
10. The device used to hold plate and negative in tight contact is the _____ .
11. Some plates are _____ in action, and need no graining.
12. Humidity is _____ in the air.
13. When air contains 70 percent of the total moisture it can hold, the relative humidity is said to be _____ percent.

Match the type grain at the left with the usual product at the right.

14. Coarse grain	a. Halftones
15. Medium grain	b. Lines, heavy type, reversals
16. Fine grain	c. Heavy solids
	d. For general run of work

List in proper order, steps at the right by matching with numbers at the left.

17. First ____	a. Expose negative to plate
18. Second ____	b. Place flat on plate
19. Third ____	c. Wash with cotton under water
20. Fourth ____	d. Counter etch
21. Fifth ____	e. Place plate under running water
22. Sixth ____	f. Apply coating solution
23. Seventh ____	g. Dry plate

Match the term listed at the left with the correct answers at the right.

24. Counter-etching ____	a. Used on stored plates
25. Coating solution ____	b. Has etching action
26. Developing ink ____	c. A cleaner for developed plates
27. Caustic solution ____	d. Makes plate more sensitive to
28. Gum Arabic desensitizer ____	e. Makes grease image visible
29. Asphaltum ____	f. Composed of acid and water
	g. Makes plate sensitive to light
	h. Usually acetic acid
	i. Becomes insoluble in water after exposure
	j. Serves as acid resistant

Match the qualities of offset plates listed at the right with the plate names listed at the left.

30. Zinc ____	a. Harder than zinc
31. Aluminum ____	b. Very shallow grain
32. Bimetal ____	c. Easily grained
	d. Cannot be grained
33. Trimetal ____	e. Initial cost lower

34. Monel and steel ____

    f. Allows finer grain than zinc.

    g. Grain wears faster

    h. Nickel plated after training

    i. Chromium plated

    j. Less water required

Plates are repaired for the following reasons:

35. _____ .

36. _____ .

37. _____ .

38. _____ .

39. _____ .

Four steps in making a presensitized plate are in what order?

40. _____ .

41. _____ .

42. _____ .

43. _____ .

Plates are grained to:

44. _____ .

45. _____ .

Plates are grained in water, under:

46. _____ .

47. _____ .

Two factors are present when plates are exposed:

48. _____ .

49. _____ .

Name six classifications of offset plates:

50. _____ .

51. _____ .

52. _____ .

53. _____ .

54. _____ .

55. _____ .

CHAPTER 7

Related Press Data

What is press fountain solution? Why is it used? What is an offset blanket? What is it made of? What do printing inks consist of and what are the primary duties of these ingredients? What colors are possible from these ingredients?

Because of the nature of the process, almost all offset presses require the use of a fountain solution, a blanket and ink. Because of this, rather than describe the use of these three subjects with each press thus repeating many paragraphs of the same information, this chapter will discuss the fountain solution, offset blankets and offset printing inks separately and in more detail before proceeding into the detailed operations of the presses in the following chapters.

In Chapters Five and Six a number of solutions were stated and several formulas were given that are necessary to proper use of the camera and proper development of the plate. From these chapters and the solutions and formulas, it can be readily observed that the offset process is both a chemical and a mechanical process. In this chapter you will see that press operations are chemical and mechanical processes as well.

The press fountain solution is a mixture of ingredients designed to serve a dual purpose. The solution adheres to the non-inked areas of the plate and prevents ink from spreading over the entire plate. In addition it keeps the plate clean to provide a clear clean image. However, in order to accomplish this, both the water flow and ink flow must be perfectly balanced. Once these settings are obtained, only a watchful eye and refilling of the ink and water fountains is required especially during long press runs.

The offset process involves the use of three cylinders: the plate cylinder, the blanket cylinder and the impression cylinder. The blanket on the blanket cylinder receives the image from the plate cylinder and transfers or "offsets" the image onto the paper as it passes between the blanket and impression cylinders. Without a good blanket, printed results will be inferior. The blanket is made of both raw and finished rubber with a fabric backing conditioned and held to tight specifications. The offset blanket is perhaps the most important single item on the press.

Offset printing inks contain much the same ingredients as ink used in the letterpress process, however offset inks are much softer and not as thick or tacky. The inks primarily consist of a *vehicle* and a *pigment*. Other ingredients are included to increase or add to the desired results required from the ink.

The vehicle contains the drying system and acts as the binder, affecting the tackiness and the distribution and transfer characteristics of the ink. The *pigment* is the solid substance added to the ink to obtain specific color. It is also responsible for the specific gravity, opacity and permanency. The type of material the ink is to be printed on may determine the choice of pigment.

Other substances that may be added to ink are: Greases and lubricants for penetration or reducing tackiness, waxes for better adhesion, dryers for faster or better drying and varnish to add "body" to the ink.

Press Fountain Etches

The press fountain etch solution (mostly water) prevents the ink from spreading over the entire plate and helps to provide a sharp clear image. The offset process is made possible by the fact that grease and water do not mix. Therefore, when the plate is clamped on the press and ink placed on the plate image, a means of providing distribution of water over the non-printing areas is needed to confine the ink to the image area, and to keep the plate clean. Offset presses are equipped with a fountain to hold the etch while it is distributed to the plate by rollers.

Many press fountain etches are available. Some are pre-mixed and bought from a manufacturer, while others are mixed by the pressman. It is a matter of choice which solution the pressman will use, but it must be one that will provide the most satisfactory results. It is advisable for the pressman to be able to mix various fountain etches for emergency purposes, as well as to determine which solution will provide the best results.

Some solutions will work well on both zinc and aluminum plates, while others will work better on zinc, and still others on aluminum only. If a solution is purchased from a manufacturer, follow his directions to obtain the best results. For those who choose to mix their own, the following formulas have been generally accepted for use:

ZINC PLATE SOLUTIONS
1

Ammonium Phosphate . . . . .4 ounces
Ammonium Nitrate . . . . .4 ounces
Ammonium Bichromate (crystals) . . . . .3 ounces
Phosphoric Acid (85%) . . . . .3½ ounces
Water to make . . . . .1 gallon

(Keep solution in a dark brown bottle as air tight as possible.) For use, mix 1½ ounces in one gallon of water (PH reading should be near 4.2).

2
MIXTURE "A"

Ammonium Phosphate . . . . .8 ounces
Ammonium Nitrate . . . . .4 ounces
Sodium Fluoride . . . . .1½ ounces

(Dissolve in order given in three quarts of water)

MIXTURE "B"

Tartaric Acid . . . . 1½ ounce
Water to make . . . . 1 quart

(Mix "A" and "B" solutions together to obtain a stock solution.) For use, mix 1½ ounces in four to six quarts of water (PH reading should be near 4).

3

Water . . . . 16 ounces
Ammonium Bichromate. . . . . 1 ounce
Phosphoric Acid. . . . . ½ ounce

(Solution should be kept in a dark brown bottle.) For use, mix 1½ ounces in one gallon of water (the pH reading should be 4).

4
SOLUTION A

Ammonium Bichromate . . . . ½ ounce
Water . . . . 3 ounces

SOLUTION B

Gum Arabic Solution (14° Baume) . . . . 12 ounces
Phosphoric Acid (85%) . . . . ¼ ounce

(Dissolve separately, then add together. For use add 1 ounce of each to 1 gallon of water)

5

Ammonium Bichromate . . . . 100 Grams
Gum Arabic Solution (14° Baume). . . . . 1 ounce
Phosphoric Acid . . . . 20 drops
Water to make . . . . 1 gallon

6
SOLUTION A

Ammonium Bichromate .... 1 ounce
Phosphoric Acid (85%)........................... 1 ounce
Gum Arabic Solution (14° Baume)................. 7 ounces
Water .... 24 ounces

SOLUTION B

Magnesium Nitrate .... 16 ounces
Gum Arabic Solution (14° Baume)................. 2 ounces
Water to make .... 1 gallon

For use add 1 ounce of Solution "A" and 2 ounces of Solution "B" to 3 gallons of water.

ALUMINUM PLATE SOLUTIONS
SOLUTION "A"

Water .... 32 ounces
Ammonium Bichromate .... 1½ ounces
Phosphoric Acid (85%) .... ¾ ounce

SOLUTION "B"

Magnesium Nitrate .... 16 ounces
Water to make .... 1 gallon

For use, mix ½ ounce Solution "A," 1 ounce of Solution "B," 1 ounce of Gum Arabic Solution (14° Baume) and add water to make 1 gallon (pH reading should be between 4.5 to 5.5).

Offset Blankets

The manufacture of good offset blankets is a complicated process because the material used must be properly conditioned. The specifications required for strength and uniformity are held within narrow limits.

A good blanket must possess qualities so that the reproduction and the life of the plate are held to the highest standards. Qualities of offset blankets include:

1. The ability to receive the ink from the plate and transfer it to the paper.
2. High resistance to oil and grease, so the absorption of ink vehicles and solvents by the rubber will be held to a minimum.
3. The ability to be compressed and expanded: Stretch across the cylinder should be held to a minimum.
4. The strength so that it can be drawn tightly around the cylinder without breaking the fabric.
5. The ability to resist normal wear.
6. Uniformity of thickness so makeready in the packing under the blanket will be held to a minimum.

There is no definite life for a blanket; that is, the number of impressions it will make. No two blankets receive the same treatment or use. No matter how well the blanket is made or how well it is treated, the blanket will wear out, because it is constantly subjected to deteriorating elements.

Preparation of the New Blanket for the Press. Some blankets for the small offset presses are already punched by the manufacturer so they can be placed on the blanket cylinder. For the blankets that are purchased without holes or slots, the following procedure may be used:

1. Check the blanket and see that it is cut true square.
2. Check the reverse side to see which way the grain of the blanket runs. (The grain indicates which direction the blanket may be more easily curved or rolled. The grain should run around the cylinder, so the blanket does not stretch, break or become distorted when it is pulled tightly around the cylinder.)
3. When marking the holes to be punched, make sure they extend in a straight line and at a right angle to both sides of the blanket. If the holes in the clamps that receive the blanket are the same on both ends, be sure to start the end holes the same distance from one side of the blanket. If there are any nicks or holes that fit over any pins or screws

on the press, be sure these line up. Every possible precaution must be taken to see that the blanket will not twist when it is placed on the press. It must be pulled evenly and uniformly across the entire cylinder surface.

4. Measure the blanket carefully with a micrometer. Do not force micrometers down into the rubber because a true reading of thickness is needed. Refer to the press specifications for blanket packing and subtract the thickness of the blanket from the amount stated or the amount it should pack to. For example: The combined thickness of blanket and packing required is .078 inches. If the blanket measures .063 inches, the required packing will be .078 minus .063 or .015 inches.

5. Cut the packing so that it is about an inch shorter than the blanket across the cylinders. This will allow ½ inch on each end. Use a good, smooth hard paper for the packing. The packing should extend the full depth of the blanket, that is, from the gripper edge of the cylinder to the tail edge.

6. Place the blanket bars on the gripper end of the cylinder and lock them in place.

7. Place the packing under the blanket up past the edge of the cylinder, centering it on both sides.

8. Move the press around to the tail of the cylinder, being careful not to wrinkle the packing, and place the blanket bars into the device for holding, and lock. Tighten the blanket well. If the press is designed to tighten the blanket on both ends, do so.

9. If desired, the press may be run a few minutes with the impression "on," but without printing. Any slack in the blanket may be taken up by tightening either or both ends of the cylinder.

10. Print a few sheets and examine the image. If the image appears weak or contains any broken characters, add another one or two thousandths to the packing. Repeat until satisfactory, but avoid overpacking. This may ruin the plate or distort the image on the blanket and printed sheets.

A magnetic packing gauge (Fig. 7-1) is available for a quick

Fig. 7-1. A magnetic packing gage may be used for a quick and accurate check of the packing on both the blanket and plate cylinders.

and easy method of checking the blanket packing as well as for checking the plate packing. This permits checking both cylinder packings without opening either the blanket or plate cylinder. It accurately measures the height of the packing in relation to the bearer height under actual running conditions and pressures.

Care and Cleaning. Offset blankets require great care and proper cleaning if the desired results are to be obtained. Following are a few helpful hints that, if practiced, will provide the required results as well as the best service from the blanket.

1. Use a non-oily or non-greasy substance for washing the blanket. A high grade, pure (white unleaded) gasoline is a good solvent for washing the blanket.

2. Powder the blanket occasionally to help absorb any oil or other volatile residue left by washing. The blanket is powdered to remove any tackiness or glaze. Cleaning, ink, gum solution and fountain etch all contribute to creating tackiness and glaze. This condition develops while a blanket is in use. The *tackiness* comes from the ink and the gum solution transferred from the plate, while the *glaze* usually comes from the fountain solution. Therefore, the blanket must be washed and powdered to keep this condition to a minimum. New blankets are washed several times before put to use, and powdered to keep the glaze down.

3. Rest the blanket periodically. To do this, two blankets must be available for each press. Before placing a blanket away for rest, scrub it with pumice stone and gasoline; then brush a caustic solution of two or three ounces of caustic soda in eight or ten quarts of

water over the blanket several times and wipe dry. Powder the blanket and hang it in a dark cool place for about two weeks.

4. At the end of each day, wash the blanket in use with water to remove any accumulation of gum. Then wash it with gasoline and powder it.

5. At the end of each week, scrub the blanket with pumice stone and gasoline. This will help to remove any oil or hard glazed surface from the blanket.

6. Do not expose blankets to the sun, to radiators, radiator pipes, or a hot room.

7. Store blankets in a cool, dark, and dry atmosphere.

8. Avoid getting any substance under the blanket when applying any of the cleaning procedures.

Offset Printing Inks

Three main ingredients are used in the making of printing ink:

A. The vehicle, or fluid ingredient
B. The pigment, or solid ingredient
C. Miscellaneous or other ingredients

The Vehicle (which contains the drying system) usually determines the type of ink, the drying system used, and the suitability of the ink for various processes of printing.

The main function of the vehicle is to act as a carrier for the pigment and other ingredients. It has, however, other functions:

1. It acts as a binder to prevent the pigment from rubbing off after the printed forms are dry.
2. It is responsible for the tackiness and flow properties.
3. It is responsible for the distributing and transferring characteristics of the inks.

Inks will dry by a combination of methods: absorption or evaporation type inks will oxidize and dry harder than other types. Moisture set inks will also dry by a partial evaporation of the vehicle.

Evaporation drying is the evaporation or drying of the solvent similar to wet clothes drying by the evaporation of the water. These inks may be allowed to dry at room temperature or heat may be applied to hasten the drying. Gravure, flexographic, and screen process inks will dry by room temperature, while heat may be used to set the inks for letterpress and offset printing. Heat-setting inks, used for letterpress and offset, contain a slow evaporating petroleum oil and a solvent which will not evaporate too fast in air, but when heat is applied drying is very rapid. Resins are mixed with oils to bind the pigments to the surface of the printed area.

Absorption drying involves the penetration of the ink into the paper stock, similarly to a blotter soaking up excess writing ink. The vehicles used are non-drying penetrating oils. Petroleum oil, castor oil, and resin oil are used in combination to allow proper tack and flow characteristics. This drying is exemplified by soft absorbent papers, such as newsprint, soft uncoated book papers, or news inks or stencil duplicating inks on mimeograph paper from the mimeograph machine.

Oxidation drying consists of the absorption of oxygen by drying oils. This drying takes place in two stages:

a. The oxygen absorption stage which takes the longest time.
b. A hardening stage when the liquid oil changes to a solid coating or film.

A dryer can be mixed into the ink to speed up both of these drying stages.

If heat is applied, oxidation rate of the drying oils increases; therefore, drying will be much faster in warm rooms.

Moisture in the air or paper also has an effect on this type of drying. An increase of moisture will slow the drying of inks.

Linseed oil and litho varnish are the most common drying oils. Linseed oil must be heated or cooked to transfer it into a litho varnish, and the length of time it is heated and the temperature used determines the "body" or viscosity of the varnish. This viscosity ranges from 00000 or 5/0 (very thin) to No. 1 or No. 0 which is a medium body, to No. 9 or 10 which is very tacky or sticky.

Some oils used in printing inks for various purposes are: soybean oil, cottonseed oil, fish oil, castor oil and resin oil.

Gloss inks and varnishes are generally combinations of varnishes or oils with suitable synthetic resins. Such combinations produce a vehicle which will not penetrate into the surface being printed, but will level out properly, and produce a glossy effect. Gloss inks dry rapidly. To obtain the best results using this type of ink, it is important to use paper that is not too absorbent.

Chemical drying has been introduced by research laboratories utilizing chemicals or gases to dry inks. These methods range from placing chemicals into the paper stock, fountain solutions, inks, and treating the printed sheets with various chemical sprays and gases.

Another method is passing the printed sheet through a chamber consisting of sulphur dichloride gas. This gas reacts rapidly with drying oils changing them from a liquid to a solid.

Special precautions are necessary to prevent the gas from corroding press and plate metals or other materials. Extreme caution should be taken to prevent constant inhalation of the gas.

Cold-set inks harden or dry upon cooling. These inks are solid at room temperature and must be heated into liquid or paste before being used. Inks of this nature are used on special presses. Rollers, plates, and other parts of the press are heated to a temperature above the melting point of the solid ink. After the ink is placed on the paper, it solidifies and is dry as soon as it cools.

Quick-set inks dry by either absorption, filtration, coagulation or a combination of these with some other drying method previously explained. Special resin oil combinations are used for the vehicles which separate, (after the ink has been printed) into a solid material. This remains on the surface while the oily material penetrates into the paper stock. This separation is very rapid and causes the quick setting or drying quality. These inks are used mostly when both sides of the paper have to be printed almost immediately, or when the printed copies require a folding operation. Quick-set inks are also used when printing on coated paper stock or when drying time required is a few seconds to a few minutes.

The Pigment. Pigments are the solid coloring substance in inks—black, white and the other colors used for printed matter. Pigments are what one sees when looking at the printed matter. These substances are responsible for:

1. the specific gravity
2. opacity or transparency
3. permanency to light
4. determining the specific end uses, such as wrappers for meat, butter, and soap labels or if work which is to be varnished, lacquered or laminated.

Black pigments used are carbon black, lamp black, furnace black and mineral black. Mineral blacks are very rarely used.

Carbon black is made by burning natural gas with an insufficient amount of air and then collecting the resultant soot. By controlling the burning process, large numbers of different grades are produced.

Lamp blacks are produced in the same manner except that oil is used instead of gas.

Furnace blacks are produced in special furnace type structures with gas. These blacks gain the necessary specific properties which are used in formulating the various types of black inks.

White pigments are classified into two main types: opaque and transparent. Opaque pigments reflect the light at the surface and have the characteristics of covering the background on which it is printed.

Transparent pigments do not reflect the light on the surface, but transmit the light through the film of ink and then reflect the light from the surface on which it is printed. These pigments do not cover the background, they allow the background material to be seen through the film of ink.

Ingredients used for these pigments are:

Opaque Pigments	*Transparent Pigments*
Titanium Dioxide	Alumina Hydrate (Hydrate)
Zinc Sulphide	Magnesium Carbonate (Magnesia)
Lithopones	Calcium Carbonate
Zinc Oxide	Blanc Fixe (Barium Sulphite)
	Barytes
	Clays

These pigment ingredients are listed in order of decreasing opacity or transparency. For example: titanium dioxide is more opaque than zinc sulphide; zinc sulphide is more opaque than lithopones, etc.

Each pigment has specific characteristics which makes each one more desirable for certain types of inks. Sometimes mixtures of several are used to obtain the proper results.

Color pigments are divided into two basic groups: inorganic and organic. Inorganic color pigments primarily come from mineral components. Some of the inorganic pigments are described below:

Iron blue (made in a number of shades, such as milori blue, bronze blue, prussian blue, etc.) is a chemical compound of iron. These blues are quite transparent, and when used at full strength as dark blues, they become permanent to light, that is, they will not fade.

Vermillion is a red mercury sulphide pigment. It is very brilliant and opaque and is very useful where extreme coverage or hiding is necessary in a red ink.

Chrome orange is composed of modified lead compounds similar to the chrome yellow.

Chrome green is a mixture of chrome yellow and iron blue.

The chrome colors are permanent or fast to light and very opaque. Some of the chrome colors tend to darken when exposed to light and they will darken considerably when exposed to sulphur gases in the air.

Organic color pigments are the largest group of pigments used, and are available in many thousands of different pigments, each with different shades and each with different characteristics and uses.

Yellow lake pigments are transparent and produced from several organic dyes and pigments of different hues by forming or depositing the colors on one of the transparent white materials previously stated, usually Alumina Hydrate.

Hansa yellows are very strong and are produced in a number of hues for strengthening chrome yellow. Hansa yellows are three to five times as strong as chrome yellows but not as opaque.

Benzidine yellows also are very strong, but not as fast to light as the Hansa yellows, but are more transparent. They are used mostly for toning the chrome yellows where extreme fastness to light is not required.

Red pigments range in shades from an orange to deep maroon, from "dirty" reds to the very clean brilliant reds as used in three and four color process work.

Para reds, and *Fire reds* are quite "dirty" in color, are semi-transparent and used mostly in poster and label inks.

Lithol reds range in shades from an orange to deep maroon. In between these extremes are some very brilliant and deep shades which are used where extreme permanency to light is not important.

Phloxine or eosine lakes are brilliant reds with a "bluish" or "purplish" cast or undertones not fast to light. These inks are mostly used for letterpress because these pigment colors bleed (run or spread from the action of water or solvent) in water.

Lake red "C" is used for making the very brilliant orange shades. It is fairly fast to light and fairly transparent.

Madder lakes are quite "dirty" in color and are used where this appearance is not objectionable. They have unusual resistance to bleed and are very permanent to light.

Blue pigments are also available in a wide variety of hues and characteristics.

Peacock blue is available both in permanent varieties and in varieties that are very poor in permanency, often bleeding in water.

Phthalocyanine blues are the most useful of the light blues with "greenish" shades. They are light fast, non-bleeding in most solvents, very clean, brilliant shades, offer a wide range of hues and have a good resistance to most chemicals. Because of these characteristics, these hues have a wide range of uses, including the bases for color process work.

Alkali blues are available in a wide range of the deep reddish shades. They are useful for "toning" blacks, their color strength and dark top-tones add density and strength to the blacks.

Metallic inks are made with metallic pigments. Although the pigment appears to be in powder form, they are actually very small, thin flakes of metal.

Silver powder is usually aluminum, and the gold powder is generally a mixture of brass flakes, copper flakes and other metals mixed together to obtain the various shades of gold. Metallic powders are available in many different shades and fineness. It is always best to consult an ink maker to obtain the best results for individual requirements.

Other Ingredients. In addition to the various vehicles and pigments, a number of other ingredients are necessary to provide special properties to the inks.

Greases and lubricants such as vaseline, petrolatum, tallow, or cup-grease are added to allow the ink to penetrate or reduce the tack. They also lubricate the ink so that it will distribute and spread properly.

Waxes and compounds are added to obtain better adhesion to certain surfaces, to help prevent offset and sheet sticking. (Offset in this sense means smudging or transfer of ink from a freshly printed sheet to the bottom of the next sheet delivered. If this "offset" is excessive, the printed sheets will stick together when the ink dries.) Paraffin wax and bees wax are only two of the many waxes used in these compounds.

Dry powder additives are used to help prevent offset or to increase the body of the ink. Corn starch or dry magnesia is used as such an additive.

Dryers were previously mentioned under "vehicles," therefore only a few types will be stated here. In general, dryers promote oxidation and will consist of lead, manganese, cobalt, calcium, iron, copper, zinc, or zirconium. Most dryers are effective when used in combination with other metals. Popular combinations are lead-manganese, paste dryers and lead-manganese-cobalt dryers.

When used individually, cobalt, manganese, and lead, in the order stated are the most effective.

Binding varnish adds "body" to the ink. It helps to improve drying and adhesion to certain surfaces. In offset inks, it also helps to keep water out of the ink and helps to prevent bleeding, washing and emulsification. Sometimes this varnish is referred to as the binder. Too much or too little of any one or more of these ingredients causes many problems. It is always best to consult your ink maker for assistance or advice whenever an ink problem appears. To save time, a good pressman should know enough about the general construction of the inks to enable him to make an emergency correction in the pressroom without causing any serious problems.

Review Questions

1. Press fountain etch prevents ink from _____ over the entire plate.
2. The mixture of sulphur coating in new blankets is called "_____".
3. All etch solutions wash well on any type of plate. True or False.
4. Absorption of grease is a necessity in an offset blanket. True or False.
5. All blankets are slotted to fit particular presses. True or False.
6. Blankets should be "rested" periodically. True or False.
   Inks consist of four major ingredients:

7. _____
8. _____
9. _____
10. _____

Inks dry by:

11. _____
12. _____
13. _____

Two types of drying oils are:

14. _____
15. _____

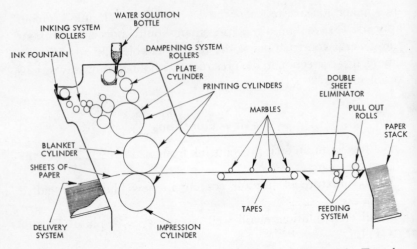

Lithography is based on the fact that grease and water will not mix. To make this principle operate, the offset-lithographic press has five basic systems: the printing cylinders, the inking system, the dampening system, the paper feeding system and the delivery system.

CHAPTER 8

Offset Presswork

What is a Ditto? What are the most significant features of the Ditto? What is an A. B. Dick? What is its most significant feature? What is a Multilith? What is the most significant feature of this press?

Basic Offset Press Operation. In the introduction of this book, you learned that lithography is based on the principle that grease and water does not mix. Later it was stated that the term lithography gave way to offset printing and is now considered a photo-mechanical process utilizing the same principle. Also, in Chapter Five you learned the important part the process camera portrays in the photography phase and in chapter six how the metal plates replaced the litho stone.

The final phase of this process, the mechanical part, is the offset press. The offset press actually employs five basic systems: the printing cylinders, the inking system, the dampening system, the paper feeding system and the delivery system.

The offset presses in these chapters contain the three cylinder system with the exception of the Davidson Press which employs only two cylinders. The three cylinders are: the plate cylinder that holds the offset plate, the blanket cylinder that holds the blanket, and the impression cylinder. A schematic diagram of a typical offset press is shown on the page facing this chapter.

During the press operation, the inking system applies the ink to the image area of the plate while the dampening system applies water to the non-image areas of the plate.

As the image is transferred from the plate cylinder to the blanket cylinder, the paper feeding system transmits the sheets between the blanket and impression cylinder where they are printed.

The grippers on the press then carry the printed sheets to the delivery system where the sheets are stacked.

The systems, with complete settings and adjustments, of several presses are described in complete detail in the following chapters.

Offset presswork requires a constant watchful eye on the many moving parts and mechanisms to see that they are functioning properly. During a press run, every spare minute not needed to watch the delivery of the printed sheets should be used to observe the other mechanisms of the press. The feeder on the press is perhaps the most complicated mechanism and should be studied and observed quite closely. A good pressman should know everything that the press is capable of doing and he should be able to handle all kinds of work from printed forms to halftones and book work. He should be able to work with all kinds of paper. Presswork involves a wide variety of work and requires years of experience for complete mastery.

The Ditto is perhaps one of the smallest offset duplicating presses. It is designed to give fast service and produce quality printing acceptable for office use. Its most significant feature is the convenient location of the controls in one place rather than have them in separated positions around the press. The operator can watch both the feeding and delivery from one position; wasted motion and body fatigue is reduced. (See Fig. 8-1.)

The A. B. Dick is another offset duplicator designed to provide fast service and quality printing. All cylinders on this press are self adjusting. In addition to its more normal functions, it can be adapted to offset check imprinting equipment with magnetic ink.

The Multilith is a third offset press designed to produce quality printing. However, it is also designed to accomplish other operations as well. As a result it is termed one of the most versatile presses. In addition to perforating, slitting, scoring, numbering, etc., much the same as other presses, it also can be adapted to three color process work.

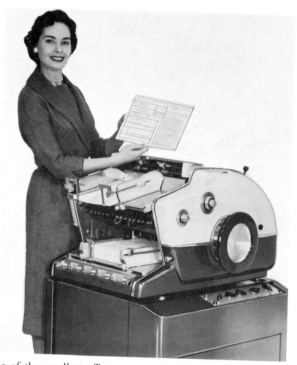

Fig. 8-1. One of the smallest offset presses, the Ditto is capable of producing quality offset printing for office use.

This chapter will explain in detail the makeready, operating, and maintenance instructions for each of these presses. No matter how well a press may be designed and built, it must be properly operated if best results are to be obtained.

Ditto Offset Duplicator[1]

Control Panel and Switches. There are five control switches located on a panel at the front of the duplicator. Facing the duplicator in the front, from left to right, they are:

1. *The elevator switch* (Fig. 8-2E) which, in an "up" or "down" position raises and lowers the paper feed table. The table may be

1. This material is rewritten and adapted from the operating manual for Ditto Offset Duplicator and is reprinted by permission through the courtesy of Ditto, Incorporated.

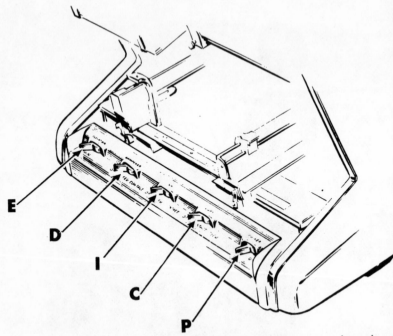

E

D

I

C

P

Fig. 8-2. Five control switches for the Ditto Offset Duplicator are shown here, at *E*—the elevator switch, at *D*—the dampener switch, at *I*—the ink switch, at *C*—the copy switch, at *P*—the power switch.

reloaded while the duplicator remains running simply by turning the elevator switch to the "down" position. An interlocking device suspends the inking process when the feed table is lowered so it is not necessary to turn off the other switches. Once the feed table is reloaded and the elevator switch is turned to the "up" position, the duplicator will continue to run off copies automatically.

2. *The dampener switch* (Fig. 8-2D) has three positions: "off," "feed," and "contact." In the feed position, the fountain solution is applied to the moistening rollers; in the "contact" position, the moistening form rollers apply the fountain solution to the master (plate) on the main cylinder.

3. *The ink switch* (Fig. 8-2I) has three positions: "off," "feed," and "contact." In the "feed" position, the ink is applied to the ink rollers; in the "contact" position, the ink form roller applies ink to the master.

4. *The copy switch* (Fig. 8-2C) also has the three positions: "off," "contact," and "feed." In the "contact" position, the master contacts the offset blanket and the image is transferred from the master to the blanket. In the "feed" position, the sheets of paper are fed into the duplicator and the image is transferred from the offset blanket to these sheets.

5. *The power switch* (Fig. 8-2P) turns the duplicator "on" and "off."

Fountain Solution and Water Settings. The nine steps in setting the fountain solution and water for the Ditto are given below.

1. Drop the left side cover to expose the fountain solution bottle (Fig. 8-3A).

2. Turn the bottle outward and away from the frame of the duplicator and pull it upward to release it from the holder (Fig. 8-3B).

3. Unscrew the cap, fill it with fountain solution, and replace cap.

4. Replace the bottle and allow it to stand until the solution

Fig. 8-3. When the left side cover is dropped, the dampening system is exposed to view, at *A*—the fountain solution bottle, at *B*—the fountain solution bottle holder, at *C*—the moistening tray, at *E*—the fountain solution tube, at *F*—the fountain solution hose.

has filled the moistening tray (Fig. 8-3C) and has covered the bottom of the fountain roller in the tray.

If the solution is not visible in the moistening tray, the hose (Fig. 8-3F) and the tube (Fig. 8-3E) may be removed to blow out any sediment that may be plugging it. When removing the hose from the tube, be careful not to drain the contents onto the working parts of the press.

5. Turn the power switch on.

6. Turn the dampener switch to "feed" position. The moistening ductor roller (Fig. 8-4C) will now contact the moistening oscillating roller (Fig. 8-4D) in the "up" position and the fountain roller (Fig. 8-4B) in the moistening tray (Fig. 8-4A) in the "down" position.

When the larger of the two knobs (Fig. 8-5A) on the right side of the press is turned to a higher numbered setting, the ductor roller will remain in contact with the fountain roller longer and will pick up more fountain solution.

The fountain solution is transferred from the fountain roller to the ductor roller, to the oscillating roller (Fig. 8-4D) to the moistening form roller (Fig. 8-4E).

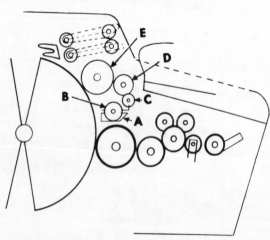

Fig. 8-4. Here is a schematic diagram of the dampening system, at *A*—the moistening tray, at *B*—the fountain roller, at *C*—the moistening ductor roller, at *D*—the oscillating roller, at *E*—the moistening form roller.

Fig. 8-5. The knobs shown here control the dampening and ink systems, at *A*—the dampening control knob, at *B*—the inking control knob.

7. Turn the large knob (Fig. 8-5A) to the 3½ setting and allow the duplicator to run with the dampener switch in the "feed" position for approximately 2 min. which should make the ductor roller "damp" but not wet.

The moistening form roller should be moistened sufficiently to prevent the master from "scumming." If the master scums or the copies come out dirty, repeat the running operation another minute to allow the ductor and form roller to become more damp.

8. Turn the large knob (Fig. 8-5A) back to the 1½ or 2 setting depending upon the room temperature and relative humidity. Very dry days will require more water to flow on the master; on humid days less water is needed. For the best results, allow as little water as possible on the master.

A perfect balance of ink and water is necessary otherwise undesired results will be obtained. If the moistening form roller is too dry, the copies will be too dark, small type or halftones will be "plugged up" or filled-in and scum will appear. On the other hand if the moistening form roller is too wet, the copies will appear gray and the paper will curl; eventually the master will break down and be of no use.

If the moistening form roller is too wet, turn off the fountain solution by turning the large knob to "0" setting until the copy starts to turn darker, then turn the large knob to a setting that will hold a balance with the ink. Only experience and close observation will help to achieve this proper balance.

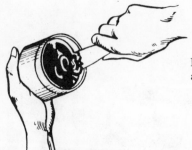

Fig. 8-6. Ink is removed from the can with an ink knife. Skim the hardened crust from the top before removing any ink.

Fig. 8-7. Ink from the can is placed in the ink fountain.

Inking and Ink Settings. Eight steps are required to prepare the inking system for a press run. These are given below.

1. Remove ink from the can (Fig. 8-6) and place a sufficient amount in the ink fountain (Fig. 8-7).

2. Turn the ink control knob to the No. 1 setting.

3. Work the ink back and forth the length of the fountain with an ink knife.

4. Turn the ink switch to "feed." The ink ductor roller (Fig. 8-8B) will move from its "neutral" position and contact the ink

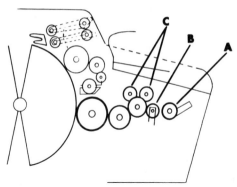

Fig. 8-8. The inking system of the Ditto Offset Duplicator is shown here, at *A*—the ink fountain roller, at *B*—the ink ductor roller, at *C*—the ink rider rollers.

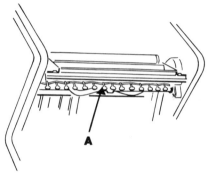

Fig. 8-9. The even distribution of ink across the roller is controlled by ink adjustment screws.

fountain roller (Fig. 8-8A) to pick up a supply of ink. It will then deliver ink to the ink rider rollers (Fig. 8-8C).

The ink fountain is equipped with 14 adjusting screws (Fig. 8-9A). Turning these screws "in" (clockwise) will decrease the flow of ink and turning "out" (counterclockwise) will increase the flow of ink.

5. Starting at the center of the fountain, adjust the fountain screws until an even flow or pickup line between the ductor roller and fountain roller is obtained across the width of the fountain.

6. Turn ink control knob to "1½" or "2" setting for most copywork.

NOTE: A heavy flow of ink will cause over-inked copy resulting

Fig. 8-10. The blanket pressure control knob (at *A*) should only be adjusted for heavy card stock, such as 90 pound Index stock. The air-flow control knob is shown at *B*.

in scum, and a very light flow will result in light copy causing the masters (plates) to break down.

Blanket Pressure Control. The blanket pressure control knob (Fig. 8-10A) is visible after the upper right hand cover is removed. It is not necessary to change this knob for various weights of paper unless heavy card stock (index) such as 90 lb is used. The knob is numbered from "3" to "9" and lines marked to indicate "2" to "10." The No. 2 setting positioned at the top is normal setting. When running heavy card stock turn the knob to a higher numbered setting. To change the setting, press the knob inward and turn.

Placing Copy Paper in the Duplicator. Proceed as follows to place the copy paper in the duplicator:

1. Fan the sheets to separate any sticking together (Fig. 8-11).
2. Check the power switch to make sure it is in "off" position.
3. Place the copy paper in the center of the feed table (Fig.

Fig. 8-11. The sheets should be fanned before they are placed in the press.

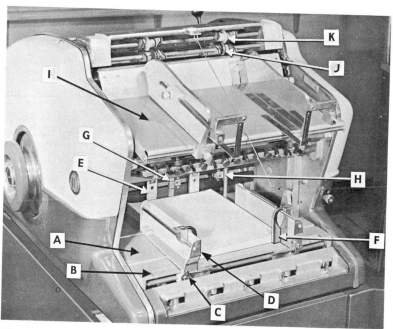

Fig. 8-12. The points lettered in the illustration above are important when placing copy paper in the machine, at *A*—the feed table, at *B*—the paper scale, at *C*—the locking lever, at *D*—the side guides, at *E*—the separator blocks, at *F* —the tail guides, at *G*—center air blow tube, at *H*—side air blow tube (one of two).

8-12A) using the scale shown in Fig. 8-12B as a guide for center-ing. This scale corresponds with a similar scale on the head clamp of the plate cylinder.

4. Release the locking lever (Fig. 8-12C) on each side of the guide (Fig. 8-12D) by moving it downward. Move the side guides into contact with the paper stack. These guides should rest lightly and not press heavily against the sides or feeding difficulty will appear.

5. Move the locking lever on each side guide upward to lock the guide into position.

6. Move the paper stack forward so that it touches but does not press too heavily against the separator blocks (Fig. 8-12E).

7. Position the tail guides (Fig. 8-12F) lightly against the end of the stack nearest to the front of the duplicator to secure it in place.

8. Slide and space each separator block evenly between the center air blow tube (Fig. 8-12E) and the side of the paper stack.

9. Slide the suction feeder feet (Fig. 8-13A) and position them directly in front of the separator blocks (Fig. 8-13B).

10. Set the side air blow tubes (Fig. 8-12G) about an inch away from the sides of the paper stack.

Receiving Tray. The side guides on the receiving tray (Fig. 8-12I) are set to approximately the same position as the guides on the feed table. The tail guides are set up or down to fit the size of the sheet being run. Accurate settings can be made while the printed copies are being delivered into the receiving tray.

Ejector Mechanism. The lower ejector wheels (black sponge rubber, Fig. 8-12J) must be moved to at least 1 in. inward from the sides of the copy sheet. The upper ejector wheels (Fig. 8-12K) must then be moved outward ½ inch from the lower wheel. Positioning ejector wheels directly over each other would cause the sheets to become crimped.

Attaching the Master (Plate). When attaching or removing a sensitized metal plate it is advisable to raise the rear part of the ejector assembly (Fig. 8-14A) up out of the way to avoid scratching the plate. Be sure to lower this rear part of the ejector assembly after building up the image.

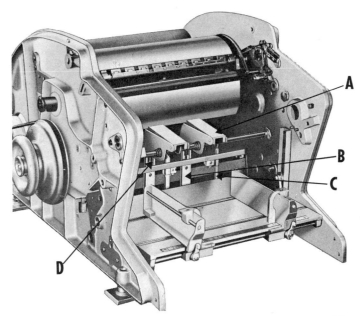

Fig. 8-13. A cutaway view of the Ditto Offset Duplicator: at *A*—one of the suction feet, at *B*—one of the separator blocks, at *C*—one of the air blow pipes, at *D*—the sheet separator.

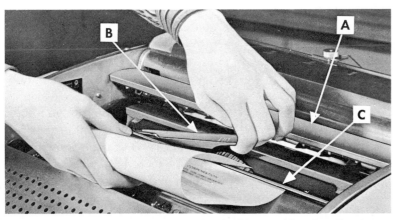

Fig. 8-14. Some of the important parts involved in attaching the offset master are shown here, at *A*—the ejector assembly, at *B*—the lever used to raise the plate clamp, at *C*—the head clamp.

1. Pre-moisten the plates on a separate table. Metal plates should be pre-moistened with diluted fountain solution, ratio: 15 to 1. Paper masters should be pre-moistened with concentrated fountain solution.

2. Clamp the plate on the main cylinder using the lever (Fig. 8-14B) to raise the head clamp (Fig. 8-14C). Use the scale on the clamp to position the master in alignment with the paper on the feed table.

3. Clamp the opposite end of the plate in the tail clamp (Fig. 8-15A). Metal plates must always be secured on the main cylinder with both the head and tail clamps. Paper masters may be attached with the head clamp alone, provided the trailing edge does not extend beyond the master cylinder surface. Both head and tail clamp handles should always be pressed down firmly.

Image Adjustments. To adjust the image on the sheet, proceed as follows:

1. Turn the copy, ink, moisture, and power switches to the "off" position.

2. Turn the plate cylinder by hand, using the hand wheel in the normal rotation direction until the head clamp (Fig. 8-16A) appears in the open area between the ejector (Fig. 8-16B) and blanket cylinder (Fig. 8-16C.)

3. While standing on the right side of the machine, turn the indicated wheel (Fig. 8-16D) on the cylinder counterclockwise to raise the image and clockwise to lower the image on the sheet of paper.

4. Using a cotton wad or soft sponge moistened with fountain solution, wipe the plate down and run more copy sheets through to check the image position. If the image is still not in proper position, repeat the previous steps. In most offset presses it is necessary to also wipe the blanket after each stop or when making an image adjustment because the blanket cylinder does not change in ratio to the plate cylinder. If an image adjustment was made and the blanket was not wiped off, the next few copies run on the press would have a double image until the first position was worn away.

On the L-16 model, it is not necessary to wipe the blanket after

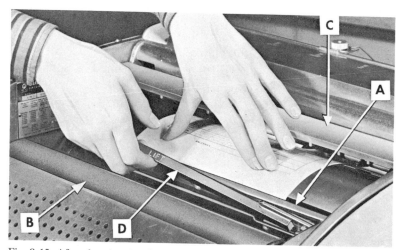

Fig. 8-15. After the plate has been secured at the head clamp, the plate cylinder is revolved and the tail of the master is secured, at *A*—the tail clamp, at *B*—the blanket cylinder, at *C*—the ejector assembly, at *D*—the tail clamp lever.

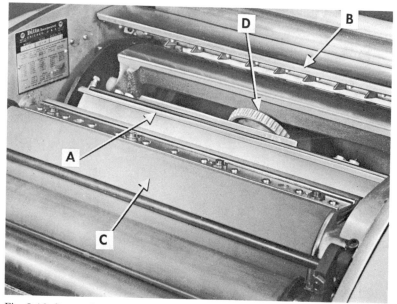

Fig. 8-16. Some of the features important to image adjustment are shown here: at *A*—the head clamp, at *B*—the ejector assembly, at *C*—the blanket drum, at *D*—the wheel used to raise and lower the copy.

each adjustment (Fig. 8-17A) because any movement of the plate up or down automatically shifts the blanket, retaining the same position of the image on the blanket.

When the blanket (Fig. 8-18) is to be cleaned, a soft cloth moistened with suitable cleaner should be used. Ink and other foreign matter collected on the blanket should be removed to prolong the life of the blanket.

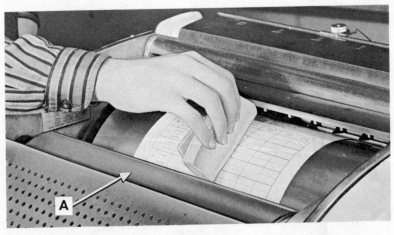

Fig. 8-17. The plate must be wiped clean after each adjustment. The blanket (shown at *A*), however, does not require wiping after each adjustment.

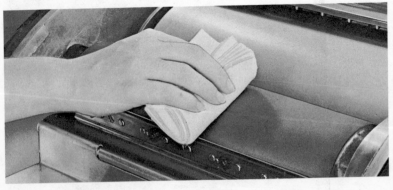

Fig. 8-18. When the blanket is to be cleaned, use a blanket and roller cleaner on a soft cloth. Most manufacturers offer such a cleaner and these are readily available.

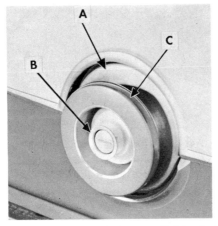

Fig. 8-19. The speed of the main cylinder is controlled by the handwheel shown here: at *A*—the handwheel and pulley assembly, at *B*—the pull-out knob, at *C*—the rim of the handwheel.

Variable Speed Control. The main or plate cylinder revolves at a speed from 4500 to 8500 revolutions per hour. To adjust the speed with the variable speed hand-wheel and pulley assembly (Fig. 8-19A) proceed as follows:

1. Make sure the power switch is "off."

2. To increase speed, pull knob (Fig. 8-19B) outward and turn to right or clockwise.

3. To decrease speed, pull knob (Fig. 8-19B) outward and turn left or counterclockwise and at the same time turn rim of hand wheel (Fig. 8-19C) in same direction.

Feed Table Height Control. To adjust the feed table height control, proceed as follows:

1. Place the stack of paper on the feed table.

2. Turn the power switch "on," turn the air blow control switch "off" and turn the elevator switch to "up." Check the level of the paper. The top of the stack should be $\frac{1}{16}$ to $\frac{1}{8}$ inch lower than the sheet separator.

If the top of the stack is more than $\frac{1}{16}$ to $\frac{1}{8}$ inch below the separators:

3. Turn the power switch "off" and turn the adjusting screw (Fig. 8-20A) inward in the direction marked "raise."

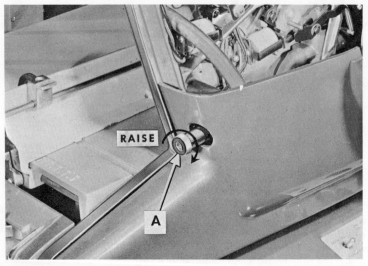

Fig. 8-20. The feed table height is controlled by turning the adjusting screw at "A."

4. Turn on the duplicator and check the height of the stock again. Repeat this until the ¹⁄₁₆ to ⅛ inch clearance between the top of the paper stack and the separators is obtained.

If the top of the stack is less than ¹⁄₁₆ to ⅛ inch below the separators:

5. Turn the power switch "off" and turn the adjusting screw outward.

6. Turn on the duplicator and allow the feed table to rise.

7. Turn the elevator switch to "down" allowing the table to drop about a ½ inch and then turn the elevator switch to "up."

8. Check the clearance between the top of the stack and the separators. Repeat if necessary until the clearance is obtained.

Daily Ink Roller Cleaning and Oiling. Turn off all switches at the control panel. Set the duplicator at its lowest speed and turn the power switch to the "on" position. Fill the small metal oil can with a good solvent and apply it to the two ink rider rollers (Fig. 8-21A). Turn the ink switch from "off" to "contact" and then turn both the ink and power switches "off." Remove the cleaner sheet (an absorbent sheet of material placed on the master cylinder

Fig. 8-21. The ink rider rollers (at *A*) should be cleaned daily.

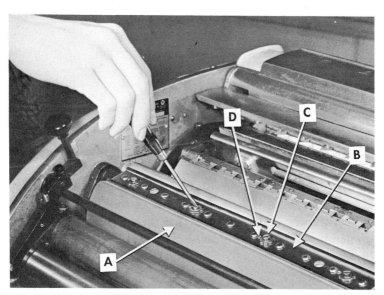

Fig. 8-22. Four parts play an important role in removing and attaching the blanket: the blanket itself (at *A*), the clamp bar (at *B*), adjusting screws (at *C*), and screws which lock the adjusting screws in place (at *D*).

to collect the ink and solvent) and repeat the operations until the roller is clean.

Removing and Attaching the Blanket. The blanket (Fig. 8-22A) is attached to the blanket cylinder with a clamp bar (Fig. 8-22B). Tension is controlled by adjusting screws (Fig. 8-22C) which are locked in position with screws (Fig. 8-22D).

1. Remove the clamp bar and the old blanket.

2. Attach the new blanket to the cylinder with the clamp bar and adjusting screws.

3. Press downward on the clamp bar with the thumb of the left hand while turning the adjusting screws with a screw driver held in the right. (Do not turn screws too tight.) The screw driver should be held lightly in the fingers and turned until the adjusting screws are snug.

4. Lock the adjusting screws in place with screws. A new blanket will stretch after being placed on the duplicator and must be tightened before the copies are printed.

5. Turn the power switch to "on" and the copy switch to "contact."

6. Allow the main cylinder to revolve for about 100 revolutions and turn switches to "off."

7. Tighten the blanket as described above.

Adjusting the Air Blow Tubes. To adjust the air blow tubes (Fig. 8-23A and B) loosen the clamp nuts (Fig. 8-23C) and adjust the top of each tube so that it is centered to the lower feed roller (Fig. 8-23D). The air holes (Fig. 8-23A and B) should be positioned so that they are at a 45° angle from the lower feed roller toward the center of the feed table.

These adjustments are for normal operation; therefore, a slight change in setting may be necessary when running paper that is heavy or uneven and excessively curled.

Separator-Finger Adjustment. The separator fingers (metal strips that prevent more than one sheet from being picked up at a time), shown in Fig. 8-23E, are adjustable upward or downward with the loosening of two screws (Fig. 8-23F). The bend in each finger should be slightly above the suction feet when the feet are in the lowest position. Each finger should extend outward from

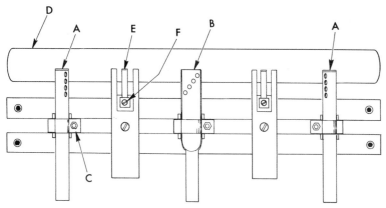

Fig. 8-23. A schematic diagram shows the air blowing system, at *A*—the side air blow tubes, at *B*—the center air blow tube, at *C*—the clamp nuts, at *D*— the lower feed roller, at *E*—separator fingers, at *F*—loosening screws.

the face of the separator block approximately ⅛ inch. Bend outward or inward as required.

Air Blow Control-Valve Adjustment. The amount of air through the air blow tubes can be regulated by turning the handle (Fig. 8-24B) located on the operator's side of the duplicator. To increase the amount of air, turn the handle counterclockwise toward the front of the machine. To decrease the air, turn the handle clockwise. It will be found that heavier weights of paper and card stock normally require a greater amount of air than lightweight papers to obtain proper sheet separation.

Moistening Form-Roller Adjustment. The over-all pressure of the moistening form roller (Fig. 8-25A) against the plate on the cylinder (Fig. 8-25B) must be equal from one end of the roller to the other. Too much pressure will cause the roller to bounce and will wear down the image on the plate. Too little pressure will not apply sufficient amounts of the fountain solution to the plate. Each time a new cover is placed on the form roller, the pressure must be checked, and, if necessary, set.

To adjust the pressure of the moistening form roller proceed as follows:

1. Place a test plate on the plate cylinder and turn the cylinder by hand until the plate is beneath the moistening form roller.

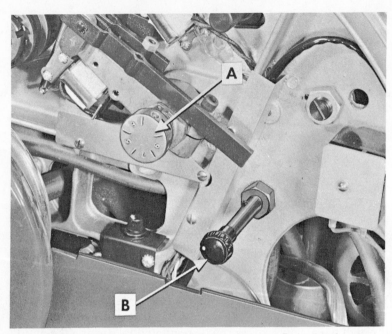

Fig. 8-24. The air-flow control knob is shown at *B*. At *A* is the blanket pressure control knob.

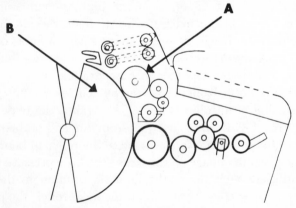

Fig. 8-25. A schematic diagram of the offset duplicator shows the moistening form roller (at *A*) and the plate cylinder (at *B*).

2. Take two strips of 20 lb. bond, one inch wide, and place one strip at each end of the roller between the roller and the plate.

3. Raise the magnet latch (Fig. 8-26A) on each side of the

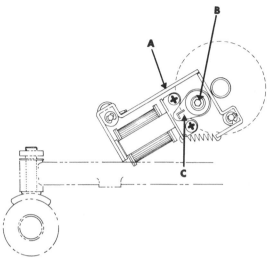

Fig. 8-26. The magnetic latch (at *A*) is an important part in adjusting the moistening form-roller. At *B*—Allen screws for the eccentric collar is shown, at *C*—the eccentric collar itself.

duplicator to drop the form roller against the paper strips and the plate.

4. Slowly withdraw the paper strips. The "pull" should be medium, rather than light or heavy, and even at both ends of the roller. To adjust:

5. Loosen the Allen screws (Fig. 8-26B) and turn the eccentric collars (Fig. 8-26C) at each side of the duplicator. To increase pressure, turn the eccentric collars toward the front of the duplicator. To decrease pressure, turn the eccentric collars toward the back of the duplicator. When the pressure has been equalized, lock the eccentric collars in position by tightening the Allen screws.

Ink Form Roller Adjustment. The overall pressure of the ink form roller (Fig. 8-27A) must be equal against the plate on the plate cylinder (Fig. 8-27B) from one of the rollers to the other. Too much pressure will wear the image on the plate and very often cause "scum," while too little pressure will not apply sufficient ink.

To adjust the pressure on the ink form roller, proceed as follows:

1. Place a test plate on the plate cylinder.

2. Turn the power switch "on" and the ink switch to "feed."

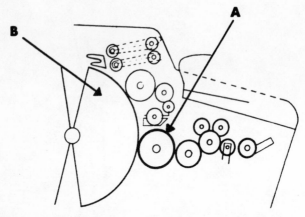

Fig. 8-27. The inking system. At *A*—the ink form roller is shown, at *B*—the plate cylinder.

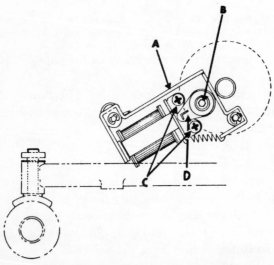

Fig. 8-28. Here you see the magnetic latch in its raised position. At *A*—the latch, at *B*—the ink form-roller shaft, at *C*—Allen screws, at *D*—the eccentric collar.

3. Turn the master ink control knob to the "½" setting and operate the duplicator for about 30 revolutions allowing sufficient ink to transfer from the fountain to the ink form roller.

4. Turn the ink and power switches "off" and turn the plate cylinder by hand until the plate is adjacent to the ink form roller.

5. Raise the magnet latch (Fig. 8-28A) on each side of the duplicator to drop the ink form roller against the plate. This will leave an inked line across the plate.

6. Using a screw driver or other tool, pull the ink form roller shaft (Fig. 8-28B) toward the front of the duplicator to enable the magnet latch to drop into position and lock the ink form roller away from the contact with the plate. Repeat this on the other end of the ink form roller shaft.

7. Rotate the plate cylinder by hand until the inked line on the test plate is visible. The line should be ⅛ to ³⁄₁₆ inches and uniform across the entire width of the plate. To adjust, if necessary:

Fig. 8-29. The A. B. Dick Offset Duplicator designed to give quality printing acceptable for office use.

8. Loosen the Allen screws (Fig. 8-28C) and turn the eccentric collars (Fig. 8-28D) at each side of the duplicator.

To increase pressure or adjust the form roller for uniform pressure, turn the eccentric collars toward the front of the duplicator. To decrease pressure, turn the eccentric collars toward the back.

9. Lock the eccentric collars in position by tightening the Allen screws.

10. Repeat the test by dropping another line on the plate. Adjust if necessary using the same procedure.

SPECIFICATIONS TO REMEMBER

Paper sizes: Maximum sheet 12 inches x 14 inches. Minimum size 3 inches x 5 inches

Maximum Image size: 10¾ inches x 14 inches

Speed: 4500 to 8500 impressions per hour

Paper weights: From 13 to 90 lb.

Paper feeder capacity: 500 sheets (20 lb. bond)

Gripper margin: ¼ inch

Paper feeder: Double suction feet with single transfer from feeder to trippers.

Motor: ½ horsepower

Floor space: 25 inches x 32 inches

A. B. Dick Offset Duplicator
Model 360[2]

Inking.

1. Using a small ink knife, remove a quantity of ink from the ink can and place it in the ink fountain (Fig. 8-30). The skin that forms in the can on fast drying ink should first be removed without too much waste.

2. Distribute the ink into the ink fountain by rotating the ink fountain roller counterclockwise at least one revolution to carry the ink down into the fountain. Rotate the hand wheel of the duplicator until the ink ductor roller contacts the ink fountain roller.

---

2. This material is rewritten and adapted from the operating manual for the A. B. Dick 360 and is reprinted by permission through the courtesy of the A. B. Dick Company.

Fig. 8-30. Ink is placed in the ink fountain with a small ink knife.

3. While rotating the ink fountain roller counterclockwise, adjust the ink fountain screws (Fig. 8-31) until an even and finely stippled effect is obtained on the ink ductor roller.

Be sure the form rollers are in the "off" position.

4. Move the ink fountain control (Fig. 8-32) to the "No. 4" position.

5. Move the aquamatic control (Fig. 8-32) to No. 45.

6. Turn the motor drive switch "on."

7. Allow the duplicator to run until an even film of ink completely covers the two rollers in the aquamatic unit. Make sure all rollers are evenly covered with a thin film of ink.

8. Move the ink fountain control to "off" position.

9. Move the aquamatic control to "off" position.

10. Turn the motor drive switch "off."

NOTE: The speed adjustment on the duplicator should be made only when the motor switch is "on." Speed "No. 5" (Fig. 8-33) should be maintained until the apprentice becomes more proficient in the duplicator's operation.

Fig. 8-31. Ink fountain screws are used to control the distribution of the ink on the ink fountain roller.

AQUAMATIC CONTROL

INK FOUNTAIN CONTROL

Fig. 8-32. The ink fountain control has five positions. The aquamatic control is used to govern the water distribution.

Fountain Solution

1. Fill the fountain solution bottle (Fig. 8-34) with fountain

Fig. 8-33. Speed adjustment of the press is controlled by the lever shown here. Speed adjustments should only be made when the motor switch is *on*.

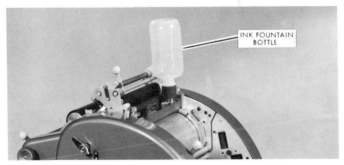

Fig. 8-34. The ink fountain bottle holds the water supply for the press.

solution; replace the cap on the bottle and place the filled bottle in position in the aquamatic unit.

2. When the flow of the fountain solution from the bottle stops, the ink and water system is in operating order.

NOTE: Make sure all ink rollers, including the two in the aquamatic unit, are inked before the fountain solution is added.

Paper Feed. A combination air-vacuum paper feed system is used on the Model 360. The top sheets of paper are fluffed or

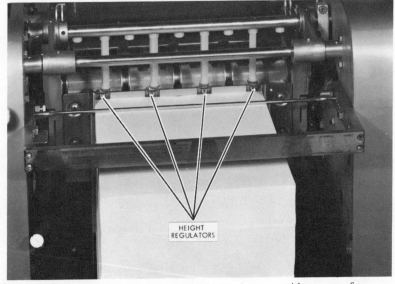

Fig. 8-35. Air holes in four paper height regulators provide a means for separating the top sheets.

separated by means of air flowing through holes in the four paper-height regulators (Fig. 8-35). Four positions are provided to aid in controlling the amount of fluff needed for a particular sheet.

The spring action of these regulators (Fig. 8-36C) floats the top sheet against the paper guide (Fig. 8-36D) and the rear guide (Fig. 8-36E) insuring lateral registration. The spring guide is positioned to the left of the paper stack for top right registration, and positioned to the right of the paper stack for top left registration.

Four suction cups (Fig. 8-36F) pick up the top sheet and carry it to the other forwarding rollers (Fig. 8-36G) which in turn bring the sheet to the paper stops. Here the paper is buckled to fit squarely and firmly against the stops, insuring vertical registration. The grippers hold the paper and carry it between the blanket and the impression cylinder. The paper is then stripped from the impression cylinder and delivered into the receiving tray.

Proceed as follows on the feeding makeready:

1. To register copies to the top right of the paper (Fig. 8-37) crank the paper guide on the non-operating side of the duplicator

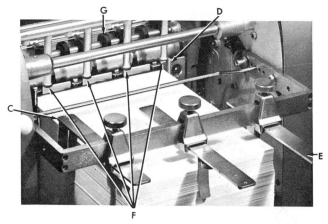

Fig. 8-36. In addition to the air-blow system, the paper feed system has five other important parts: at *C*—spring action regulators, at *D*—the paper guide, at *E*—the rear guide, at *F*—suction cups, at *G*—the forwarding rollers.

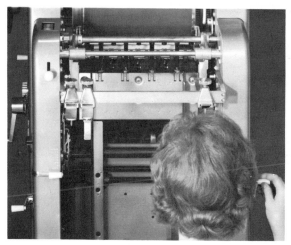

Fig. 8-37. The paper-guide crank is used to register copies right or left.

to the correct scale setting according to the width of paper being used.

To register copies to the top left of the paper, crank the paper guide on operating side of duplicator to correct setting.

2. Position the opposite paper guide as required.

3. The paper stack supports should be positioned so that the

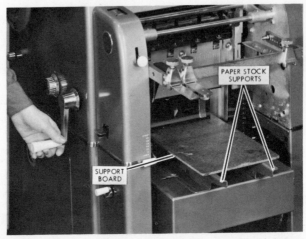

Fig. 8-38. The paper stock supports and the support board hold the paper before it is delivered to the press.

Fig. 8-39. The paper height regulators should be in their lowest position before beginning the feeding operation.

back stop clears both supports when the table is at its maximum height. The tapered ends of the supports must face outward to prevent damage. A paper stack support board (Fig. 8-38) is placed on the stack supports and should be cut slightly smaller than the paper size being run.

4. Engage the paper elevator crank (Fig. 8-38) by pushing in and lower the paper feed table by turning the crank counterclockwise while depressing the table release (Fig. 8-38.)

5. Turn the hand wheel until the four paper height regulators (Fig. 8-39) are in their lowest position.

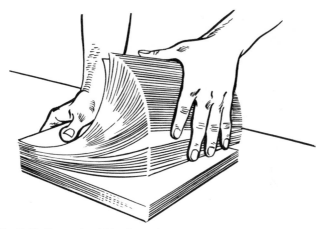

Fig. 8-40. Paper should be fanned or "winded" before it is placed on the feed table board.

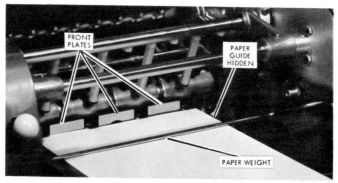

Fig. 8-41. The lead edge of the paper should be flush with the front plate and the paper guide.

6. Fan the paper (Fig. 8-40) and load it into the paper feed table, being careful to keep the reams neatly stacked.

7. Raise the feed table by turning the paper elevator crank clockwise until the top sheets contact the paper height regulators.

8. Square the top few sheets of paper so the edge of the paper being used for registration touches the correct paper guide. The lead edge of the paper should be flush with the front plate (Fig. 8-41).

9. Adjust the rear guide near the tail of the stack so that it just touches the paper as shown in Fig. 8-42.

Fig. 8-42. The rear guide should just touch the paper stock.

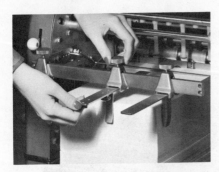

Fig. 8-43. The back stop must be adjusted to the size paper being used.

Fig. 8-44. The paper weight should be positioned differently for different weights of paper; "forward" for light papers and farther back for heavier stock.

10. Adjust the back stop so that it just touches the tail end of the stack (Fig. 8-43) but does not bind the stack against the front

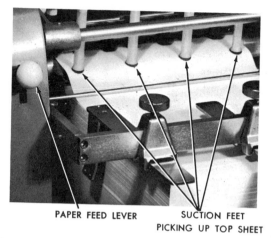

PAPER FEED LEVER   SUCTION FEET
                         PICKING UP TOP SHEET

Fig. 8-45. The suction cups or "pick-up feet" are movable to any of nine positions.

Fig. 8-46. The paper stack height adjustment shown here governs the height of the paper stack.

plate. On heavy card or bristol stock the back stop should be approximately ⅛ inch away from the stack of paper.

11. Turn the motor drive switch "on" until the stack reaches its maximum height.

12. Place the paper weight (Fig. 8-44) in the "forward" position for light papers and further back for heavier papers. If necessary for heavy card stocks, the paper weight may be removed.

13. All four suction cups or feet are movable to any of nine positions (Fig. 8-45) depending on the size of the paper. If possible, utilize as many suction feet as possible for the size of paper being

used. To reposition a suction cup, loosen and remove the cup by using a wrench. Determine the required position and remove the plug (Fig. 8-45). Secure the suction cup into place and seal the open position with the plug.

Paper Stack Height Adjustment. A paper stack height adjustment thumb screw (Fig. 8-46) is used to govern the height of the stack of paper. The lever may be adjusted through six graduations depending upon the weight of paper stock being printed. The heavier the paper, the higher adjustment number required.

Air-Vacuum Adjustment

1. Turn the air and vacuum control knobs (Fig. 8-47) clockwise as far as they will go.

2. Turn both knobs counterclockwise approximately three full turns. Be sure the paper feed lever is in the "off" position.

3. Turn the motor drive and vacuum pump switches "on." The top sheets of paper should fluff up and follow the four height regulators. It may be necessary to increase the air setting by turning air control knob clockwise until sheets fluff up properly.

4. Turn the motor drive "off" and lift the paper feed lever (Fig. 8-45) to the "on" position. Turn the hand wheel counterclockwise and manually feed one sheet of paper through the duplicator. If the sheet is not picked up properly by the suction

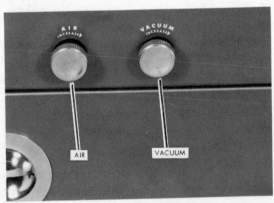

Fig. 8-47. The air and vacuum control knobs are shown here.

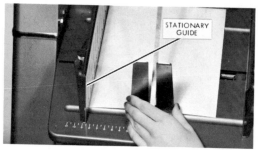

STATIONARY GUIDE

Fig. 8-48. The stationary guide is adjusted to the width of paper; the front stop is adjusted to the lengths.

duplicator. If the sheet is not picked up properly by the suction cups, increase the vacuum setting by turning the vacuum control knob clockwise.

5. Turn the vacuum switch and paper feed lever "off."

Receiving Tray

1. Set the stationary guide at the same setting used for the paper stack (Fig. 8-48).

2. Place one sheet of paper in the tray and adjust the front paper stop for the length and center it to the width of the paper being used. An approximate setting may be used first by setting the trailing edge (opposite the lead edge) of the paper with the back edge of the tray.

3. Rotate the hand wheel until the jogging guide is in the inward position. Adjust the guide so that it just touches the sheet of paper (Fig. 8-49.)

4. Position the tray bail (Fig. 8-49) in the slot in the front stop which is shaped to provide best stacking for the type of paper being used.

5. Turn on the vacuum pump switch and paper feed lever. Turn the hand wheel counterclockwise to feed a sheet of paper through the duplicator manually until it is just past the lower ejector wheels (Fig. 8-50.)

6. Position the metal ejector wheels so that they ride inside the margins of the paper. The metal ejector rings (Fig. 8-50) may be positioned about a ½ inch outside the ejector wheel when using

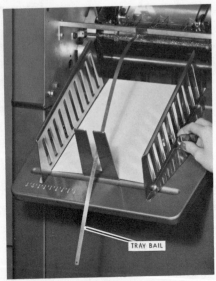

Fig. 8-49. The guide should be adjusted so that it meets the paper; the tray bail is positioned in the slot as shown.

Fig. 8-50. The ejector wheels operate to deliver the printed paper from the press. The ejector rings serve as "rollers" for the paper to ride on.

flat or curled down paper. For curled up paper, position the rings inside the ejector wheels.

7. Turn vacuum pump switch and paper feed lever "off."

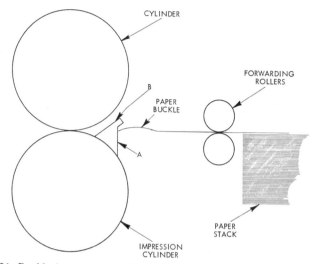

Fig. 8-51. Buckle is necessary to deliver each sheet firmly to the paper stops. At *A*—the paper stops, at *B*—the grippers.

Fig. 8-52. The buckle control knob is calibrated for adjustment: "0" produces minimum buckle, "15" produces a maximum.

Buckle Control Registration. An adequate buckle or bulge in the sheet of paper is required to deliver each sheet firmly against the paper stops (Fig. 8-51) in the grippers. This insures accurate vertical registration.

The "0" on the buckle control (Fig. 8-52) produces a minimum buckle and "15" produces maximum buckle. Generally, the buckle control is set from "0" to "3" for card stock, and "3" to "7" for 20 lb. paper and as high as "15" for very light paper. The buckle is set too high if the card stock is being nicked at the lead edge. Changing the buckle setting may alter the registration slightly; therefore, the buckle setting should not be changed during a press run especially when close registration is required.

Fig. 8-53. Here a paper master is being inserted in the head clamp. The plate is inserted until it reaches the stops.

Fig. 8-54. The lead end of the master is attached to the head clamp, and then creased.

Attaching the Plate (Paper Master). To attach the straight edge plate, proceed as follows;

1. Open the straight edge clamp by depressing the head clamp lever (Fig. 8-53).

2. Insert the plate until it touches the stop (Fig. 8-54) evenly across the width of the plate. Release the head clamp lever and crease the plate.

3. If no tail punchings are available in the plate, it will be necessary to punch the plate with the teeth of the clamp.

For attaching a pinbar plate, proceed as follows:

Fig. 8-55. Once the lead end of the master is attached the cylinder is rotated by the hand wheel and the master is pulled around the plate cylinder.

Fig. 8-56. Hold the master in place and lift the tail clamp.

1. Attach lead end of master to head clamp (Fig. 8-54). Crease plate at the head clamp while holding the plate taut.

2. While still holding the plate taut with the right hand, rotate the hand wheel with the left hand until the tail clamp is within 1 inch of the aquamatic fountain (Fig. 8-55).

3. Hold plate tightly against the cylinder surface with the left hand and crease the plate. With the right hand lift the tail clamp up (Fig. 8-56) and over the tail punchings of the plate. Drop the tail clamp down into the plate punchings.

4. The tail clamp automatically adjusts to the position of the tail punching of the plate.

(Two knurled knobs, Fig. 8-57, are used to tighten or lock *metal* plates to the cylinder.)

Fig. 8-57. These knurled knobs are used to tighten and lock metal plates to the cylinder.

Fig. 8-58. Form roller and water controls are shown here.

Ink and Water Settings

1. Etch or wash down the plate following the instructions supplied with the type of plates being used.

2. Turn the motor drive and vacuum pump switches "on."

3. Move the aquamatic control to "No. 25."

4. Move the upper and then the lower form roller control levers to the "on" position (Fig. 8-58).

Look at the plate while it is running and be sure it is clean in the non-image area. If the plate tends to pick up ink in the non-image area, there is either too much ink or too little water being fed into the system.

5. Move the image development control knob (Fig. 8-58) down toward the paper stack for several revolutions, and watch the blanket. When the good solid image appears on the blanket (about two to four revolutions) release the image development control knob.

6. Lift the paper feed lever to feed one sheet of paper through the duplicator. Inspect the copy for position, clarity and general acceptability. Image adjustments are discussed in the next section of this chapter.

7. Once correct position is established, set the copy counter (Fig. 8-58) to the left to "0" and the paper feed lever to the "on" position.

NOTE: During the press run, it may be necessary to adjust the ink or water controls to adjust for ink uniformity or for heavy or light copy on one side of the plate. To adjust, turn the ink fountain adjusting screws clockwise to decrease the ink supply and counterclockwise to increase the ink supply. "No. 1" setting is for the minimum amount of ink supply while "No. 4" is for maximum amount.

8. When the press run is completed, turn the two roller levers to the "off" position.

9. Turn the aquamatic control to the "off" position.

10. Turn the paper feed lever "off" and turn both the vacuum and motor drive switches "off."

Image Adjustments. The duplicator must be stopped when making any copy adjustments.

Fig. 8-59. Angular and lateral adjustments are shown here.

Angular adjustments are made by loosening the plate from the tail clamp and adjusting the knurled knob (Fig. 8-59A) so that the right end of the master cylinder head clamp moves in the proper direction. If the image appears to be running "downhill" from left to right, turn the knurled knob counterclockwise to raise the image. If the image appears to be running "uphill" from left to right, turn the knurled knob clockwise to lower the image. This adjustment may have to be done several times until the operator learns how many turns of the knob are necessary to raise or lower the image the required amount. Wash the blanket before beginning the job.

Lateral adjustments up to about ¼ inch can be made by removing the plate from the tail clamp and turning the knurled knob (Fig. 8-59B) so that the head clamp moves in the desired direction. When straight edge plates are used, release the hand clamp and move the plate in the desired direction without removing it

Fig. 8-60. This view of the A. B. Dick Duplicator shows some of the parts involved in image adjustments.

from the cylinder. The paper stack must also be moved in the proper direction when making this adjustment, especially when the move exceeds ¼ inch. Wash the blanket after making this adjustment.

Vertical image adjustments are also made by rotating the blanket cylinder until the locking nut lines up with the built-in print adjusting lock (Fig. 8-60). Push the lock handle in and loosen the locking nut (Fig. 8-60) by turning it counterclockwise. Continue to hold the handle in, and move the scale (Fig. 8-60) by turning the hand wheel following the arrows to raise or lower the image. After the adjustment is made, tighten the locking nut.

It is not necessary to wash the blanket after making a vertical adjustment because the relationship of the plate cylinder to the blanket always remains the same.

Removing and Attaching the Blanket

1. Loosen the four socket-head setscrews on the two blanket cylinder bars; then loosen and remove the four socket-head cap screws (Fig. 8-61).

2. Remove the cylinder bars and the blanket from the cylinder.

3. Remove the screws from the reverse side of the bars to release the blanket (Fig. 8-62). Attach a new blanket to the bars, replace the screws and tighten them.

Fig. 8-61. The set screws shown here must be loosened and the cap screws loosened and removed in order to replace the blanket.

Fig. 8-62. The blanket and cylinder bars are removed together. To release the blanket, remove the screws from the opposite side.

4. Attach the blanket to the cylinder, and secure it with the four set screws (Fig. 8-63).

Care, Cleaning and Lubricating

To wash the duplicator, follow these steps:

1. Remove the fountain solution bottle.

2. Remove the fountain solution from the fountain with a sponge or syringe.

3. Use an ink knife to remove and discard the ink from the ink fountain.

4. Remove the ink fountain by lifting it up to a vertical position (Fig. 8-64). Clean the ink fountain with a rag moistened with an appropriate wash or solvent.

Fig. 8-63. Attach the blanket and screw it down with the four cap screws.

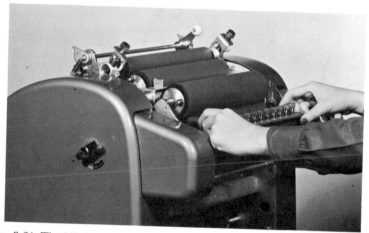

Fig. 8-64. The ink fountain may be removed by lifting it to a vertical position.

5. Clean the ink fountain roller.

6. Remove the excess ink from the rollers by manually feeding a sheet of paper into the rollers. Hold on to the end of the sheet while manually turning the handwheel. Back the sheet out and discard it. Repeat this process several times to make the washup easier and faster.

7. Attach a cleanup mat to the plate cylinder and start the duplicator. *Turn the Speed Down to Minimum.*

8. Squirt a small amount of wash over the ink oscillating roller, allowing it to work into the ink system.

9. Move the two form rollers to the "on" position and the aquamatic unit control to No. 45. Continue to add small amounts of wash until the rollers appear clean. Do not use too much wash at one time.

10. Turn the two form rollers and the aquamatic control to the "off" position. Stop the duplicator, remove the clean up mat and discard it. Repeat the operation with another clean up mat, and a third if necessary.

11. After all ink is removed, moisten a soft, lintless rag with wash, and wipe all the rollers clean of any ink residue or lint.

To prepare the duplicator for idle periods:

Fig. 8-65. The duplicator is made ready for idle periods as shown here.

1. Lift and tilt the ink oscillating roller toward the ink fountain so it does not contact any other rollers (Fig. 8-65).

2. Lift the aquamatic oscillating roller into the support bracket.

3. Turn night latch lever to "night latch" position.

4. Remove the fountain solution bottle and set it on a stable flat surface.

5. Move the aquamatic unit night latch lever to "off."

Lubricating. As with any piece of equipment having movable parts, the duplicator must be oiled regularly to keep it at its best performance with the least amount of wear. The duplicator should be lubricated every 36 hours of running time with an S.A.E. No. 20 nondetergent oil. A high grade grease should be applied in the places specifically indicated on the machine.

SPECIFICATIONS TO REMEMBER

Paper size; 3 x 5 inches to 11 x 17 inches—automatic fed

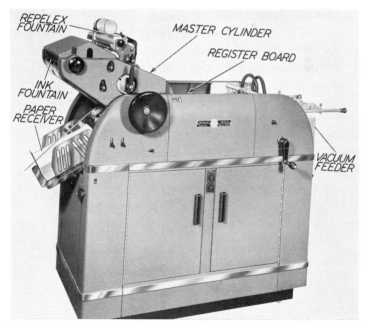

Fig. 8-66. The Multilith Offset Duplicator, Model 1250, is a press capable of quality offset printing acceptable for office use.

Paper weight: 12 lbs. bond to 110 lb. Bristol

Maximum copy area: 10½ inches wide x 16¼ inches long

Gripper margin: ¼ inch

Speed: Variable from 4500 to 9000 copies per hour

Paper feed: Vacuum type

Feed table: 5000 sheets 20 lb. capacity

Weight: 611 lbs.

Dimensions: 45 inches long, 28 inches wide, 52 inches high, floor area 8.7 sq. ft.

Ink Roller System: 3 oscillating rollers, 2 ductor rollers, 5 distributor rollers and 2 form rollers

Motors: Drive motor ¼ H.P., pump motor ⅓ H.P., A.C. 110V-60 cycle standard, D.C. available.

Multilith Offset Duplicator [3]
Model 1250

Dampening System. Fill the fountain bottle (Fig. 8-67) with fountain solution and replace the plastic screw cap on the bottle. Place the bottle on the dampening unit with the valve in the cap seated firmly in the opening in the fountain. The valve automatically maintains the solution in the fountain at a constant level.

The feed control lever (Fig. 8-67A) is adjustable over a range of six notched positions, to regulate the flow of the fountain solution. When the lever is in the "up" position, the maximum amount of solution will be fed from the fountain to the rollers. As the lever is lowered the flow of the water is decreased. When the lever is in its extreme position, the feed of the solution is cut off entirely.

The ductor roller contact lever (Fig. 67B) makes or breaks the contact between the ductor and fountain roller. When the lever is in the "off" position, it interrupts the flow of the solution without disturbing the adjustment of the feed control lever. Move the lever away from the fountain to "off" position to stop the flow of the solution. When dampening the rollers, the lever must be in the "on" position or toward the fountain.

---

[3] The following material is rewritten and adapted from the operator's manual for the Multilith 1250 and is reprinted by permission of Addressograph-Multigraph Co.

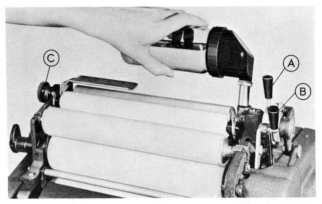

Fig. 8-67. The fountain bottle is an important part of the dampening system. Other parts indicated here are: at *A*—the feed control levers, at *B*—the ductor roller contact lever, at *C*—the fountain roller knob.

The fountain roller knob (Fig. 8-67C) may be used when an extra supply of fountain solution is needed quickly to prevent "scumming" or "filling in." This knob is turned quickly 1 or 2 turns clockwise by hand, but care must be taken to avoid flooding the rollers.

To moisten the rollers (when they are dry) proceed as follows:

1. Move the ductor roller contact lever to the "on" position, toward the fountain.

2. Set the feed control lever to the extreme "down" position, then place it on the second notch.

3. Turn the handwheel until the ductor roller contacts the fountain roller.

4. Revolve the fountain roller knob about five complete turns then turn on the press and allow to run for approximately 30 revolutions. This will usually provide enough moisture to the rollers to start the run but may be necessary to provide an extra few revolutions to obtain the correct dampness. Never allow the rollers to become saturated.

When the press is not in use, place the ductor roller contact lever in the "off" position to prevent the ductor roller from becoming saturated with solution.

Fig. 8-68. Ink is placed in the ink fountain with a small ink knife.

Fig. 8-69. Three controls are used to govern the inking system: the ink feed lever (or disengaging knob), the fountain roller knob and the adjusting screws.

The Multilith 1250

Inking System. Before placing the ink in the ink fountain, be sure the ink form roller control knobs (Fig. 8-68C) are in the "off" position (pointing upward). This is to prevent the ink rollers from contacting the cylinder. The disengaging knob must be in the operating position (horizontal). To ink the press, proceed as follows:

1. Turn the handwheel until the ductor roller (Fig. 8-68B) is out of contact with the fountain roller (Fig. 8-68A).

2. Remove and discard dried skin from the ink surface.

3. Using a circular motion with an ink knife, remove ink from the ink can and place it in the ink fountain. Do not fill the fountain completely. Additional ink may be added if required during the press run.

4. While turning the fountain roller knob (Fig. 8-69B) counterclockwise with the right hand, adjust the 14 adjusting screws (Fig. 8-69C) with the left hand, starting in the center and working to the outside. Turn the screws "in" to decrease the flow of the ink and "out" to increase the flow of the ink. Each screw controls the flow of ink directly in front of it. Adjust the screws until an even film of ink covers the roller from end to end.

5. Turn the handwheel to contact the ductor roller to the ink fountain roller.

6. Rotate the fountain roller knob counterclockwise to inspect the ink on the ductor roller for evenness. Adjust if necessary.

Once the image has been positioned correctly on the paper, it may be necessary to re-adjust the adjusting screws to provide a graduated ink coverage for the specific plate being run or for images on any area of the plate that may require more or less ink.

When the desired inking has been obtained, inking during the run may be made by the ink feed control lever (Fig. 8-69A).

The ink feed control lever may be regulated over a range of four notched positions. When the lever is all the way down, the ink feed is shut off. As the lever is raised notch by notch, the flow of ink increases accordingly until the lever is in its fourth position (pointing upward) when the maximum flow is obtained.

To prepare the ink unit for operation:

1. Set the ink feed lever (Fig. 8-69A) to the second notch from the left.

2. Start the press and allow it to turn until the ink rollers are covered with a light even film of ink. Be sure the ink roller control knobs (Fig. 8-68C) are in the "off" position.

Attaching Plates. The 1250 model duplicator is equipped with a master clamp, that is, a quick-change hook-bar clamp for slotted plates or a variation of this clamp consisting of a quick-change pin-bar clamp for punched plates.

To attach a slotted or serrated plate (quick-change hook-bar clamp):

1. Place slotted holes at the lead end of the plate on the hooks.

2. While holding the trailing end of the plate with your right hand, form the lead end of the plate to the lead edge of the cylinder with your left thumb.

3. Hold the plate taut and turn the handwheel counterclockwise until the trailing clamp becomes accessible.

4. Change hands and hold the plate securely to the edge of the cylinder with the left thumb and index finger.

5. Raise the trailing clamp up under the plate with your right hand and line up the hooks with the slots in the end of the plate.

6. Press the end of the plate over the clamp, and allow the clamp to return to its normal position.

7. Tighten the lock screw (Fig. 8-70B) snugly, then tighten the lock-nut. Do not tighten the screw when using paper masters. Check and tighten, if necessary, the lock screw on the lead edge (Fig. 8-71B) and tighten the lock nut.

For lateral adjustment (side-to-side) when for some reason the image is not squarely in position on the plate, the lateral adjustment trailing clamp (Fig. 8-71A) and the lateral adjustment lead clamp (Fig. 8-71C) are used. To square the image:

A. Loosen the knurled lock screws (Fig. 8-71B & D) slightly.

B. Turn the lateral adjusting screw (Fig. 8-71B) to swing the top of the image on the plate in the direction as much as it is to be moved on the top of the paper.

C. Turn the lateral adjusting screw (Fig. 8-71A) in the opposite direction.

Fig. 8-70. How to attach a slotted or serrated plate to the
plate cylinder is shown here.

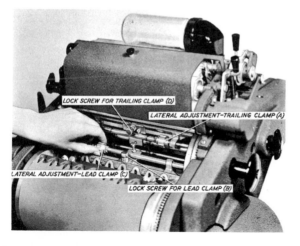

Fig. 8-71. Lateral adjustment of the master involves the four
adjustment points shown here.

Since both the lead edge and trailing edge are moved to make this adjustment, it is advisable to move each adjusting screw only half the distance necessary to square the image on the paper.

D. Re-tighten the knurled lock screws (Fig. 8-71B & D) and tighten the lock nuts.

To attach a punched plate with a quick-change pin-bar clamp, proceed as follows:

1. Using the right hand (Fig. 8-72) insert the lead end of the plate under the metal guide on the clamp, with the holes in the lead end of the plate engaging the pins in the pin-bar clamp.

2. Form the lead end of the master to the edge of the cylinder with your left thumb, while holding the trailing end of the plate with your right hand.

3. Hold the plate taut with your right hand, and turn the hand-wheel counterclockwise with your left hand until the trailing clamp becomes accessible.

4. Change hands and hold the plate securely against the cylinder with your left thumb and index finger.

5. Raise the trailing clamp up over the plate with your right hand (Fig. 8-73) and line up the pins in the clamp with the holes in the trailing end of the plate.

6. Press the end of the plate down over the clamp pins with your left thumb and index finger, and allow the clamp to return to its normal position.

For lateral adjustments (side-to-side) refer to "attaching slotted plates."

If the press is equipped with a combination plate clamp, a hinged hook-bar clamp for straight-edge and slotted masters (or a variation of this clamp consisting of a hinged pin-bar clamp for straight edge and punched plates) then the following procedure will apply:

1. Place the slotted holes at the lead end of the plate over the hook on the lead clamp.

2. Form the lead edge of the plate to the lead edge of the cylinder with your left thumb while holding the trailing end of the plate with your right hand.

3. While holding the trailing edge of the plate with your right

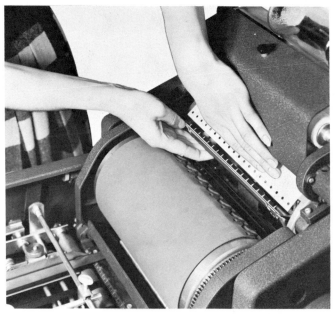

Fig. 8-72. The lead end of the plate is inserted under the metal guide and the punched holes are lined up with the pins in the clamp bar.

hand, turn the handwheel counterclockwise with your left hand until the trailing clamp becomes accessible.

4. Change hands and hold the trailing edge of the plate to the cylinder with your left thumb and index finger.

5. Raise the trailing clamp up and over the trailing end of the plate with your right hand and line up the pins in the clamp with the slots in the trailing end of the plate; then allow the clamp to return to its normal position. The pins in the clamp will engage the slots in the plate. *There is no lateral or side-to-side adjustment.*

To attach a punched plate with a hinged pin-bar clamp:

1. With your right hand, insert the lead end of the plate under the metal guide of the clamp. The holes in the lead end of the plate engage the pins in the pin-bar clamp.

2. Form the lead end of the plate to the lead edge of the cylinder with your left thumb while holding the trailing end of the plate with your right hand.

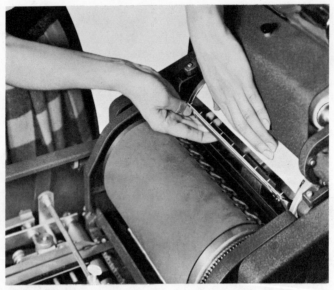

Fig. 8-73. Once the lead end has been inserted, the cylinder is turned and the tail of the master is secured in the tail clamp.

3. While holding the plate taut with your right hand, turn the handwheel counterclockwise until the trailing clamp becomes accessible.

4. Change hands and hold the plate securely against the cylinder with your left thumb and index finger.

5. Raise the trailing clamp up and over the trailing edge of the plate with your right hand (Fig. 8-73). Line up the pins in the clamp with the holes in the trailing end of the plate and then allow the clamp to return to its normal position, and the pins in the clamp will engage the holes in the plate.

There is no lateral adjustment using this clamp.

To attach a straight edge plate (paper) with a hinged hook-bar with a clamp or hinged pin-bar clamp.

1. Insert the lead end of the plate squarely into the slot with your right hand while depressing the clamp handle with your left hand. The edge of the plate should touch the strap plate at the right end of the clamp jaw to insure uniform side register.

2. Release the clamp handle, allowing the clamp to seat firmly.

3. Form the lead end of the plate to the lead edge of the cylinder with your left thumb.

4. While holding the plate taut with your right hand, turn the handwheel with your left hand until the trailing clamp becomes accessible.

5. Change hands and hold the plate securely to the trailing edge of the cylinder with your left thumb and index finger.

6. Raise the trailing clamp up and over the trailing edge of the plate with your right hand.

7. Press down on the clamp until the pins in the clamp pierce the trailing edge of the plate. Be sure the clamp seats firmly.

8. Form the trailing edge of the master to the trailing edge of the cylinder with your thumb.

There is no lateral adjustment with this clamp.

Automatic Vacuum Paper Feeder. The register board (Fig. 8-74) performs a very important part in obtaining accurate registration by providing a mechanism to jog each sheet into exactly the same position for entry into the head of the press.

The paper jogger guide (Fig. 8-74J) has three adjustments: the first for the approximate positioning of the guide (Fig. 8-74H), the

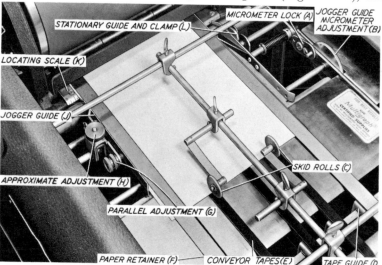

Fig. 8-74. Accurate registration is obtained through the use of the register board shown here.

second for the fine micrometer setting (Fig. 8-74B) and the third for squaring the lead edge of the sheet with the paper stop finger.

The approximate setting is made by placing a sheet of paper on the register board, in the position necessary to produce the image as it must appear on the finished copy. Measure the distance from the left edge of the master to the left edge of the sheet. Revolve the handwheel until the jogger guide has reached the inward limit of its stroke. Loosen the knurled lock (Fig. 8-74H) and set the jogger guide.(Fig. 8-74J) to the dimension on the scale (Fig. 8-74K) as determined by the measurement of the distance between the left edge of the plate and the left edge of the sheet then re-tighten the lock screw.

The parallel setting of the jogger guide is made by the parallel adjusting screw (Fig. 8-74G). To set the guide parallel with the sheet, first turn the handwheel until the feed rollers are apart, then lightly press the paper under the upper feed roller and against the stop fingers. Loosen the lock screw and turn the adjusting screw until the guide is parallel with the sheet of paper. Re-tighten the lock screw.

The micrometer adjustment of the jogger guide is made by the micrometer disc (Fig. 8-74B). To make this adjustment, release the tension disc by pressing the lock pin (Fig. 8-74A) upward and revolve the disc clockwise to move the jogger guide outward or counterclockwise to move the jogger guide in toward the tapes.

The right stationary guide is adjusted by squeezing the clamp (Fig. 8-74L) and moving the guide inward until the flat spring is compressed about ¹⁄₁₆ in. against the paper. Each sheet is registered by the jogger guide; therefore, it is necessary that each sheet be held uniformly against the jogger guide by the spring action of the stationary guide.

The conveyor tapes (Fig. 8-74E) are spaced evenly between both guides (the jogger guide and the right stationary guide) by means of the tape guides (Fig. 8-74D) which are moved laterally on the guide bar. The conveyor tapes are bands of cloth which carry the sheet of paper from the feed board to the grippers by rotating on the register board. The outside tapes should be placed to run over the flanges of both guides.

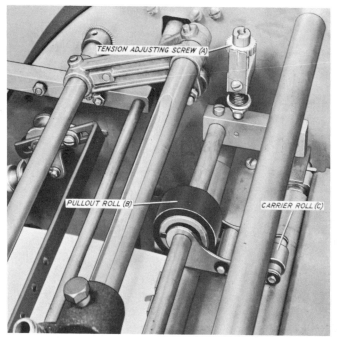

Fig. 8-75. Important parts of the Multilith feeding system are shown here.

The conveyor paper retainers (Fig. 8-74F) keep the paper flat on the conveyor tapes. These retainers are placed directly over the outside conveyor tapes with a light pressure. Too much pressure will retard the paper.

The skid rolls (Fig. 8-74C) provide better control of the sheet as it travels down the register board. These rolls are positioned just off the trailing edge of the sheet when the sheet is under the upper feed roller frame and against the paper stops.

The upper pullout rolls (Fig. 8-75) pull the sheet off the paper stack after it is raised into feeding position by the suction feet. The pull-out rolls are placed equally from side to side in relation to the suction feet and vertical magazine guides (Fig. 8-76A).

The tension of the pullout rolls against the lower pullout roller must be light and even on both sides, otherwise, as the sheet is pulled onto the register board it will be pulled unevenly causing mis-register. To adjust the tension of the pullout rolls, turn the

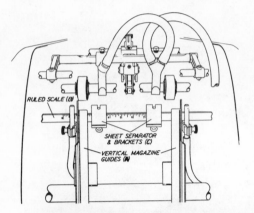

Fig. 8-76. This pictorial diagram shows the parts of the Multilith feeding system.

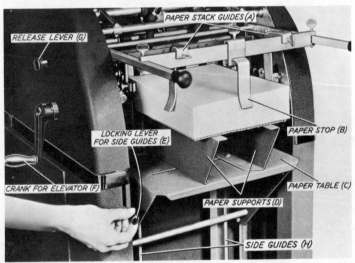

Fig. 8-77. This view of the "feed" end of the Multilith Offset Duplicator shows the controls and adjustment points necessary to operate the machine.

tension adjusting screw (Fig. 8-75A) on either or both sides until the light and even pressure is obtained. Use a screwdriver and turn clockwise to decrease tension, counterclockwise to increase tension.

The carrier rolls (Fig. 8-75C) carry the sheet from the pullout rolls to the conveyor tapes. These rolls are mounted on the pullout roll unit and therefore are positioned with the pullout rolls.

The vertical magazine guides (Fig. 8-76A) hold the paper stack in alignment. Partially lower the paper table by holding the release lever (Fig. 8-77G) to the right, and turn the crank (Fig. 8-77F) counterclockwise. The right and left vertical magazine guides (Fig. 8-77H) hold the paper stack in alignment for the proper image margins. The locking lever (Fig. 8-77E) is used to lock the guides after they are positioned. When the lever is down, the guides are locked.

The left magazine guide is adjusted first by determining the figure on the scale (Fig. 8-74K) of the register board. Then the outer edge of the left vertical magazine guide is aligned with the corresponding figure on the magazine locating scale (Fig. 8-76B). Next the right magazine guide is adjusted until a sheet of the paper being run can be placed between the guides.

The paper supports (Fig. 8-77D) are mounted on the paper table (Fig. 8-77C) and should be positioned equi-distant from the outside edges of the paper to provide support for the paper stack. The supports are locked in place by wing nuts on the underside of the table. A stiff cardboard backing sheet cut slightly smaller than the sheet size should be placed on the supports first. This gives added support to the paper stack by preventing the paper from concaving in the center or the ends of the paper from turning down.

Place about 500 sheets of paper in the paper magazine with the lead edge of the paper squarely against the front part or flange of the vertical magazine guides, then position the right guide about ⅛ inch from the edge of the paper. Press the locking lever (Fig. 8-77E) down to lock the magazine guides in position.

The suction feet (Fig. 8-78E) and sheet separators (Fig. 8-78C) are set approximately as illustrated. Adjustments toward the center or sides are made according to the width of the paper being run.

The suction feet are moved by loosening the lock screws (Fig. 8-78A) and moving them laterally on the bar. Be sure to re-tighten the screws after the positioning of the suction feet.

The sheet separators prevent the suction feet from picking up more than one sheet of paper from the stack. Each separator is attached to a bracket (Fig. 8-76C) which may be positioned by loosening a winged nut on the bottom. The sheet separators are positioned directly under the suction feet.

Fig. 8-78. The lock screws must be loosened to move the suction feet laterally on the bar.

Fig. 8-79. The air blow tubes must be adjusted to the heights of the paper stack

The flat protruding surface of the separators should project about ³⁄₁₆ inch out over the edge of the stack of paper and about ¼ inch above the bottom of the suction foot when the foot is in its lowest position.

After the separators are positioned, raise the paper by turning the crank lever (Fig. 8-77F) into the "feeding" position, about ⅛ inch below the bottom of the suction foot when the foot is in its lowest position.

The blower tubes (Fig. 8-79A) are adjusted next. They aid in the sheet separation by blowing air against the front of the top sheets. The blower tubes are held in position by lock screws (Fig. 8-79C). Adjust the blower tubes by loosening the lock screws and set the top hole just above, and directed toward, the top of the paper stack at the normal height, i.e., about ⅛ inch below the suction feet when running 20 lb. paper stock.

NOTE: Do not position the blower tubes when the suction pump is running. When the pump is turned on after the positioning is obtained, the air-stream should flutter the top sheet of the stack.

Re-adjustment of the blower tubes is not very necessary except at times when changing weights of paper stock.

The paper height adjustment (Fig. 8-79B) is made so the height of the paper stack is in relation to the bottom of the suction feet. This adjustment is only necessary when the paper does not maintain the proper height to feed the sheets consistently.

To raise the stack automatically, turn the control knob, in the direction marked "raise" or "lower" as indicated on the knob.

Be sure there is sufficient vacuum at the suction feet to pick up the sheets before changing this adjustment.

The blower and vacuum controls (Fig. 8-80) may be finely regulated by means of the two pointer knobs on the control panel. When in operation, only a sufficient vacuum and air pressure to obtain consistent feeding of single sheets should be used.

The paper stop is positioned to contact the trailing edge of the paper lightly enough to hold the paper in contact with vertical guides. The paper stop should be centered on the stack of paper by

Fig. 8-80. The air blow and vacuum are controlled by means of the two pointer control knobs shown here.

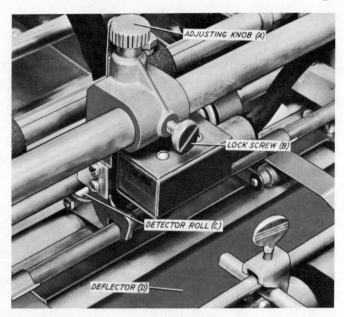

Fig. 8-81. The Multilith is equipped with a multiple sheet detector which prevents more than one sheet from entering the press at one time.

loosening the wing screw on the top and sliding the guide on the cross bar into position and retightening the screw, (Fig. 8-77B).

The paper stack guides are positioned until they just clear the sides of the paper stack. Make sure the lead edge of the stack of paper is directly contacting the vertical guides, (Fig. 8-77A).

The paper height control bar (Fig. 8-79D) determines the speed at which the paper stack rises. The normal position of bar is about 1½ inch in front of suction feet when feet are in their lowest position. When feeding thin paper, move the bar toward the suction feet to make the stack rise slowly. When feeding heavy card stock, move the bar away from the suction feet to allow the stack to rise more quickly. These two adjustments are not used very often because, once set in the normal operating position, the feeding procedure does not require the control bar to be moved. If it is necessary to position the bar, loosen the lock screws at each end.

The multiple sheet detector prevents more than one sheet from being fed through the press at a time. This unit is positioned by a lock screw (Fig. 8-81B) between the two suction feet, but in no case

Fig. 8-82. The impression cylinder is adjusted by means of the micrometer screw (at *A*), the sector (at *B*), and the clamp screw (at *C*).

should the unit be placed so close to a suction foot that the detector roll (Fig. 8-81C) may be hit during the operation.

To adjust the detector, start the press, but not the vacuum pump, and turn the adjusting knob (Fig. 8-81A) slowly towards "lower" until the detector roll just contacts the lower pullout roller. Then turn the knob towards "raise" until the detector roll stops revolving, and then raise the roll two more notches.

When properly adjusted, the detector will pass only a single sheet through at one time. Two or more sheets will be deflected by the deflector plate (Fig. 8-81D) into the tray below the register board. Occasionally, single sheets will be deflected into the tray. If this happens, turn the knob one more notch towards "raise." Once set, the detector normally handles 16 and 20 lb. paper without resetting, but will require resetting when changing to thinner or heavier paper stock.

The impression cylinder is factory adjusted for 20 lb. paper. When different weights of paper are to be run, the impression cylinder must be adjusted accordingly. To change the impression pressure proceed as follows:

If changing from light to heavy stock:

1. Loosen the clamp screw (Fig. 8-82C) with the T-wrench provided with the press.

2. Decrease the pressure by turning the micrometer screw (Fig. 8-82A) clockwise 2 or 3 times.

3. Turn a sheet of paper of the size and thickness to be run between the blanket and the impression cylinder by using the handwheel.

4. Turn the micrometer screw counterclockwise by drawing the index finger over the knurled edge until the screw can no longer be turned in this manner. At this point, an additional quarter turn of the screw by means of the thumb and forefinger may be necessary to obtain the correct pressure.

5. Re-tighten the clamp to lock the sector (Fig. 8-82B).

If changing from heavy to light stock:

1. Run a sheet of paper of the size and thickness to be used between the blanket and the impression cylinders.

2. Turn the micrometer screw counterclockwise (to increase pressure) by using the finger as outlined in step 4 above.

3. Re-tighten the lock screw.

NOTE: It is not necessary to first decrease the pressure as stated when changing from light to heavy stock.

The ejector rolls (Fig. 8-83B) can be moved from side to side on the shaft to which they are attached. To determine the correct position for these rolls, run a sheet of paper through the press by turning the handwheel until the lead edge of the sheet is just past the lower ejector roller. Position the rolls so that they will ride on the extreme right and left margins of the sheet. If placed to ride over the inked image, they may streak the copy.

The ejector rings (Fig. 8-83A) also can be moved from side to side on the shaft to which they are mounted. The rings aid in obtaining positive ejection of the sheet. When the paper has a tendency to curl downwards, set the rings outside the ejector rolls, and for paper that curls upwards, set the rings inside the rolls.

The paper receiver should be set before the sheet is completely ejected from the press.

Position the side guides (Fig. 8-83E) ⅛ inch from the edges of the sheet. The paper end stop (Fig. 8-83C) is set to allow the trailing edge of the sheet to completely clear the ejector mechanism. The paper retainer (Fig. 8-83D) deflects the sheet into the paper receiver and is positioned as illustrated.

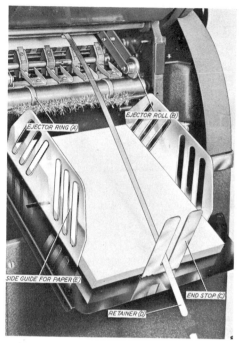

Fig. 8-83. The delivery system of the Multilith has many of the features of large offset presses.

The paper magazine (Fig. 8-84) is now loaded to its full capacity after all the positioning adjustments have been completed.

To load the paper magazine, lower the paper table by holding the release lever to the right and turning the crank counterclockwise. Load the paper stock to within ¼ inch of the sheet separators. The stack will automatically rise to the feed level when the press is turned on, provided the paper height control is set correctly.

The variable speed control knob is located beneath and to the right of the paper receiver. The speed control should be adjusted only when the press is running. The speed may be varied from 4000 to 7500 copies per hour by turning the control knob. A dial, located on the side of the press, below the two press switches and to the left, indicates the speed setting of the press.

The sheet counter, located near the handwheel, automatically counts the number of copies being printed up to 99,999. Before beginning to print, set the counter by turning the knurled knob in

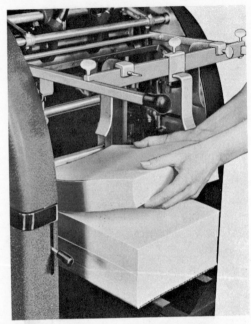

Fig. 8-84. After all positioning adjustments have been made, the paper magazine is loaded to its fullest capacity.

the direction the numbers rotate until all zeros appear in the window. (The counter is so arranged that it only counts the sheets of paper as they pass through the press.)

Vertical positioning of the image on paper may be done as follows:

1. Revolve the handwheel until the clamp screw at the lead end of the cylinder is in line with the socket of the vertical positioning control (Fig. 8-85B).

2. Press the control knob inward and "rock" the cylinder slightly using the handwheel until the socket engages the clamp screw.

3. While pressing the control knob inward, turn the knob counterclockwise to loosen the clamp screw. Continue to press the knob inward, and carefully turn the handwheel clockwise to raise the image on the sheet, or counterclockwise to lower the image

4. Tighten the clamp screw and release the control knob.

As a guide in obtaining the correct vertical positioning, a

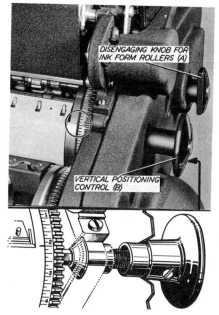

Fig. 8-85. Vertical positioning of the image involves the use of the vertical positioning control shown here.

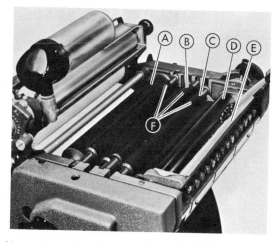

Fig. 8-86. The inking unit contains the ink fountain and seven removable rollers.

graduated scale is provided on the gear of the master cylinder. When the figure "2" on the scale is in line with the reference mark on the edge of the cylinder, the lead edges of the master and blanket cylinders are in line. Moving the gear in relation to the reference mark will change the vertical position of the image on the paper. For example, moving the gear up an inch in relation to the reference mark will lower the image on the sheet a corresponding inch.

Ink Unit Adjustments. The ink unit (the ink fountain and ten rollers) distributes a thin film of ink to the plate. The fountain and seven rollers are removable, Fig. 8-86 illustrates the inking unit:

A. Upper ink form roller (lower ink form roller not shown)
B. Upper distribution roller (lower roller not shown)
C. Ductor roller
D. Ink fountain roller
E. Ink fountain
F. Intermediate idler rollers (3)

A fixed oscillating roller is not shown.

The upper ink form roller (Fig. 8-87B) is mounted on eccentric shafts which provide contact with the plate. To insure that this roller is placed properly according to the factory, check the center-

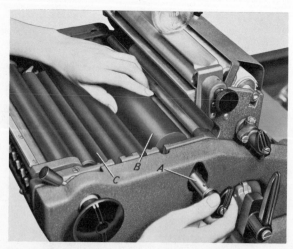

Fig. 8-87. The disengaging knob (at *A*) may be turned to raise the ink roller (at *B*) out of contact with the other press parts. At *C*—the distribution roller is shown.

punch marks on the edge of the end bearings. One center-punch mark is for the upper form roller, and two center punch marks are for the lower form roller. The rollers are installed with the punch marks facing the operating side of the press.

The disengaging knob for the ink form rollers (Fig. 8-87A) may be turned to raise the ink form roller out of contact with other parts of the press. This is usually done so that the roller will not obtain low spots when the press stands idle for a period of time.

Place the form roller into the ink unit by holding the roller as illustrated and insert the shaft through the bearing, into the roller, and then into the bearing on the opposite side. Press the shaft inward, and turn the knob slightly until the shaft locks in position.

The ductor roller (Fig. 8-88D) is placed into the U-shaped bracket (Fig. 8-88C) when the bracket is centered between the lower distributor roller and the fountain roller. The ductor roller is held in position by spring latches (Fig. 8-88B) at each end. The brackets are centered by turning the handwheel.

The three idler rollers (Fig. 8-86F) with bearings attached, fit into slots in the side plates. The first idler contacts the upper form roller; the second idler contacts the oscillating roller (Fig. 8-88A) and the third idler contacts the lower distribution roller.

The upper distribution roller (Fig. 8-86B), without bearings, fits into the side plates and is in contact with the second and third idler rollers.

Fig. 8-88. Here the ink ductor roller is being inserted, at *A*—the oscillating roller, at *B*—the spring latch, at *C*—the U-shaped bracket, at *D*—the ink ductor roller.

Fig. 8-89. Here the ink fountain is being inserted, at *A*—the fountain, at *B*—the U-shaped opening, at *C*—the fountain roller bearings.

Place the ink fountain (Fig. 8-89A) over the fountain roller, as illustrated, with the U-shaped openings (Fig. 8-89B) at each end of the fountain roller bearings (Fig. 8-89C) and press the fountain down firmly. Turn the fountain backwards until seated into position.

To adjust the ink form rollers, proceed as follows:

1. Place a dry plate on the cylinder, but do not apply any fountain solution.

2. Turn the handwheel until the plate is under the ink form rollers, and place the ink form roller control knob to the "on" position, momentarily contacting the plate. Then turn the knob to the "off" position.

The inked line or "bead" on the plate (Fig. 8-90) should be between ⅛ inch and ³⁄₁₆ inch evenly across the plate. Both the upper and lower rollers are checked in the same manner.

To adjust the overall pressure:

3. Loosen the setscrew (Fig. 8-90A) in the form roller control knob, and with a screwdriver, turn the eccentric shaft (Fig. 8-90A) clockwise to decrease the width of the "bead" and counterclockwise to increase the width of the "bead." Retighten the set screw.

To adjust the parallel pressure:

4. Remove the right side plate from the ink unit. The disengaging cam (Fig. 8-91B) must be out of contact with the eccentric brackets when making this adjustment. A cam is the projecting

Fig. 8-90. The inked line on the plate is shown here, at *A*—the set screw, at *B*—the eccentric shaft.

Fig. 8-91. Ink form roller adjustments are shown here, at *A*—the lock screw, at *B*—the disengaging cam, at *C*—the eccentric bearings.

part on a wheel or shaft to govern the motion of a roller, pin, or valve with which it comes in contact. The eccentric bearing (Fig. 8-91C) lowers or raises the right end of the ink roller.

5. Loosen the lock screw (Fig. 8-91A) and turn the eccentric bearing counterclockwise to increase the width of the right end of the contact line (the inked or "bead" line) or clockwise to decrease the width. Re-tighten the lock screw.

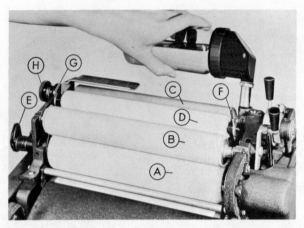

Fig. 8-92. The water dampening rollers are shown here.

NOTE: The overall pressure and parallel pressure of both form rollers are adjusted in the same manner.

Inserting and Adjusting Water Dampening Rollers. The dampening unit consists of a water fountain and four rollers.

In Fig. 8-92, the parts are:

A. Form roller
B. Rider roller
C. Fountain roller
D. Ductor roller

The form roller inserted first is mounted on an eccentric shaft which brings the roller in contact with the plate. Place the roller in the unit with the slot in the end of the roller-engaging coupling on the drive gear. Insert the shaft, through the bearing in the side plate, into the roller, then into the bearing in the opposite side plate. Press the shaft inward while turning the knob (Fig. 8-92E) slightly until the shaft locks in position.

The rider roller is inserted into slots in the side plates so it will contact the form roller.

The ductor roller is placed into U-shaped brackets on both sides and held in position by spring latches (Fig. 8-92F). Before inserting it into place, turn the handwheel until the brackets are centered between the rider roller and the fountain roller.

The fountain roller normally remains in the fountain tray and is

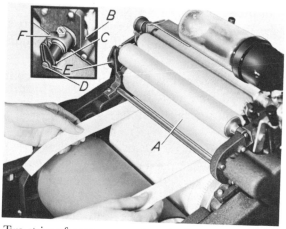

Fig. 8-93. Two strips of paper are used to check parallel pressure. At *A*—the form roller is shown, at *B*—the set screw on the eccentric bearing, at *C*—the set screw on the form roller control knob, at *D*—the roller control knob, at *E*—the form roller control knob, at *F*—the eccentric bearing.

removed only to clean the roller itself or the fountain tray. To remove it loosen the set screw and pull the knob (Fig. 8-92H) outward until the roller is released.

To adjust the form roller pressure, the roller must first be "run-in" or "broken-in." To do this, the press must be running with the rollers down on the plate. When a new cover is placed on the roller, wet the cover with fountain solution, place the roller in contact with the plate and allow the press to revolve a few minutes. Then make the following checks and adjustments:

For parallel pressure:

1. Cut two strips of 20 lb. paper, 1 inch wide and place them between the plate and form roller (Fig. 8-93). Avoid placing the strips under the seam (if any) of the cover.

2. Contact the form roller (Fig. 8-93A) to the plate and slowly withdraw the paper strips, paying particular attention to the "drag" or tension of both strips. If the tension is unequal:

3. Loosen the setscrew (Fig. 8-92B) and turn the eccentric bearing (Fig. 8-93F) counterclockwise to increase tension on the left end of the roller or clockwise to decrease the tension.

4. Re-tighten the set screw when the tension is equal.

NOTE: This adjustment only affects the left end of the roller.

For overall pressure:

5. Replace the two strips of paper as stated before and turn the form roller control knob (Fig. 8-93E) to "on" position contacting the roller to the plate.

6. Loosen the set screw (Fig. 8-93C) in the roller control knob and with a screwdriver, turn the eccentric shaft (Fig. 8-93D) counterclockwise until a fairly strong "drag" is felt as the strips are withdrawn.

7. Lock the adjustment by means of the lock screw. The knob must point to the left when the form roller is contacting the plate.

Attaching the Blanket. To place the blanket on the press, proceed as follows:

1. Turn the handwheel until the lead clamp of the blanket (Fig. 8-94A) cylinder is accessible (Fig. 8-94B), and place the holes of the blanket over the hooks in the clamp.

2. Hold the blanket taut with the right hand and turn the handwheel with the left hand until the trailing clamps (Fig. 8-95A) are accessible.

3. Attach the holes of blanket to the hooks of the clamp and tighten all clamp screws (Fig. 8-95C) with the fingers (do not use pliers).

Fig. 8-94. The clamp of the cylinder (at *B*) must be accessible in order to attach the blanket (*A*).

Fig. 8-95. Once the head of the blanket is attached, the cylinder is turned and the tail is attached, at *A*—the trailing clamps, at *B*—the lock nuts, at *C*—the clamp screws.

4. Draw up the lock nuts (Fig. 8-95B) snugly with the fingers to hold the clamp screws.

Since the blanket has a certain amount of stretch, this stretch should be taken up before the blanket is actually used on a job.

NOTE: On the model 1250, the blanket must be washed off each time the press is stopped, or each time the position of the image on the paper is changed.

Plate-to-blanket Pressure Adjustment. When the image on the plate is completely inked, but the image on the blanket contains broken lines and indistinct characters throughout, more contact pressure is required between the plate and blanket. To obtain proper pressure, proceed as follows:

1. Place a plate on the plate cylinder, start the press and allow the plate to ink up completely black (Fig. 8-96B). (Do not apply water.)

2. Turn the ink form roller knobs "off" and stop the press.

3. Turn the handwheel until the duplicating surfaces of the cylinders are directly opposite, and turn operating handle (Fig. 8-97A) to the "on" position, momentarily contacting the blanket. Then return to the "off" position.

4. Revolve the cylinders by means of the handwheel until the

Fig. 8-96. The plate cylinder should be inked completely black. Shown at *B*—the plate on the plate cylinder, at *C*—the contact ink line on the blanket.

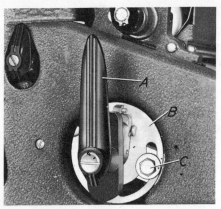

Fig. 8-97. The controls shown here govern the master-to-blanket pressure adjustment. Shown at *A*—the operating control handle, at *B*—the adjusting disc, at *C*—the clamp screws.

contact line (Fig. 8-96C) can be seen on the blanket. This line should measure ⅛ inch to 3⁄16 inch width uniformly across the blanket.

To adjust if necessary:

5. Loosen the clamp screw (Fig. 8-97C) for the adjusting disc (Fig. 8-97B) and rotate it together with the operating control handle (Fig. 8-97A) clockwise to decrease contact pressure, or counterclockwise to increase contact pressure.

Fig. 8-98. This view of the Multilith Offset Duplicator shows the following points:

A. Cam	E. Scale	H. Lock nut
B. Adjusting nut	F. Strips of paper used in	J. Lock nut
C. Lock screw	parallel pressure adjustment	K. Adjusting screw
D. Elevating frame	G. Lock washer	

6. Re-tighten the lock screw after making this adjustment.

7. Wash off the blanket and repeat operations 3 to 6 until the correct pressure is obtained.

Paper feed roller adjustment: The paper feed rollers must be accurately set to insure registration of the sheets. The pressure between the upper feed roller and lower feed roller must be equal at all points to obtain this registration.

For parallel adjustment:

1. Cut two strips of 20 lb. paper, 1 inch wide and place them between the feed rollers (Fig. 8-98F).

2. Turn the handwheel until the upper feed roller contacts the lower feed roller.

3. Withdraw the strips slowly, paying attention to the "drag" or tension. The tension should be firm and offer moderate resistance but should not be enough to tear the strips of paper.

4. If tension is unequal, loosen the lock screw (Fig. 8-98C) and lightly turn the bearing until equal tension is obtained. It may be necessary to lighten the overall pressure at this point in order to level the lower feed roller. Turning the bearing counterclockwise lowers the left end of the lower feed roller and reduces pressure between the left end of the feed rollers; clockwise raises the left end of the lower feed roller and increases pressure between left end of feed rollers.

5. Re-tighten the lock screw (Fig. 8-98C) to hold the bearing in the proper adjustment.

6. If overall pressure is necessary, loosen the lock nut (Fig. 8-98H) and lightly turn the adjusting nut (Fig. 8-98B) counterclockwise to increase overall pressure or clockwise to decrease pressure.

7. Re-tighten the lock nut.

Paper finger shaft adjustment: This adjustment should be slightly below the surface of the ruled scale (Fig. 8-98E) when the paper feed rollers are in contact. If the fingers are too high, they will nick the lead edge of the sheet as it is fed through the press. If they are too low, they will not stop and will hold the sheet until the feed rollers close. The fingers may be seen under the elevating frame, Fig. 8-98D.

To adjust if necessary, loosen the lock nut (Fig. 8-98J) on the adjusting screw (Fig. 8-98K) and turn the screw clockwise to lower the fingers or counterclockwise to raise them. Re-tighten the lock nut.

Cam Adjustment. The engaging cam is factory adjusted for average weights of paper and seldom requires re-adjusting unless considerably lighter or heavier stock is to be run. This cam (Fig. 8-99A) controls the timing of the sheet with the grippers on the impression cylinder. This adjustment is important in obtaining registration. The timing in turn is directly affected by the pressure of the feed rollers; therefore, before disturbing the cam, be sure the feed roller pressure is correct for the stock being run.

If necessary to adjust.

1. Place a sheet of paper to be run on the conveyor tapes between the feed rollers and squarely in contact with the paper stop fingers.

Fig. 8-99. The cam must be adjusted to the weight of paper being run. The cam (at *A*) controls the timing of the sheet with the grippers on the impression cylinder. Other parts shown here are: the reference mark (at *B*), the slot used in moving the cam band (at *C*), and the locking screws (at *D*).

2. Turn the handwheel counterclockwise until the grippers (Fig. 8-100B) begin to open.

The cam is correctly adjusted when the lead edge of the sheet is under the grippers and firmly against the stop plates (Fig. 8-100A).

If the lead edge of the sheet is under the grippers, but not in contact with the stop plates, the cam is retarded too far. Inaccurate registration will result. The paper will fail to enter the grippers and will flutter out of the press.

If the lead edge of the sheet is under the grippers, but extends over the top of the stop plates, or if the sheets are actually jumping over the grippers, the cam is advanced too far. Nicking of the lead edge of the sheet will result or the sheets will flutter out of the press.

3. Turn the handwheel until the trailing clamps of the blanket and plate cylinder are approximately 1 inch apart.

The cam band is locked in position on the blanket cylinder by three lock screws equally spaced around the circular edge of the cylinder. Avoid moving the cylinder after all three screws have been loosened. To do so will throw the cam completely out of adjustment.

Fig. 8-100. Shown here are the stop plates (at *A*) and the grippers (at *B*).

4. Loosen the two lock screws accessible through the two holes in the side plates, Fig. 8-99D.

5. Turn the handwheel counterclockwise until the open part of the blanket cylinder is about in line with the reference mark (Fig. 8-99B) on the side plate.

6. Loosen the third screw near the lead clamp of the blanket cylinder.

7. Move the cam band in the desired direction by inserting a screwdriver into the slot in the band (Fig. 8-99C).

NOTE: Only a very slight, almost unnoticeable, movement is needed: therefore, be careful in making this adjustment. If the cam should happen to be moved too far in either direction, return the cam to the original factory setting by turning the cam band until the center of slot (Fig. 8-99C) is in line with the punch mark on the rim of the gear. Then start all over again to obtain the proper adjustment.

CAUTION: Be sure to re-tighten all three lock screws before attempting to check adjustment or operate the press. In retightening, tighten the screw nearest the lead clamp, then turn the cylinder by hand until the other two screws are in line with the holes in the side plate. Tighten these screws.

Vacuum Pump. An automatic oiling system assures correct lubrication of the vanes as they ride against the interior of the

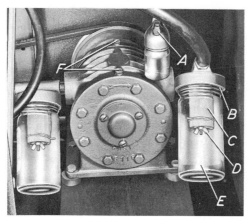

Fig. 8-101. The vacuum pump system is shown here, at *A*—the snap filler cap, at *B*—the gasket, at *C*—the filter, at *D*—wing nuts, at *E*—the glass jar, and at *F*—.

pump housing (a container for the vanes). A wick in the oiler (a container for the oil) allows an adequate supply of oil through the pump.

Whenever the oil level in the oiler is within ½ inch of bottom, add sufficient oil to fill the glass reservoir through the snap filler cap (Fig. 8-101A). Do not fill beyond the rim of the jar.

The pump bearings should be lubricated once a week by removing the caps (Fig. 8-101A) and filling the oil channels.

Air filters provided in the vacuum blower parts of the pump, prevent paper lint and other foreign material from being drawn into the mechanism. The filter elements consist of layers of fine and coarse metal mesh (Fig. 8-101C) and for efficient operation, must be frequently cleaned.

To clean the filter, remove the glass jar (Fig. 8-101E) and wing nuts (Fig. 8-101D), then the washers and clips. Unroll the screens and wash them in a suitable cleaner to remove all foreign matter. Reroll the screens and reassemble them on the pump. Wash the jars and replace them, being sure the gaskets (Fig. 8-101B) are in place and the jars are seated snugly.

Auxiliary Equipment. The mechanical jogger (Fig. 8-102) smoothly and quietly stacks copies evenly in the paper receiver, making them ready for a second run, folding, or padding. The

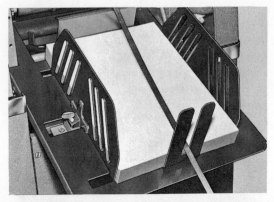

Fig. 8-102. The mechanical jogger stacks paper evenly in the receiver tray.

Fig. 8-103. A numbering device can be installed on the Multilith to automatically number the printed sheets.

capacity is 1000 sheets of 20 lb. paper or the equivalent number in other weights at one time.

A numbering device (Fig. 8-103) can be installed which can automatically number simultaneously with the printing in either color of aniline ink. From one to 24 numbering heads can be used at one time to provide one or multiple numbers in almost any location on a sheet. Numbering heads can be obtained to number forward or backward in consecutive, triplicate, skip 2 or skip 3 sequence to handle practically any numbering requirements.

Fig. 8-104. The Multilith can be adapted to perforate printed sheets as they are delivered.

Fig. 8-105. The slitting unit may be used to run two small forms at the same time.

A *perforating device* (Fig. 8-104) may be added to the numbering device or it may be obtained as a drive by itself. The perforating is done simultaneously with the printing and is parallel with the direction of the sheet travel. From one to three perforating wheels can be used at a time. Slitting or scoring units can also be installed on this device.

The slitting unit (Fig. 8-105) may be used when running two small forms two up. Economy of operation can be obtained by this operation which eliminates a second operation of cutting apart on the cutter.

The roller cleaning attachment (Fig. 8-106) is a convenient method of cleaning the ink rollers at the end of each day or changing from one color to another. The rollers can be cleaned without removing them from the machine.

Advanced Models (Figs. 8-107–108) have some very definite advantages:

1. Larger image coverage
2. Maximum sheet size 11 x 17 in.
3. Elimination of the handwheel
4. Chain delivery with receding stacker which delivers, jogs, and stacks up to 5000 copies without interruption.
5. Facilities for:
   a. Three color process
   b. Electrical static elimination
   c. Alternate sheet feeding
   d. Right and left jogging
6. Automatic blanket cleaners

Fig. 8-106. The Multilith roller cleaning attachment allows the rollers to be cleaned without removing them.

Fig. 8-107. The Multilith 1000 is shown here.

Fig. 8-108. The Multilith 2550 is fully automated.

7. Overload clutch
8. Chrome plated cylinders
9. An electrical control unit in the base of the machine which positions the plate, coordinates the flow of ink and moistening solution, and begins feeding the paper stock. When the predetermined number of copies has been run, the paper feeding is stopped, the blanket is automatically cleaned and the press is prepared for the next cycle. Step-by-step control can be returned to the pressman at the flick of a switch.

10. Magnetic ink encoded checks can be personalized, serially numbered, and imprinted with characters printed in magnetic ink. The press is programmed to provide for the production of deposit and reorder forms in the course of a standard operating cycle.

SPECIFICATIONS TO BE REMEMBERED
MULTILITH MODEL 1250

Paper sizes: Maximum—11 × 14 inches. Minimum size—3 × 5 inches.

Paper weights: 13 lb. to 140 lb. index

Image: 9½ × 13 inches

Gripper margin: $\frac{5}{16}$ inches

Feeder magazine: 5000 sheets—20 lb. paper

Speed range: 4000 to 7500 copies per hour

Weight: Press 600 lbs.

Motors: ½HP AC 115V or 230V. 50 or 60 cycle for press; ⅓HP for the vacuum pump

Review Questions

1. Do not write in the book, but on the test sheets provided.
2. Questions are in several forms: multiple choice, true or false, one or a few words, or matching.
3. Place T in the space provided if the statement is true, F if it is false.
4. Select from the list of statements or words the most logical answer.
5. Use one or a few words in the one-word answers.
6. In the matching questions, select the correct letter of the alphabet.

DITTO OFFSET DUPLICATOR
MODEL—16

1. Scum is the result of too much ink and not enough water applied to the plate. True or False   ( )
2. It is necessary to wash the blanket each time a vertical adjustment is made of the image. True or False   ( )

3. Metal plates should always be secured with both the head and tail clamps. True or False ( )

4. How many control switches are there on the Ditto Model L-16? Name them: ( )

5. Maximum sheet size is:

a. 10 × 14
b. 11 × 14

c. 12 × 14
d. 12 × 15 ( )

6. Minimum sheet size is:

a. 3 × 6
b. 3 × 5

c. 4 × 5
d. 4 × 6 ( )

7. The maximum image area is:

a. 10 × 14
b. 10¾ × 14

c. 10¾ × 15
d. 10½ × 14 ( )

8. The speed range is:

a. 4500 to 8000 imp. per hour
b. 4000 to 8000 imp. per hour
c. 4500 to 8500 imp. per hour
d. 4000 to 85000 imp. per hour ( )

9. The fountain solution is transferred to the plate from:

a. Fountain roller to oscillating to ductor to form roller
b. Fountain roller to ductor to form to oscillating roller
c. Fountain roller to ductor to oscillating to form roller
d. Fountain roller to form to ductor to oscillating roller ( )

10. Line up the left column to the corresponding right column in proper sequence:

a. Elevator switch ____
b. Ink switch ____
c. Copy switch ____
d. Dampener switch ____
e. Power switch ____

a. Up & down position
b. Off, contact & feed position
c. Off, feed & contact position
d. On & off position
e. Off, feed & Contact position

A. B. DICK OFFSET DUPLICATOR
MODEL—360

1. Maximum sheet size is:

    a. 11 × 14   c. 10 × 17
    b. 11 × 17   d. 10 × 14   ( )

2. Minimum sheet size is:

    a. 4 × 5   c. 4 × 3
    b. 4 × 6   d. 3 × 5   ( )

3. Maximum image area is:

    a. 10¼ × 16½   c. 10½ × 16¼
    b. 10 × 16   d. 10½ × 16   ( )

4. When adjusting the duplicator for speed, the speed adjustment should be made only when the motor switch is on. True or False   ( )

5. A vacuum type feeding system is used on the Model 360. True or False   ( )

6. It is necessary to wash the blanket after making each vertical adjustment. True or False   ( )

7. The paper height adjustment thumb screw is turned clockwise to raise the stack of paper. True or False   ( )

8. How many rollers are there in the inking system?

9. What are the three image adjustments called?

    1.

    2.

    3.

10. What is required to insure accurate vertical registration of the sheet?

MULTILITH DUPLICATOR MODEL—1250

1. Maximum sheet size is:

    a. 10 × 14   c. 11 × 15
    b. 11 × 14   d. 11 × 13   ( )

2. Minimum sheet size is:

    a. 4 × 5   c. 3 × 5
    b. 5 × 6   d. 4 × 3   ( )

3. Speed range is:

    a. up to 5000   c. up to 6000
    b. 4000 to 7500   d. 4000 to 8000   ( )

4. What two auxiliary devices are available on the 1250 model

    a. drilling   c. folding   e. trimming
    b. numbering   d. perforating   ( )

5. In the dampening system, water is applied from:

    a. Fountain roller to rider to ductor to form roller
    b. Fountain roller to ductor to form to rider roller
    c. Fountain roller to ductor to rider to form roller
    d. Fountain roller to rider to form to ductor roller   ( )

6. The dampening system consists of what four rollers?

    1. _____   3. _____
    2. _____   4. _____

7. The inking unit consists of _____ rollers.

8. Lateral adjustment is possible using a slotted plated with a hinged hook-bar clamp. True or False   ( )

9. Each time the position of the plate image is changed, the blanket should be washed. True or False   ( )

10. More than one different type of plates may be run on the 1250. True or False   ( )

CHAPTER 9

ATF Chief 15 and Davidson Dual 500

What is the ATF Chief "15"? What is its most significant feature?
What is the Davidson? What is its most significant feature?

The ATF Chief 15 is another offset press and is similar in appearance to the Multilith press. ATF are the initials of the manufacturer—American Type Founders. Operational efficiency is perhaps the most significant feature of this press.

The Davidson offset press is another press designed and manufactured to produce quality work. This press is noted for its versatility; however, this versatility includes types of printing other than lithography. The Davidson press employs a two cylinder principle rather than the three cylinder principle.

This chapter will describe the operation of, and makeready procedures for, these two offset presses.[1]

The Inking System

The inking system of any press supplies ink to the plate so that the image on the plate may be transferred to paper. The inking system of the offset press has a minimum of six parts: The ink fountain, the fountain roller, a ductor, a vibrator, a rider, and a form roller. A schematic diagram of a typical offset inking system is shown in Fig. 9-1.

[1] This material is adapted from the ATF Chief Model 15 Manual and reprinted by permission through the courtesy of American Type Founders Co., Inc.

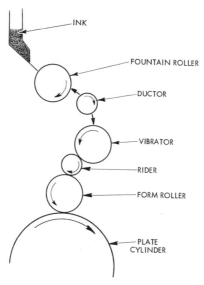

INK

FOUNTAIN ROLLER

DUCTOR

VIBRATOR

RIDER

FORM ROLLER

PLATE
CYLINDER

Fig. 9-1. A schematic diagram of a typical small offset inking system is shown. Such systems have a minimum of six parts: the ink fountain, the fountain roller, a vibrator, a rider roller and form rollers.

The Ink Fountain. The reservoir that supplies ink to the offset press is held in the ink fountain. The *ink fountain roller* rotates slowly and intermittently. Ink flows from the ink fountain to the ink fountain roller. The *ductor* swings backward and forward between the ink fountain roller and the vibrator taking ink from the rollers and depositing it on the vibrator. The *vibrator* rotates and shakes to condition the ink, making it more pliable. Ink from the vibrator is deposited on the *rider* which transfers it to the *form roller*. From the form roller, the ink is placed on the plate.

Operating Controls

The Inking System. The ink fountain roller control knob (Fig. 9-2A) controls the ink flow from the fountain and, when used with the ink fountain adjusting screws, provides proper inking.

The ink volume control (Fig. 9-2B) with its 7 positions, controls or regulates the amount of ink being delivered to the system. No ink is delivered in the extreme left position. As the control is moved

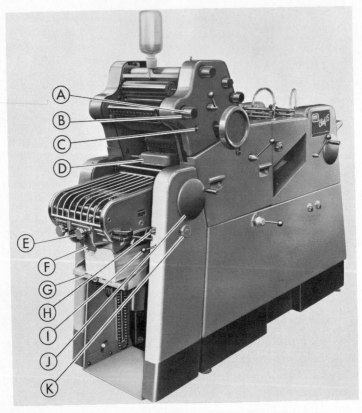

Fig. 9-2. The controls for the ATF Chief "15" inking and delivery systems are shown here. At *A*—the ink fountain roller knob, at *B*—the ink volume control, at *C*—the ink fountain manual control lever, at *D*—the delivery light, at *E*—the side-guide controls, at *F*—the delivery sheet stop, at *G*—the delivery board, at *H*—the delivery lock release, at *I*—the delivery paper-feed control, at *J*—the delivery pile handwheel, at *K*—the delivery rate lowering control.

to the right, the amount of ink is increased until the maximum is delivered in the 7th position.

The ink fountain manual control lever (Fig. 9-2C) is used to supply ink to the entire ink system. Since the ink fountain roller turns only when paper is being fed, this lever is depressed to provide ink to the system when paper is not being fed.

The delivery side-guide control knobs (Fig. 9-2E) permit the side guides to be moved to accommodate the stock being run. (For this adjustment, a counterclockwise movement loosens the delivery side guides.)

The delivery sheet stop (Fig. 9-2F) stops the sheet as it is delivered after being printed. The paper is jogged from the rear against the stop which swings up so that the sheets may be easily removed for inspection.

The delivery board (Fig. 9-2G) that receives the printed sheets has four casters located on the bottom. These casters allow the board to be rolled away when it is full and reaches floor level. The capacity of the delivery board is about 20¾ in. of stock.

The delivery lock release (Fig. 9-2H), when depressed, allows the paper pile to be raised manually.

The delivery paper-feed control (Fig. 9-2I) controls the feed of paper from the delivery end. The feed is "on" when this control is pulled "out" and the feed is "off" when the control is "in."

The delivery pile handwheel (Fig. 9-2J) raises or lowers the delivery board. Turn the handwheel counterclockwise to lower the delivery board. To raise the board, depress the delivery lock release and turn the handwheel clockwise.

The delivery rate lowering control (Fig. 9-2K) determines the rate at which the delivery board will drop to maintain the top of the pile at a constant height. It can be set for various thicknesses of stock by turning the control clockwise to increase the drop or counterclockwise to decrease the drop.

The Dampening System. The inking system has been previously described, but the peculiarity of offset-lithography is that it requires both ink and water for operation. The water is supplied by the dampening system.

The dampening system (Fig. 9-3) is quite similar to the inking system; it requires at least the following parts: a *fountain, fountain roller,* a *ductor* and one or more *form rollers.*

The *fountain* holds the water supply. The *fountain roller* picks up water from the fountain and carries it to the *ductor.* The ductor *oscillates* (moves backward and forward) between the fountain roller and the form rollers, supplying water intermittently to the form rollers. The form rollers deposit the water to the plate.

The dampener fountain roller control knob (Fig. 9-4A) permits the operator to turn the dampener fountain roller by hand.

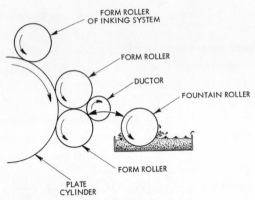

FORM ROLLER
OF INKING SYSTEM

FORM ROLLER

DUCTOR

FOUNTAIN ROLLER

FORM ROLLER

PLATE
CYLINDER

Fig. 9-3. A schematic diagram of a typical dampening system for a small offset press is shown here. It has a minimum of five parts: the water fountain, the fountain roller, the ductor roller and two form rollers.

The dampener volume control (Fig. 9-4B) has 11 positions that regulate the amount of fountain solution delivered to the dampening system. When the control is in the extreme right position, no solution is delivered; as the control is moved to the left, the amount of solution is increased until the maximum amount is being delivered in the 11th position.

The dampener and ink form roller control lever (Fig. 9-4C) is a simplified 3-position operating lever. "Off" is to the extreme left. In the center position, the dampener form roller is placed in contact with the plate, and in the 3rd position the ink form rollers drop and are in operating position.

The handwheel (Fig. 9-4D) manually turns the press through the full cycle. It is used when placing or removing plates and blankets and can be moved in either direction.

The drive motor switch (Fig. 9-4E) is "off" in the left position and "on" in the right position.

The air vacuum pump switch (Fig. 9-4F) operates the air vacuum pump. This switch may be left in the "on" position during the press operation because the feeding of the paper is controlled by the front and back paper feed controls. The "off" position of the switch is to the left and "on" is to the right.

The speed control lever (Fig. 9-4G) with 8 positions is adjustable from 3400 to 7200 impressions per hour. The lever is moved down

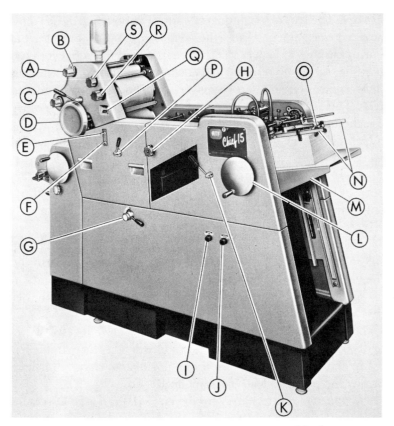

Fig. 9-4. The controls for the ATF Chief "15" dampening and feeding systems are shown in this illustration. At *A*—the dampener fountain roller control knob, at *B*—the dampener volume control, at *C*—the dampener-ink form roller control lever, at *D*—the handwheel, at *E*—the drive motor switch, at *F*—the air-vacuum pump switch, at *G*—the speed control lever, at *H*—the jogger control knobs, at *I*—the air blow control, at *J*—the vacuum control, at *K*—the back paper-feed control, at *L*—the paper platform handwheel, at *M*—the paper platform, at *N*—the paper-stack side guides, at *O*—the paper-stack back guides, at *P*—the manual plate-to-blanket impression control, at *Q*—the automatic copy counter, at *R*—the vertical positioning control knob, at *S*—the control knob for the auxiliary form roller in the dampening system.

to increase the speed, and up to decrease it. Speed changes should be made gradually and only when the press is in operation.

The last operation performed by the press is "jogging." Jogging is the process of keeping the printed sheets evenly stacked in the delivery. The left and right jogger control knobs (Fig. 9-4H) move the side jogger, the ball race (the metal strip that contains the ball bearings as they ride over the feed board), and the conveyor tape all at the same time. The left jogger control (maroon) and the right jogger control (green) can be moved independently or simultaneously. They should be used only when the press is running, otherwise the tapes will become distorted.

The air blower on the ATF Chief "15" *winds* (pronounced a "the wind blows") the sheets before being fed to the press for printing. *Winding* keeps the sheets from sticking together. The air blower control (Fig. 9-4I) regulates the amount of air delivered to the center and side air blow paper separators. A turn to the right increases, and to the left decreases, the amount.

Suction feet are used to pickup the paper from the "feed" stack and hold it so that the sheet can be fed into the press for printing. The vacuum control (Fig. 9-4J) regulates the suction delivered to the suction feet. A turn to the right increases, and to the left decreases, the suction.

The back paper-feed control (Fig. 9-4K) lever located at the paper feeder end is in the "off" position when at the extreme left and in the "off" position when at the extreme right. This lever permits the paper to feed on to the feedboard.

The paper platform handwheel (Fig. 9-4L) raises or lowers the paper platform. First, push in the handwheel, then turn it clockwise to raise the platform or counterclockwise to lower the platform.

The paper platform (Fig. 9-4M) is made of solid steel and is tilted slightly forward to provide better sheet control. The platform capacity is approximately 5000 sheets of 20 lb. bond or equivalent.

The left and right paper stack side guides (Fig. 9-4N), "flip-up" or "lift-up" guides, are adjustable for various widths and lengths of paper stock by using the movable side guide extensions.

The paper stack back guides (Fig. 9-4O) are also adjustable for various widths and lengths of stock. These guides are also "flip-up" guides which facilitate loading and which contain two sets of "wings." The front wings are in position when they rest on the top of the paper stack, and the back wings are in position when they rest against the back of the paper stack.

The manual plate-to-blanket impression control (Fig. 9-4P) is used if pre-inking of the blanket is desired. By turning this control to the left (towards the delivery end), the plate and blanket cylinders are placed on "impression," permitting the pre-inking of the blanket.

The automatic copy counter (Fig. 9-4Q) should be set on 00,000 before starting the run; this will inform the operator of the number of copies that are printed upon completion of the run. A built-in reset wheel is provided for setting the counter. The counter will register up to 99,999.

The vertical positioning control knob (Fig. 9-4R) is used for the vertical positioning of the image on the paper being run. When engaged with the plate-cylinder lock nut, and turned to the left, it allows the image to be raised or lowered. A turn to the right re-locks the cylinder ready for use. A scale is provided on the plate cylinder for positioning.

The control knob for the auxiliary form roller in the dampening system (Fig. 9-4S) has three functions: when in the "up" position, the dampener form roller is taken out of contact with the plate; when moved one position to the right, it places the roller in normal operating position, and when moved to the extreme right, it releases the retaining arms permitting the dampening form roller to be easily removed.

Adjustments

Ink and Ink Adjustments. Before placing the ink in the ink fountain, inspect the ink rollers to make sure they are clean of all lint and glaze. Remove the fountain and clean it along with the ink fountain roller. Replace the fountain and turn the handwheel until the ink ductor roller is out of contact with the ink fountain roller, then proceed as follows:

1. Fill the ink fountain until it is about half full (Fig. 9-5).

2. While turning the ink-fountain roller control knob with one hand (Fig. 9-6), adjust the ink-fountain adjusting screws with the other hand, until a thin film of ink is evenly distributed over the fountain roller. Turning the screws counter-clockwise increases the flow of the ink and clockwise decreases the flow.

Fig. 9-5. The ink fountain is filled half-way before ink adjustments are made.

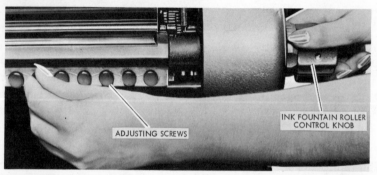

INK FOUNTAIN ROLLER CONTROL KNOB

ADJUSTING SCREWS

Fig. 9-6. Ink is evenly distributed over the fountain roller by adjusting the ink fountain adjusting screws as you turn the ink fountain roller control knob.

3. Place the ink feed volume control on the 3rd notch and turn the drive motor switch on (see Fig. 9-7).

4. Depress the ink fountain manual control lever (Fig. 9-7) and let the press run until all the ink rollers are properly covered with a thin film of ink.

5. Raise the manual control lever and turn the drive motor switch "off" after a sufficient amount of ink has been distributed. The inking system is now ready for use. After the plate is placed on the press it may be necessary to adjust the ink control for the image area of the plate. If heavier inking is needed for solids or large type, increase the setting from the 3rd notch to the 4th, 5th or higher until the desired inking is obtained. If less ink is required, decrease the setting. The ink fountain adjusting screws are used to allow the flow of ink to be evenly distributed across the plate. They may also be used to vary the horizontal flow when running line drawings, halftones, and solids on the same plate.

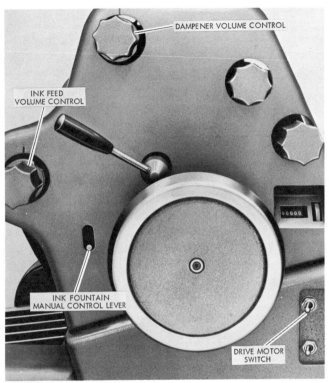

Fig. 9-7. A view of the operator's side of the ATF Chief "15" is shown here with the ink feed volume control, the dampener volume control, the ink fountain manual control lever and the drive motor switch which all have a part in inking

Fountain and Water Settings. The dampener fountain roller should also be clean and free of dirt. Clean if necessary; then proceed as follows:

1. Fill the fountain bottle with the fountain solution and re-cap it.

2. Invert the bottle with the spout down over a waste basket or can to be sure it does not leak, then bring the bottle over the side of the press and insert it in its holder, being careful not to spill any on the ink rollers.

3. With a pad or sponge moistened with fountain solution, go over the entire surface of the ductor roller and form roller until each is thoroughly moistened, but not wet.

Fig. 9-8. The paper platform, a part of the feeding system, is shown here with th elevator control knob which governs the height of the platform; the suction fee air blower and stock guides which must be adjusted to the size sheet being rur

4. Place the dampener volume control (Fig. 9-7), on the 2nd notch and allow the press to run for about 20 revolutions; the dampening system should now be ready for use.

Paper Platform. To set up the paper platform:

1. Lower the paper platform by pushing in on the paper plat form handwheel and turn counterclockwise.

2. Set the inside of the left paper stack side guide on the scal marking for the size sheet being run (Fig. 9-8).

3. Lay a sheet of paper to be run into position, then set the righ paper stack side guide so that it is about ¹⁄₁₆ inch away from th edge of the paper.

4. Set the front guides (Fig. 9-8) so they are about on a line representing ¼ inch of the front edge of the paper.

5. Center the suction feet (Fig. 9-8) on the front guides directl above the sheet separators.

6. Position the front air blower (Fig. 9-8) in the center of th sheet.

AIR BLOW
PAPER SEPERATORS

BACK SIDE
GUIDE EXTENSIONS

FRONT WINGS

BACK WINGS

Fig. 9-9. The paper stack shown here is ready to be fed into the press. Note the position of the front and back wings on the stock and the back side guide extensions.

7. Load the paper platform with the stock to be run, and bring the paper stack up to within ¼ inch of the paper separators.

8. Set the paper stack back guide so that the front wings are on the top of the paper stack and the back wings are behind and up to the stack (Fig. 9-9).

9. Set the back-side guide extensions so that they are about ½ inch from the back of the sheet or at their extreme distance when running larger size paper stock.

10. Set the side air blow paper separators so that they blow about ⅔ of the way back and across the paper. The second hole (Fig. 9-10) in the air blower tube is in line with the top of the paper when the stack is ¼ inch below the sheet separators.

11. Lower the paper platform a few inches and turn the drive motor switch on to allow the platform to rise automatically.

12. Adjust the elevator control knob (Fig. 9-8) so that the paper stack stops about ¼ inch below the sheet separators. Turn the knob clockwise to lower and counterclockwise to raise the height.

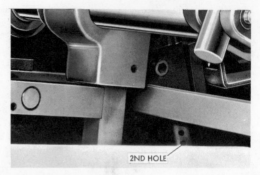

Fig. 9-10. The second hole of the air blower should be in line with the top of the paper stack as shown here.

Fig. 9-11. Reverse the backstop when running minimum size stock as shown in this illustration.

NOTE: If the minimum size 3 inch stock is being run, reverse the paper stack back stop (Fig. 9-11) so that the wings can be brought in closer. It is recommended that all jobs be centered when running. When running minimum size stock, only one of the paper feeler fingers and two of the seven tumbler grippers are needed to obtain accurate sheet control.

Helpful hint for fast positioning:

When 11 inch wide paper is being run, the right paper stack side guide should be set to the 11 inch mark on the scale and the left side guide set so that it will be about $\frac{1}{16}$ inch away from the paper.

For fast and accurate positioning of the front guide and center blower, fold a sheet of the paper to be run in half lengthwise (Fig

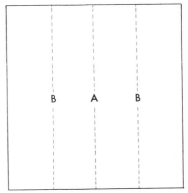

Fig. 9-12. For fast, accurate positioning of the front guides and center blower, fold a sheet of paper as shown here and direct the air blower down the center crease, and position the side guides along the two other creases marked *B*.

9-12), then in half again. Unfold the sheet and lay it on top of the stack on the paper platform. Then turn the blow direction indicator so that the air is directed to the center of the sheet as indicated by line "A," and position and center the front guides on line "B."

Paper Feedboard. The paper is picked up from the paper stack by suction feet forwarded to the paper pull-out roll (Fig. 9-11), and then delivered to the paper feedboard. On the feedboard (Fig. 9-13), conveyor tapes carry the sheet to the paper stop bar and joggers where it is straightened into its correct feeding position.

The press contains a left hand and a right-hand side jogger. In most instances, when only one side of the sheet is printed, the left hand side jogger is used because it is on the operator's side of the press and more convenient to set. When two sides of the sheet are printed, then both side joggers are used. First the left side jogger is used on the first side printed and then when the paper is turned over to print the other side, the right hand jogger is used. This practice insures better register because the same side of the sheet is used to jog it into feeding position.

Both joggers are set into motion while the press is running. To set the left hand jogger in motion, hold the right jogger with your left hand and pull it toward you while you move the jogger selector (Fig. 9-14) back toward the feeder. To set the right hand jogger in motion, hold the left jogger with your left hand, and push it away

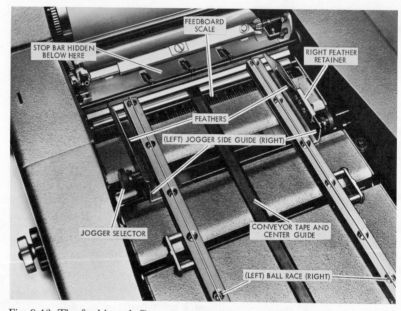

Fig. 9-13. The feed board. Conveyor tapes carry the sheet to the paper bar stop (not shown) as the joggers, guides and feathers straighten it for correct feeding.

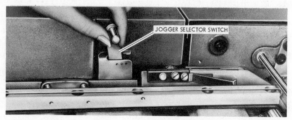

Fig. 9-14. The jogger selector switch shown here sets the joggers into motion.

from you while you move the jogger selector into its forward position. Both joggers can be set into motion by placing the jogger selector in its center position.

Sometimes it will be necessary to set the feathers on the jogger to obtain side register. When they are used, the feathers on the jogger should be raised. This is done by pressing down on the back end of the feather retainer. The feather on the idle jogger should be lowered; this is done by pressing down on the front end of the feather retainer. When in use, the idle jogger should be set so that when the sheet is moved against the feather, it does not move the feather more than $\frac{1}{16}$ inch.

To square the jogger to the paper, turn the handwheel until the jogger being used is at the maximum jogging position. Turn the jogger control knob until the jogger side guide is positioned to the feedboard scale marking (Fig. 9-13) at the width of paper being run. Place a sheet of paper on the feedboard with one side against the active jogger side guide, then feed a few sheets of paper through to check the jogger action.

Chain Delivery. After the paper is brought forward by the conveyor tape to the paper stop bar and jogged into feeding position, tumbler grippers pick up the paper and carry it through the impression cycle, then transfer it to the delivery grippers where it is delivered to the pile. To obtain good delivery proceed as follows:

1. Raise the delivery board to its uppermost position by depressing the delivery lock release, and turning the delivery pile handwheel clockwise.

2. Feed a sheet of paper through the entire cycle, allowing it to drop in its normal delivery position on the delivery board.

3. Loosen the two delivery side guide control knobs (Fig. 9-16), and bring the stationary side guide in against the sheet, then tighten its control knob.

4. Turn the handwheel until the automatic side jogger is in its extreme inward position, slide this side guide in until it is about $\frac{1}{16}$ inch away from the paper when the paper is against the stationary guide, and then re-tighten.

5. Place a sheet of paper against the front guide, then turn the handwheel until the back jogging guide (Fig. 9-16) is in its extreme inward position.

6. Loosen the back jogging guide and slide it in against the sheet until it is about $\frac{1}{16}$ inch away from the back edge of the paper and then retighten.

Delivery Rate Lowering Control. This control (Fig. 9-16) determines the rate of descent of the delivery board. Graduated notches accommodate the entire range of stock that the press can run. If the top of the paper stack remains at a point about halfway

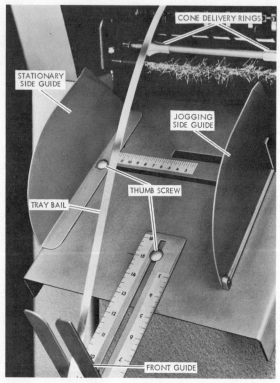

Fig. 9-15. The jogging side guide and the delivery scales must be adjusted to the size sheet being run.

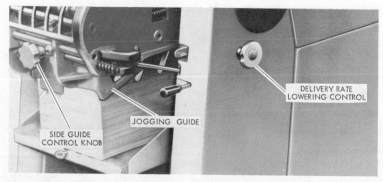

Fig. 9-16. For effective chain delivery on a press equipped with such, the delivery guide knobs must be loosened and then tightened after the stationary guide is brought in to meet the sheet.

up on the side guide, then the control is set correctly. If the top of the paper stack descends below the half-way point, turn the control counterclockwise to decrease the rate of descent. If the top of the paper stack climbs higher than the half-way point, turn the control clockwise to increase the rate of descent.

Delivery Chute. To set the delivery chute:

1. Using the scale provided (Fig. 9-15) set the left hand stationary guide for the width of the paper to run.

Note: The adjusting knobs for all chute adjustments are located on the underside of the chute.

2. Also using the scale provided, set the front guide for the length of paper being run.

Note: Stock less than 9 inches long may require the front guide to be turned around. The scale also turns around for your convenience.

3. Adjust the jogger by turning the handwheel until the jogger is in its "inward" position.

4. Loosen the adjusting knob on the underside and slide the jogger in until it is about ¹⁄₁₆ inch away from the paper when the paper is against the stationary side guide on the left.

5. Set the cone delivery rings on the shaft so that the edges of the paper will curl slightly. Both rings are adjusted by sliding them on the shaft.

The angle of the entire delivery chute can be changed to accommodate light or heavy weight stock. To do this, loosen the thumbscrews (Fig. 9-15) and either raise or lower the chute for the type of stock being run.

6. Lift the tray bail and place it in the slot of the front guide (Fig. 9-15). Humidity and temperature from day to day are important factors that may change the running qualities of certain stock. It is recommended that several sheets be run through the press until the proper adjustment of the angle of the chute is made.

Attaching the Plate. Be sure that the plate cylinder is thoroughly cleaned before attaching the plate. Even a small particle of dirt under the plate can ruin the plate after a few impressions. After the cylinder is cleaned, attach the plate as follows:

1. Turn the handwheel until the lead plate clamp is in position to attach the plate (Fig. 9-17).

Fig. 9-17. After the lead clamp is in position, attach the lead edge of the plate to the plate clamp.

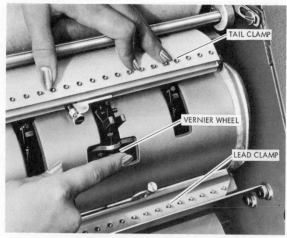

Fig. 9-18. After the tail edge of the plate has been attached, turn the vernier wheel to tighten the plate clamp.

2. Attach the lead edges of the plate to the plate clamp. Start at the far side and work towards the operator's side, holding the tail of the plate squarely and tightly down to prevent it from coming detached.

3. Hold the tail of the plate with the right hand, and turn the handwheel clockwise with the left until the tail clamp comes into position to attach the tail of the plate (Fig. 9-18).

Fig. 9-19. The first step in changing the plate clamps is releasing the safety screw as shown here.

Fig. 9-20. The paper stop bar must be adjusted properly to obtain a correctly positioned image on the paper.

4. Bring the tail clamp up and attach the trailing edge of the plate to the clamp.

5. Turn the plate-clamp vernier wheel clockwise to tighten the plate clamp. A lock nut is provided to prevent the plate from loosening on long runs.

The pin bar clamp is the standard plate clamp on the Chief 15, but for those who prefer to use the oval-serrated or straight edge plates, oval-serrated and straight edge clamps are available.

To change the plate clamps:

1. Turn the safety screw counterclockwise until fully opened (Fig. 9-19).

2. Press the safety screw to release the lock, and lift the clamp from its retaining studs.

3. To attach, the plate clamps, merely reverse this procedure.

Positioning the Image on the Paper. A crooked image that appears to be running "uphill" or "downhill" from the left to right is positioned squarely on the paper by adjusting the paper stop bar (Fig. 9-20). This adjustment is made by loosening the binder screw

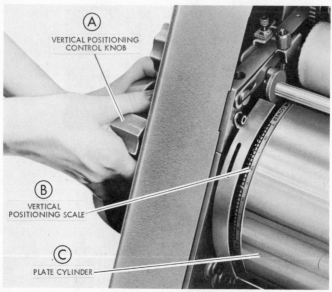

Fig. 9-21. Push the vertical positioning control knob (A) in and turn to the left to unlock the plate cylinder (C). Use vertical positioning scale (B) to move image desired amount.

which allows the bar to be tilted in either direction. Any need for adjusting the angle of the plate on the cylinder is thus eliminated.

Horizontal positioning of the image on the paper is made by moving the right and left jogger control knobs simultaneously in the desired direction. When the image has been centered correctly, the paper stack is then adjusted correspondingly.

The position of the image may be adjusted a full 360°. Proceed as follows to make this adjustment:

1. Turn the handwheel until the vertical-positioning control knob (Fig. 9-21A) is aligned with the plate cylinder lock nut located on the end of the plate cylinder. The lock nut is now visible through the slot in the cylinder guard.

2. Engage both the vertical control knob and the lock nut by pushing and holding the vertical positioning control knob in.

3. Turn the control knob to the left to unlock the cylinder, and then, by turning the handwheel and using the vertical positioning scale (Fig. 9-21B) just opposite the plate cylinder (Fig. 9-21C), the image can be raised or lowered to the desired position.

Fig. 9-22. To change the blanket, first turn the blanket cylinder until the lead clamp is in position to attach the blanket. The cylinder is turned by the hand-wheel (not shown here).

4. Turn the control knob to the right to relock the plate cylinder.

NOTE: This adjustment must be made while the press is idle.

Changing Blankets. Due to the various chemicals and inks used, it becomes necessary to change blankets periodically despite the high quality of materials used in their construction. In addition, dirt and other dust particles will impregnate the blanket. To attach the blanket:

1. Turn the handwheel until the lead blanket-clamp is in position to attach the blanket (Fig. 9-22).

2. Hook the blanket onto the lead blanket-clamp.

3. While holding the blanket tight with the left hand, turn the handwheel with the right until the blanket tail clamp comes into position.

4. Hook the tail end of the blanket onto the blanket tail clamp and turn the vernier wheel counterclockwise to tighten it (Fig. 9-23).

Paper Pull-out Roll and Double-sheet Eliminator. The paper pull-out and double-sheet eliminator are attached on the same unit. The unit should be positioned so that the pull-out roll is in the center of the paper. To move the unit, loosen the unit retaining screw (Fig. 9-24), depress the release lever for the pull-out roll, then move the pull-out roll until it is centered. Retighten the unit retaining screw and reset the pull-out roll release lever.

A thumb screw controls the pressure of the pull-out roll. There should be just enough pressure to move the paper through to the

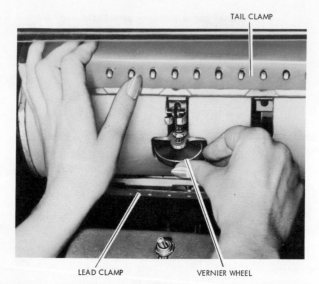

Fig. 9-23. After the blanket has been attached to both the lead and tail clamps, turn the vernier wheel to tighten it.

feedboard. Too much pressure may distort the sheet. If the sheet was printed a second time through the press, the pull-out roll may mark the sheet, if the ink is not thoroughly dry. Insufficient pressure will cause the sheet to delay or arrive late at the paper stops.

A thumb screw (Fig. 9-24) also controls the double-sheet eliminator. To set it correctly, start up both motors and allow some sheets through. As the sheets are going through, loosen the locknut and turn the screw counterclockwise until single sheets are rejected. Then turn clockwise slightly, until the ejector does not operate on a single sheet. Retighten the locknut.

Elevator Control Knob. The elevator control knob (Fig. 9-25) regulates the maximum height to which the top of the paper pile will be elevated automatically. To change the height of the pile, turn the knob clockwise to lower it, or counterclockwise to raise it.

Water Roller Adjustment. The water oscillating roller and dampener form roller should be parallel to each other. To set them:

1. Back the oscillator-adjusting eccentric studs (Fig. 9-26) away from the water oscillator roller bearing arms. These studs are

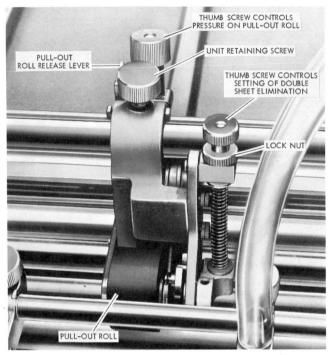

THUMB SCREW CONTROLS
PRESSURE ON PULL-OUT ROLL

UNIT RETAINING SCREW

PULL-OUT
ROLL RELEASE LEVER

THUMB SCREW CONTROLS
SETTING OF DOUBLE
SHEET ELIMINATION

LOCK NUT

PULL-OUT ROLL

Fig. 9-24. The paper pull-out roll and double-sheet eliminator are both attached to the same unit.

located on the outside of the water unit side frames at the feeder end of the oscillator bearing arms.

2. With the dampening form roller in its "down" position and the press "on impression," place two 1 inch strips of 16 lb. paper between the dampener form roller and the water oscillator roller (Fig. 9-27), one on each end, and check for an even pull on both strips. If the water oscillator roller is not parallel to the dampener form roller:

3. Loosen the set screw in the water oscillator drive gear (Fig. 9-27) located on the far side, and rock the gear slightly back and forth until an even pull is obtained.

4. Lock the set screw in the drive gear.

5. Place a strip of identical paper between each of the water oscillating bearing arms and the oscillator-adjusting eccentric studs.

Fig. 9-25. The height of the paper stack is elevated automatically. The elevator control knob regulates the desired height of the stack.

Fig. 9-26. The first step in adjusting the water roller is to back the eccentric stud away from the water oscillator roller bearing arms.

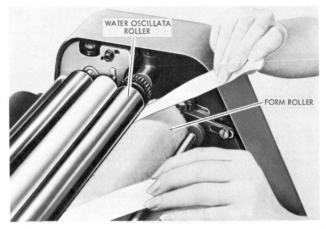

Fig. 9-27. Two strips of paper are used to check the pressure between the form roller and the water oscillator roller.

6. Adjust these studs until there is a slight even pull on the strips of paper.

7. Lock the set screws on the eccentric studs.

To set the water ductor roller:

1. Turn the handwheel until the water ductor roller contacts the water oscillator.

2. Insert two strips of 16 lb. paper between these two rollers, and check for an even "pull" (Fig. 9-28).

3. Turn the handwheel until the water ductor roller contacts the water fountain roller and place the same two strips of paper between these two rollers.

4. Adjust the eccentric cam roller stud (Fig. 9-29) on the water ductor drive lever located on the operator's side until the same even "pull" on the paper strips is obtained.

NOTE: *Newly covered water rollers will slightly shrink in size while being "run in." It is important to check the settings of the dampener form roller and water ductor roller often and make any necessary adjustments using the procedures described.*

To set and adjust the dampener form roller:

1. Place a plate on the plate cylinder, raise the feeder fingers, and turn the handwheel by hand about three-quarters of a revolution until the press goes on "impression."

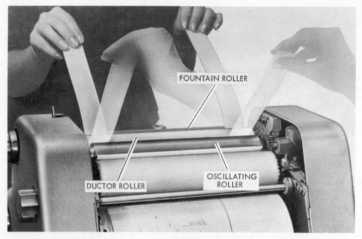

Fig. 9-28. To check the pressure on the water ductor roller, use two strips of paper between the water ductor roller and the water oscillating roller.

Fig. 9-29. The "Pull" on the two strips can be changed by adjusting the eccentric cam roller stud.

2. Tear two strips of 16 lb. paper, 1 inch wide and insert one strip on each end of the roller between the plate and the dampener form roller as shown (Fig. 9-30).

3. Drop the dampener form roller into operating position by placing the dampening and ink form roller control lever in its second position. Make sure the auxiliary dampener form roller control is in its "on" position.

Fig. 9-30. The pressure between the dampener roller and the plate cylinder is checked by using two strips of paper as shown here.

Fig. 9-31. The adjusting screw and lock nut are important in adjusting the dampener roller.

A slight but equal amount of tension or resistance should be felt as the two strips are pulled out. An adjustment will be necessary if there is too much, if too little resistance, or if it is unequal on either end.

4. Using the small wrench provided, loosen the locking nut (Fig. 9-31) and turn the dampener form adjusting screw counterclockwise if the paper strip is too loose, clockwise if the paper strip is too tight.

5. Retighten the locking nut and repeat the paper strip test to be sure proper adjustment has been made. If not, repeat the operation as stated in step 4.

Ink Form Roller Adjustment. The Chief 15 contains two ink form rollers, an upper and a lower. To set them, proceed as follows:

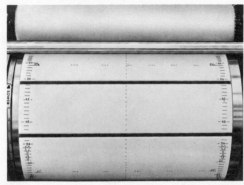

Fig. 9-32. When the ink form roller is properly adjusted, two parallel lines of ink will appear on a clean dry plate as the plate is turned back into view.

1. Attach a clean, dry plate to the plate cylinder, then turn the handwheel until the plate clamps are facing the feeder, and the plate is facing the ink form rollers.

2. Drop the ink form rollers by placing the dampening and ink form roller control lever in the 3rd position. Allow the rollers to remain on the plate no more than a second or two. If the form rollers are in proper adjustment, two parallel lines of ink (Fig. 9-32) will appear on the plate as the plate is turned back into view. These lines of ink should be an identical $\frac{3}{16}$ inch wide. If necessary to adjust either or both:

3. Loosen the ink form roller lock screw (Fig. 9-33) on the side requiring the adjustment. Turn the ink form roller adjustment screw clockwise to decrease, or counterclockwise to increase, the width of the stripes.

NOTE: The form rollers should be set so that when they are placed in contact with the plate, and the press is running, no appreciable "bounce" or up and down movement is noticed. If the rollers bounce, they will give uneven inking and wear out the plate.

Plate-to-blanket Impression Adjustment. To adjust the impression between the plate and blanket, proceed as follows:

1. Attach a plate to the plate cylinder.

2. With the auxiliary dampener form roller control "off," drop the dampening and ink form roller control lever into its 3rd position until the plate is solidly inked.

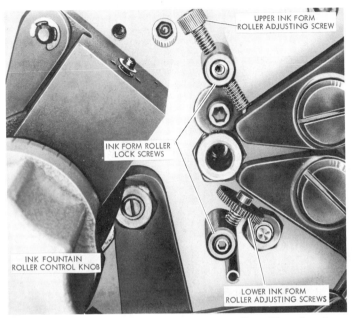

UPPER INK FORM
ROLLER ADJUSTING SCREW

INK FORM ROLLER
LOCK SCREWS

INK FOUNTAIN
ROLLER CONTROL KNOB

LOWER INK FORM
ROLLER ADJUSTING SCREWS

Fig. 9-33. Both the upper and lower rollers can be adjusted by using the appropriate adjusting screws. The adjusting screws are held in position by lock screws.

3. Turn the handwheel until the plate is in position to contact the blanket about half way around.

4. Move the plate-to-blanket tumbler block (Fig. 9-34) to the right to throw the impression "on" between the plate and the blanket. Even stripes (Fig. 9-35) about ³⁄₁₆ inches should appear on the blanket. If not properly adjusted:

5. Loosen the locking screw and turn the plate-to-blanket impression-adjusting screw clockwise to increase, and counterclockwise to decrease, the width of the stripe.

6. When properly adjusted, retighten the locking screw.

Blanket-to-paper Impression Adjustment. To make this adjustment:

1. Attach a plate to the plate cylinder.

2. With the auxiliary dampener form roller control "off," drop the dampening and ink roller control lever into the third position.

3. Move the manual plate-to-cylinder control lever to the left until the blanket is thoroughly inked.

Fig. 9-34. Plate-to-blanket impression is adjustable through the use of the adjusting screw shown here. The screw is held in position by a locking screw which must be loosened before any adjustment is made.

4. Turn the handwheel until the inked surface of the blanket is next to the impression cylinder. Insert a sheet of the paper stock to be run between the impression cylinders and the blanket.

5. Place the blanket and impression cylinders on "impression" by moving the blanket tumbler block to the right for a second or two, then release the tumbler and remove the paper. A ³⁄₁₆ inch stripe should appear on the paper. If the stripe is more or less:

6. Loosen the locking screw (Fig. 9-36) and turn the impression adjusting screw clockwise until the stripe is very light.

7. Turn the adjusting screw counterclockwise until the desired impression on the paper is obtained.

8. Retighten the locking screw and the adjustment is complete.

Fig. 9-35. An even strip like the one shown here should appear on the blanket when the plate-to-blanket pressure is properly adjusted.

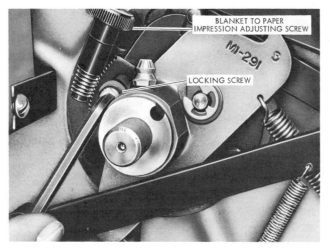

Fig. 9-36. Blanket-to-plate impression can be adjusted by turning the adjusting screw. A locking screw also holds this adjusting screw in position.

SPECIFICATIONS TO REMEMBER

Sheet sizes: Maximum—11 × 15, minimum—3 × 5 inches
Paper weights: 11 lb. manifold to 2 ply card stock
Maximum image area: 9¾ × 13¼ inches
Gripper Margin: ³⁄₁₆ × ⁵⁄₁₆ inches
Plate sizes: Pin-bar 10 × 15 inches; Serrated-Oval 10 × 15⅜ inches
Plate thickness: .006 inches
Blanket size: 9⁵⁄₁₆ × 15½ inches
Blanket thickness: .065 inches

Impressions per hour: 3400 to 7200

Feeder capacity: 21¾ inches

Delivery capacity: Chute 2⅞ inches; Chain 20¾ inches

Drive and pump motor: ⅓HP each

Length—61 inches, width—28 inches, height—50 inches

Net Weight: Chute delivery 740 lbs. Chain delivery 870 lbs.

Inking unit: 10 rollers—1 ductor, 1 fixed, I auxiliary oscillator, 5 idlers, 2 form

Dampening unit: 4 rollers—1 fountain, 1 ductor, 1 oscillating vibrator, 1 form

Davidson Dual, Model 500

The Davidson Dual[1] is perhaps the most versatile offset press in the printing industry today. (Several models of the Davidson line are shown in Figs. 9-37 through 9-39.) In addition to being able to print by offset, the press can easily be adapted to relief printing, dry offset printing, dry offset embossing and perfecting. (*Perfecting* is printing on both sides of the sheet at the same time.) In this chapter offset printing by the Davidson Dual (Fig. 9-40) will be described in detail. Complete instructions for any of the other printing methods are furnished with the purchase of every additional segment or cylinder required.

Dampening Unit. Fill the bottle with the fountain solution in use and mount it over the dampening fountain tray (Fig. 9-41A). A special bottle cap will keep the solution in the tray at the proper level at all times. The tray is mounted on two spring pins in the side frame (Fig. 9-41B and C).

The fountain roller (Fig. 9-41D) revolving in the fountain tray (Fig. 9-41E) is supplied by the bottle of solution mounted above it. This solution distributes itself along the entire length of the metal fountain roll.

As the fountain roll turns, it carries the moisture to the ductor roller (Fig. 9-42A) which ducts back and forth between the fountain roll and the form roll covers (Fig. 9-42B). From the form roll,

1. This material is adapted from the Davidson Dualith 500 operators manual and is reprinted by permission of the Davidson Corporation.

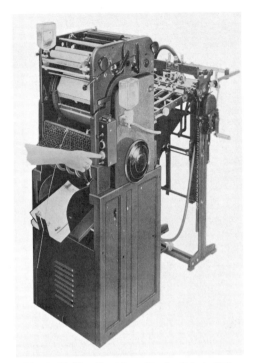

Fig. 9-37. The Davidson Dual-a-Matic 242.

the solution is transferred to the dampening form roller which places the moisture on the plate.

Only two controls are necessary to regulate the dampening of the rollers. The flow control lever (Fig. 9-42C) controls the amount of moisture, and the fountain roll knob (Fig. 9-42D) brings the form roller in contact with the plate.

The amount of solution which is available for transfer by the ductor roller is dependent upon how fast the fountain roll revolves in the fountain tray. The flow control lever regulates the revolving of the fountain roll and therefore controls the flow of the solution. With the control lever in its uppermost position, the fountain roll does not turn and no moisture is transferred. With the lever in the lowest or horizontal position, the maximum quality of moisture is transferred. The fountain roll knob (Fig. 9-42D) provides manual turning of the dampening fountain roll.

Fig. 9-38. The Davidson Model 238.

Inking Unit. The inking unit consists of the ink fountain (Fig. 9-43A) a fountain roll (Fig. 9-43B) which rides in the ink fountain, a ductor roller (Fig. 9-43C) which ducts the ink from the fountain roll to the rest of the inking system, two distributing rollers (Fig. 9-43D—only one is shown), one idler roller (Fig. 9-43E) and two form rollers (not shown).

The flow of ink is regulated by three controls:

The ink ductor lever (Fig. 9-43F) determines whether the ductor roller ducts back and forth between the fountain roll and the other rollers distributing the ink, or whether it remains in contact with the other roller and does not transfer ink. The lever permits the transfer of the ink when it is in the operating or horizontal position.

The flow control lever (Fig. 9-43G) regulates the speed with which the fountain roll turns in the fountain. In the lowest position, the roll does not turn at all and no ink is transferred. As the lever is raised, the rate increases; therefore, the rate of ink transfer increases accordingly.

The ink-fountain adjusting screws (Fig. 9-43H) regulate the

Fig. 9-39. The Davidson Model 239.

amount of pressure exerted against the ink fountain roll by the metal ink blade. The ink blade is tightened against the fountain roll by turning the adjusting screws clockwise; less ink is transferred. To increase the flow of the ink, turn the adjusting screws counterclockwise.

To properly adjust the fountain screws when in operation, proceed as follows:

1. Remove a quantity of ink from the ink can as previously explained and place it in the ink fountain, spreading it evenly across the width of the ink fountain. Turning the ink-fountain roller manually by means of a knob (Fig. 4-43I) will help keep the ink in the fountain.

2. Move the ink ductor lever so that the ductor roller contacts the ink fountain roll.

3. Set the flow control lever on the third notch from the top and turn on the press. As the ductor roller ducts back and forth, the uniformity of the ink transfer can be seen. Where the ink is

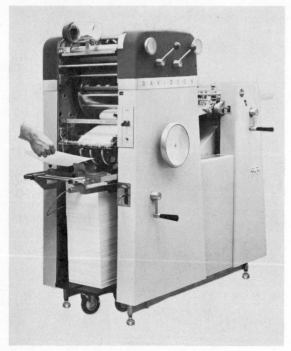

Fig. 9-40. The Davidson Dualith 500.

Fig. 9-41. The dampening unit is shown here, at *A*—the fountain solution bottle, at *B* and *C*—the spring pins, at *D*—the fountain roller, at *E*—the fountain tray.

Fig. 9-42. A close-up view of one corner of the dampening unit system is shown here, at *A*—the ductor roller, at *B*—the form roller, at *C*—the flow control lever, at *D*—the fountain roll knob.

Fig. 9-43. The inking system consists of: at *A*—the ink fountain, at *B*—the ink fountain roll, at *C*—a ductor roller, at *D*—a distributor roller, at *E*—an idler roller, at *F*—the ink ductor lever, at *G*—the ink flow control lever, at *H*—the adjusting screws, at *I*—the ink fountain roller knob.

deposited heavily, the adjusting screws are open too far and should be turned in. Where there is very little ink being deposited, the adjusting screws are too tight and should be opened up. Adjust the screws by turning in or out. Start from the center and move toward both ends until an even flow of ink is being deposited across the

Fig. 9-44. The fountain solution flow and the ink flow are regulated by the two levers shown here: at *A*—moisture control and at *B*—ink control.

Fig. 9-45. Mounting the plate on the plate cylinder: at *A*—the top of the plate segment, at *B*—a "T" wrench, at *C*—the head clamp screws, at *D*—the head clamp.

ductor roller. Then lift the ink ductor roller so that it no longer transfers ink to the other rollers, thus, preventing any build-up of excess ink.

The moisture-flow control lever (Fig. 9-44A) and the ink-flow control lever (Fig. 9-44B) may be set to the required positions depending upon the amount of copy on the plate being run.

Mounting the Plate. To mount the plate on the cylinder, proceed as follows:

1. Turn the press by hand until the top of the plate segment (Fig. 9-45A) is accessible. The top of the plate is anchored to the plate segment by means of a head clamp across the entire width of the plate (Fig. 9-45D). The head clamp is held in place by screws (Fig. 9-45C) which are loosened to attach the plate. A T-handle wrench (Fig. 9-45B) is provided with the press to loosen the screws.

2. Open the head clamp and insert the lead edge of the plate under the clamp, making sure that it is seated all the way into the clamp.

3. Center the plate using the scale provided (Fig. 9-45E) and tighten the head clamp screws.

4. Turn the plate cylinder around with one hand while holding the trailing end of the plate with the other. Turn the cylinder until the tail clamp becomes accessible.

5. Secure the plate by pressing your thumbs against the plate and cylinder (Fig. 9-46A). With the right forefinger, depress the tail clamp release (Fig. 9-46C), and raise the clamp (Fig. 9-46B).

6. Insert the bottom edge of the plate into the clamps, and pull the release back to its original position. Throughout the press run, the spring on the tail clamp will insure that the plate is firmly held.

To remove the plate, release the tail clamp, hold the trailing edge of the plate with one hand and turn the press with the other,

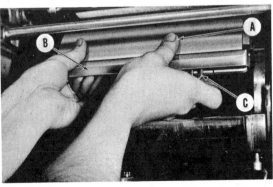

Fig. 9-46. Secure the plate by pressing your thumbs against the plate and cylinder (*A*), with the right forefinger depress the tail clamp release (*C*) and raise the clamp (*B*).

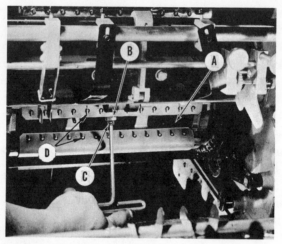

Fig. 9-47. The parts affected by changing the blanket are: *A*—the gripper bar, *B*—the lock nuts, *C*—the tightening screw and *D*—the mounting hooks.

until the lead clamp becomes accessible. Loosen the head-clamp holding screws with the T-wrench and pull the lead edge from under the plate head clamp. (NOTE: Depending on the type of plate being used, the model press, and the plate cylinder involved, it may be necessary to underlay the back of the plate to bring it up to the correct printing pressure.)

Changing the Blanket. To change the blanket on the Davidson Dual, proceed as follows:

1. Turn the handwheel until the gap in the blanket drum appears without the gripper bar (Fig. 9-47A).

2. Loosen the lock nuts (Fig. 9-47B) on the blanket tightening screws.

3. With the T-handle wrench, unloosen the blanket tightening screws (Fig. 9-47C) until enough play is obtained to release the edge of the blanket from the hooks of the blanket clamp.

4. When one end is free, the other end will be released quickly as soon as the slack is provided. Pull one end and the blanket is removed from the drum.

5. Place one end of the new blanket over the row of mounting hooks (Fig. 9-47D). Hold the blanket on the drum with one hand while turning the handwheel with the other until the drum has

made two complete revolutions and the gap appears without the gripper bar.

6. Place the other end of the blanket over the hooks and retighten the clamp by turning the tightening screws with the T-wrench. Tighten each screw a ½ turn at a time so that tension on the blanket is evenly distributed.

7. Retighten the lock nuts when the bar has been properly adjusted.

When a new blanket is placed on the press, check periodically to see if it is tight enough. A loose blanket will result in a blurred image.

Positioning Image on the Sheet. To obtain correct horizontal positioning of the image on the sheet, the sheet of paper itself is moved to the left or right. If it is necessary to move the image on the sheet to the left, the sheet is moved in the opposite direction or to the right. If the image is to be moved to the right, the sheet must be moved to the left.

This is done on the conveyor table by moving the jogger and register guide. If a large adjustment (½ inch or more) is required to position the image horizontally, it will also be necessary to move the magazine channels (side paper guides) in the same direction. Otherwise, the sheet will run too close to the jogger or register guide (depending on the direction of the movement) and cause mis-register. The sheet also may hit the jogger or the register guide and cause other troubles.

To move the image on the sheet vertically, the plate cylinder is moved up or down on the upper cylinder. No adjustment of the paper is necessary. To make this particular adjustment:

1. Place the adjusting-pin segment (Fig. 9-48A) in the positioning-hole segment (Fig. 9-48B).

2. Loosen the two segment-holding screws (Fig. 9-48C) with the T-handle wrench.

3. Apply pressure against the adjusting-pin segment and the plate may be moved by the handwheel up to ¾ inch in either direction.

Since the plate cylinder is held stationary during this adjustment and the movement is made using the handwheel, the adjustment

Fig. 9-48. When adjusting the image vertically, the following parts are used: at
A—the adjusting-pin segment, at *B*—the positioning-hole segment, at *C*—two
segment-holding screws, at *D*—the scale.

is made in the opposite direction. To raise the image on the sheet,
the plate cylinder is moved downward. This is done by:

4. Turning the handwheel counterclockwise to raise the image
on the sheet or clockwise to lower it on the sheet. A scale (Fig.
9-48D) is provided with the press to assist in vertical positioning.

NOTE: In making this adjustment, hold the plate cylinder posi-
tioning-pin in position with the thumb. If you forget to remove it,
a safety built into the construction will automatically remove the
pin as the press is started.

When the image for some reason appears to be running "uphill"
or "downhill" from the left to right, it is necessary to loosen the
plate to make correct alignment or to "square" the image. To
do so:

1. Release the tail of the plate and turn the press by hand until
the head clamp is accessible.

2. Draw a line across the top edge of the plate with a pencil
using the head clamp as a guide.

3. Loosen the head-clamp screws and grasp the plate on both
sides. Drop either the left or right corner the required distance to
bring the image into alignment by judging the distance between
the pencil line against the edge of the plate head clamp.

4. Retighten the plate head-clamp screws and remount the
trailing edge.

Each time the plate cylinder or plate is moved, it is necessary to wash the blanket or a double image will appear on the next few sheets, and a true measurement of image positioning will be difficult to obtain.

Press Adjustments for Speed and Pressures

The speed of the Davidson Dual can vary from 3000 to 5400 impressions per hour on Model 233, from 3000 to 6000 on Models 244 and 251, and 4000 to 8000 on the Model 500. Each model has a different control to change speed. Consult the operating manual of the press in use to set the variable speed control.

Dampening Unit Pressures. To adjust the ductor roller to the fountain roller, proceed as follows:

1. Allow the press to run to duct water and moisten the ductor roller.

2. Pressure is maintained by a spring located under the side cover. To make sure the spring is operating properly, turn the press by hand until the ductor contacts the fountain roll.

3. Place two 1-inch strips of 20 lb. paper (Fig. 9-49A) one at each end, between the ductor and fountain roll.

4. Pull the paper from between the rolls and check for even

Fig. 9-49. To check the pressure between the ductor roller and the fountain roller, two 1-inch strips of 20 lb. paper are used as shown here.

Fig. 9-50. When testing the pressure between the ductor roller and the fountain roller, be sure the ductor roll bracket (*A*) is able to pivot freely on the bracket cross rod (*B*). If not, remove the holding screws (*C*) and the bracket; clean and lubricate the top surface of the bracket cross rod.

Fig. 9-51. Adjusting the pressure of the ductor to the distributor roll involves *A*—the cam roller, *B*—the high part of the cam, *C*—the lock nut, and *D*—the eccentric shoulder screw.

pressure. Be sure the ductor roll bracket (Fig. 9-50A) is able to pivot freely on the bracket cross rod (Fig. 9-50B). If not, remove the holding screw (Fig. 9-50C) and the bracket; clean and lubricate the top surface of the bracket cross rod. Accumulation of dirt will cause a bind in the pivot.

To adjust the ductor roller to the distributing roller:

1. Place the cam roller (Fig. 9-51A) on the high part of the cam (Fig. 9-51B) and insert two 1-inch strips of 20 lb. paper on each side between the ductor roller and the distributing roller (Fig. 9-52A).

2. Loosen the lock nut (Fig. 9-51C) and turn the eccentric shoulder screw (Fig. 9-51D) until a light, even tension is obtained on both strips and retighten the lock nut.

To adjust a form roller to the distributing roll:

The pressure on both ends of the rollers and the overall pressure must both be correct to obtain the desired results. To check and make any adjustments between these two rollers:

1. Place two 1-inch strips of 20 lb. paper, one at each end, between the distributing roll (Fig. 9-53B) and the form roller (Fig. 9-53A). Turn the handwheel until the strips are pulled in between the two rollers.

2. Pull on both strips (Fig. 9-53C) to check the tension.

3. Loosen the setscrew (Fig. 9-54A) holding the eccentric bearing (Fig. 9-54B) through which the form roller shaft passes.

4. Turn this bearing with a screwdriver (Fig. 9-54C) so that the top surface moves away from the distributing roller to increase pressure or toward the distributing roller to decrease pressure. Use

Fig. 9-52. Two strips of 1-inch paper (*A*) are used to check the pressure between the ductor and distributing roller.

Fig. 9-53. To check pressure between the distributor roller and the form roller, use two 1-inch strips of 20 lb. paper as shown. At *A*—the form roller, at *B*—the distributor roller, at *C*—the strips of paper.

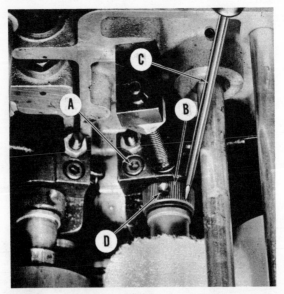

Fig. 9-54. Adjusting the form to the distributor roller pressure: at *A*—the set screw, at *B*—the eccentric bearing, at *C*—a screw driver (used to turn the eccentric bearing), at *D*—the depressed markings used as a guide on the bearing.

Fig. 9-55. The end play adjustment utilizes: (*A*) the set screw, (*B*) a screw driver and (*C*) the eccentric bearing.

the depressed marks (Fig. 9-54D) on the bearings as a guide to obtain pressure. They should be opposite each other.

5. Check to be sure no end play exists in the rollers. If there is end play:

6. Loosen setscrew (Fig. 9-55A) and insert a screwdriver between the form roll bracket and the eccentric bearing (Fig. 9-55B) and move the bearing toward the roll.

7. Retighten the setscrew (Fig. 9-55A). Do not set the eccentric bearings (Fig. 9-55C) too tight against the form-roll bearing as it will effect the free turning of the dampening form roll.

To adjust the form roller to the plate:

1. Mount the proper plate as previously explained ("Mounting the Plate" page 405) and turn the handwheel until the plate is directly below the dampening form roll.

2. Insert two 1-inch strips of 20 lb. paper under each end of the form roll and on top of the plate.

3. Lower the dampening form roll by moving the operating handle straight to the "on" position and pull on the strips of paper (Fig. 9-56A). If uneven:

4. Loosen the locknut with a small wrench (Fig. 9-57A) and turn the adjusting screw (Fig. 9-57B) counterclockwise, until the

Fig. 9-56. The pressure between the form roller and the plate is checked with two 1-inch strips of paper (A) as shown here.

Fig. 9-57. To adjust the form roller to the plate the following parts are used: at A—a lock nut, at B—an adjusting screw, at C—a lock nut, at D—an adjusting screw, threads are shown at E.

bottom of the screw does not touch the round metal banking stud directly under the dampening form roll brackets.

5. Loosen locknut (Fig. 9-57C) and turn adjusting screw (Fig. 9-57D) until the spring (Fig. 9-57E) exerts an even pressure which is slightly more than normally needed for running.

6. Retighten locknut, Fig. 9-57C.

Ink Unit Pressure Adjustments

Ductor Roller to the Fountain Roll. Make sure that the spring attached to the ink ductor lever is functioning properly and that the ductor roller can pivot at its center thus pressing against the fountain roll evenly. The pressure remains fixed by a spring (Fig. 9-58A) and should not require any adjustments.

Ductor Roller to the Intermediate Distributing Roller. Pressure is adjusted in the same manner as the dampening ductor roller to distributing roll on page 411.

To adjust the form to the distributor rollers:

Fig. 9-58. This spring (*A*) maintains the pressure of the ductor roller to the fountain roller.

1. Place two 1-inch strips of 20 lb. paper and two pieces of paper 2½ inches wide folded (Fig. 9-59C), one on each end of the roller, between the ink form roller (Fig. 9-59A) and the distributor roller (Fig. 9-59B).

2. Pull on the inside pieces to get an indication of pressure. The three layers of paper are used because a single piece may give an inaccurate pressure indication, depending on the tack of the ink, and a single sheet may cut the surfaces of the soft rollers.

NOTE: *This strip arrangement for checking pressures when the rollers are inked may be used on any of the offset presses.*

3. Loosen the setscrew (Fig. 9-60A) holding the eccentric bearing (Fig. 9-60B) through which the form roller shaft passes.

4. Turn the eccentric bearing with a screwdriver (Fig. 9-60C) so that the top surface moves away from the vibrator roller to decrease the pressure or toward the vibrator roller to increase pressure. Use the depression marks (Fig. 9-60D) on the eccentric bearing as a guide to obtain even pressure.

5. Check and take up end play as previously shown (Fig. 9-55).

To adjust the form rollers to the plate:

1. Mount a plate of proper thickness and turn the handwheel until the plate is directly under the ink form rollers.

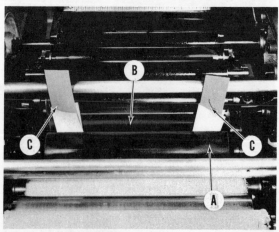

Fig. 9-59. Two strips of paper are used to check the pressure between the ink form and the distributor rollers. At *A*—the ink form roller, at *B*—the distributor roller, at *C*—two 1-inch strips of paper inside two folded 2½ inch sheets.

Fig. 9-60. To adjust the ink form roller to the distributor, the following parts are used: at *A*—a set screw, at *B*—the eccentric bearing, at *C*—a screw driver, at *D*—the depression marks used as a guide.

Fig. 9-61. If the form rollers are properly adjusted to the plate, two lines of ink "bead" (*A*) will appear on the plate. These beads should be uniform in width and parallel. If adjustment is necessary, the following parts are used: at (*B*) the lock nuts, at *C*—the adjusting screws.

2. Lower the ink form rollers to the plate by moving the form roller handle to the "on" position momentarily then raise them.

3. Turn the handwheel until the lines of ink "bead" are visible on the plate (Fig. 9-61A). If any adjustment is necessary:

4. Loosen the locknuts (Fig. 9-61B) on the adjusting screws (Fig. 9-61C) located in the form roller bracket (similar to dampening form roller bracket) and turn the adjusting screw clockwise with a screwdriver. This raises the roller, thereby decreasing the width of the mark.

5. Retighten the lock nuts.

6. Wash the plate and repeat until both roller marks are exactly ⅛ inch wide and equal across the entire width of the plate.

Paralleling the two Cylinders

Both the plate cylinder and the blanket cylinder must be parallel to each other. To parallel these cylinders:

1. Turn on the press and allow the entire plate to ink up by lowering the ink form rollers.

2. Stop the press and turn it by hand until the center of the inked plate is directly over the blanket.

3. Remove the main frame cover on the operating side by removing the single screw in the center at the top with the T-handle wrench to expose the blanket drum latching mechanism.

4. Place a large screwdriver inside the blanket latch (Fig.

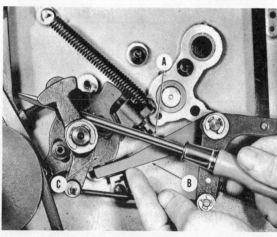

Fig. 9-62. To parallel the cylinders, the blanket latch is adjusted. Using a large screw driver (A), and applying pressure on the detent pawl (B), the blanket latch (C) is engaged.

9-62A) and apply pressure downward on the detent pawl (Fig. 9-62B) which engages the blanket latch (Fig. 9-62C).

This contacts the plate and the blanket. Push down on the detent pawl and the blanket drum will be unlatched and will drop to the nonprinting position.

5. Turn the press by hand until the ink mark on the blanket becomes visible. Inspect to see if the line is even across the entire width of the blanket (Fig. 9-63A). If not:

6. Remove the other frame cover. This end of the blanket drum is raised or lowered to parallel the cylinders.

7. Loosen the set screws (Fig. 9-64A) and move the disc to the right to raise it, or to the left to lower it. Only a slight movement is necessary.

8. Retighten the set screws and latch the blanket manually once again. Check the new line and repeat until an even line is obtained. When obtained, replace the main cover on this side.

Plate to Blanket Pressure. Once the parallel line is obtained, the overall pressure between the two cylinders (the plate and blanket) must be set. To do this:

1. Turn the press by hand until the inked plate is once again directly over the blanket.

2. Latch the blanket manually and examine the inked line. This line which is now even across the width of the blanket should measure exactly 3/16 inch wide (Fig. 9-63A). If not:

Fig. 9-63. If the plate-to-blanket pressure is correct, an even line (*A*) 3/16″ wide will appear on the blanket.

Fig. 9-64. To parallel the cylinders the appropriate set screws (A) are loosened adjustment is made and set screws are retightened.

Fig. 9-65. Overall pressure between the plate and blanket brings the following parts into use: (A) two latch holding screws, (B) a lock nut and (C) a hexagon headed screw

3. Loosen the 2 blanket latch holding screws (Fig. 9-65A).

4. While holding the adjusting screw with a screwdriver, loosen the lock nut (Fig. 9-65B) on the adjusting screw and turn the hexagon headed screw (Fig. 9-65C) clockwise to make the line wider, or counterclockwise to make the line narrower.

When the disc (Fig. 9-64) was adjusted only the opposite side of the blanket was raised or lowered, but this adjustment raises or lowers the entire drum. Move the blanket drum adjusting screw only a quarter turn at a time.

5. Retighten the adjusting screw lock nut and the blanket holding latch screws, and again latch these by hand.

6. Repeat the operation until the ³⁄₁₆ inch line is obtained.

Feeding and Delivery

For the magazine channel adjustment: A scale (Fig. 9-66A) on the elevator table is used to position the magazine channels (Fig. 9-66E) for the sheet size being run. Fold a sheet in half to locate the center and bring the channels into position by pressing downward on the lock lever (Fig. 9-66B) so that the paper enters the table ⅛ inch to the right of the center position.

Fig. 9-66. The magazine channel adjustments utilize: a scale (*A*) to position the channels (*E*). The lock nuts (*B*) are used to move the channels, and the elevator table brackets (*C*) support the pile of paper.

The elevator table brackets (Fig. 9-66C) support the pile of paper in the magazine. The brackets are spaced so that the weight of paper is equally balanced on them. A piece of cardboard, cut slightly smaller than the sheet size being run, should be placed on the brackets first. This keeps the stock perfectly level to the last sheet and makes it easier to handle.

The paper guide wires (Fig. 9-66D) hold the top of the pile exactly square with the pull-out rolls so that the sheets will enter the conveyor table evenly. These guides are mounted on a cross bar, one on each side of the stack, and locked in place by thumb screws. The guides should be set against the stack lightly. If set too tight, they may cause the top sheets to bind and interrupt the feeding. If set too loose, the sheets may twist while feeding and travel on the conveyor board in a crooked position.

How the elevator is lowered:

1. Hold the crank with the right hand (Fig. 9-67A) and depress the elevator release with the left hand (Fig. 9-67B).

2. Turn the crank counterclockwise to lower the elevator.

A safety stop is provided to prevent damage in case the release is accidently depressed when the magazine is loaded with paper. To pass or disengage this safety stop:

3. Pull the crank handle out, and lower the elevator to the bottom.

Fig. 9-67. The elevator table is lowered by turning the crank (*A*) with right hand and depressing the release (*B*) with the left hand.

Fig. 9-68. Fan the paper before placing it in the magazine.

4. To raise it manually, turn the crank handle clockwise.

The feeder magazine holds approximately 5000 sheets of 20 lb. paper. The actual capacity varies with the thickness of the stock.

The paper should be loaded in convenient quantities of about 500 sheets at a time and fanned before placing in the magazine (Fig. 9-68). Each load should be placed carefully on top of each previous load so that the pile will be uniform and squarely placed. If the paper stock has a curl in it, make sure the curl runs in the same direction.

After the first 1000 to 1500 sheets have been placed in the magazine, the opposite magazine channel may be positioned so that the channel touches the paper firmly without buckling it.

The back stop (Fig. 9-69C) keeps the paper pile in position against the front portion of the paper channels. If not set tightly enough, the paper will back away from the channels. The suction foot will pick up the sheet too far forward and prevent the sheet from feeding into the pull-out rolls.

To set the back stop, loosen the two thumb screws on the back stop cross bar (Fig. 9-69A), and slide the bar forward until the back stop rests firmly and squarely across the tail end of the stack. Retighten the thumb screws. The back stop may be moved along the cross bar (Fig. 9-69B) after being loosened with the thumb

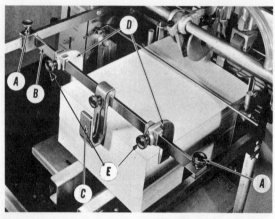

Fig. 9-69. The pile of paper is properly placed in the magazine by loosening the two thumb screws (*A*) and moving the back stop cross bar (*B*) with back stop guide (*C*) into position. The side guides (*D*) are brought into position using the thumb screws (*E*).

Fig. 9-70. The paper separator bracket (*A*) and paper separator (*B*) are moved along the cross bar using the thumb screw (*C*).

screw and centered on the stock. Model 233 has two stops and when positioned should divide the stack equally.

The side guides (Fig. 9-69D) are set one on each side of the stack as shown to prevent the stack of paper from shifting or moving during the feeding operation. The side guides may be moved along the cross bar by loosening thumb screws (Fig. 9-69E).

The paper separator (Fig. 9-70B) and paper separator bracket (Fig. 9-70A) are mounted directly below the suction foot, with the separator spring projecting ³⁄₁₆ inch over the top of the lead edge of the stack. This prevents the suction foot from picking up more than one sheet at a time. It must not extend so far as to touch the suction foot and should be level with the suction foot when the foot is in its lowest position. Whenever the suction head is moved, the paper separator is also moved by loosening the thumb screw (Fig. 9-70C) and sliding it along the cross rod. The separator is sometimes removed when feeding heavy paper stock.

The raising mechanism is adjusted for the proper height which is dependent on the weight of paper being used. The proper height to maintain is about a ¼ to ⅛ inch below the paper separator spring. If the paper pile is set too high, the paper separator becomes inoperative and the suction foot will pick up more than one sheet at a time. If set too low, the suction foot will be unable to reach the sheets and will misfeed.

To set the mechanism to maintain the proper height, lower the stack, place the raising control wire lever (Fig. 9-71C) in the "on"

Fig. 9-71. Proper feeding of the paper requires the adjustments of: the drive motor (*A*), the height control knob (*B*), the raising control wire (*C*), the blower tubes (*D*) and the thumb screws (*E*) to adjust the blower tubes. *F* is the suction cut-off switch.

position, and turn on the drive motor (Fig. 9-71A). Allow the stack to come up automatically and stop. If it stops before it reaches the ¼ to ⅛-inch distance below the paper separator spring, turn the height control knob (Fig. 9-71B) counterclockwise one half turn at a time until it reaches the required height. If the stack rises too high, turn the knob clockwise and lower the elevator by hand. Repeat until the required height is obtained. (On model 251, the height control knob operates in reverse.)

The raising control wire, when in its forward position (Fig. 9-71C) will allow the stack to continue to rise while the press is running until it reaches the height the stack is set for. To stop the stack from rising, especially while loading paper with the press running, lift the wire and pull it back into the idle position. Moving it forward again will cause the stack to rise again. When running ordinary stock, the control wire should be set 1⅜ inch behind the blower tubes (Fig. 9-71D). When running heavy card stock, the wire may be moved an additional inch away from the blowers.

The blower tubes are set after the proper height of the stack is obtained. The tubes (one on each side of the stack) are mounted on the magazine channels. These tubes introduce air between the top sheets, thus separating the top few sheets, and assist the suction foot in lifting one sheet at a time from the pile.

Each tube has three small openings and is connected to the feeder pump by a hose. The center hold should be level with the top of the stack when the pump motor is off. The openings should be pointed to the lead edge of the sheets. The tubes may be moved by loosening thumb screws (Fig. 9-71E). Model 233 has an additional blower for the center of the stack that is set at the same height as the others, except for the openings which face the paper stack.

The pump which supplies the air for the blowers is controlled by the switch (Fig. 9-72B). The amount of air delivered to the stack may be regulated depending upon the kind of stock being run. The thinner the stock, the less the amount of air needed. To adjust the amount of air, turn the air blower control valve (Fig. 9-73A) in the desired direction. When the proper amount of air is obtained, turn the pump motor switch to the "off" position. Too much air

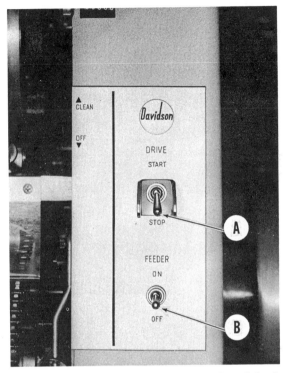

Fig. 9-72. A close up view of the drive motor switch (A) and the feeder control switch (B) are shown here.

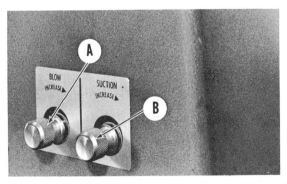

Fig. 9-73. A close up view of the air blower control (A) and the suction control (B) are shown here.

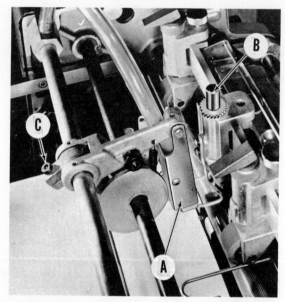

Fig. 9-74. The suction foot (*A*) lifts the top sheet off the pile and the set screw (*C*) is used to position the foot on the mounting bar. The double sheet detector (*B*) prevents more than one sheet feeding at one time.

curls the edge of the sheet; too little fails to separate the sheets and induces two at a time to be fed.

The suction foot (Fig. 9-74A) lifts the top sheet from the stack and brings it forward to feed into the pull-out rolls. The suction foot may be moved along the mounting bar by first loosening the set screw (Fig. 9-74C), then sliding it. It should be centered on the sheet and directly behind the double sheet detector (Fig. 9-74B) so that it lifts the sheet in the center. The same pump and the same switch controls the suction foot and the suction. Suction requirements will change when lifting different kinds of stock. The suction control valve (Fig. 9-73B) is used to adjust the amount of suction needed. To obtain the proper amount of suction:

1. Turn the drive motor switch (Fig. 9-72A) to the "start" position until the pile height is reached, then turn the switch to "stop."

2. Place the suction "cut-off" lever (Fig. 9-71F) in the "on" position and turn the suction control valve (Fig. 9-73B) counterclockwise to eliminate all suction.

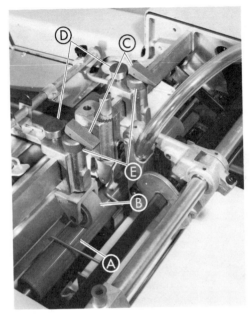

Fig. 9-75. The lower pull-out rolls (*A*) and the upper pull-out rolls (*B*) take the sheet from the suction foot. The pull-out rolls are adjusted by the levers (*C*), thumb screws (*D*) and the knurled adjusting barrel (*D*).

3. Turn the drive and motor switches "on" again, and turn the suction control valve clockwise until just enough suction is obtained to lift and consistently feed a single sheet of paper into the feed rolls. Use only the amount of suction required to lift one sheet, then increase the suction by an extra ¼ turn.

The pullout rolls upper (Fig. 9-75B) and lower, take the sheet from the suction foot and propel it onto the conveyor table. The lower pull-out rolls (Fig. 9-75A) are stationary. The upper pull-out rolls can be moved horizontally to adjust for various widths in stock being fed. A downward pressure adjustment is also provided.

The upper rolls should be set as close to the center as possible, one on each side of the suction head, so that if there is any difference of pressure present, the effect will be kept to a minimum. If unequal pressure is present on the edges of the sheet, the sheet may twist as it enters the conveyor table and cause mis-register. The rolls are moved by placing levers (Fig. 9-75C) in the "up" position

Fig. 9-76. When setting the double sheet detector at *A* the following units are used: *B*—the micrometer adjusting knob, *C*—the detector paper control wire, *D*—the detector foot and *E*—the deflector plate.

and loosening the thumb screws (Fig. 9-75D). Model 233 has four pull-out rolls and should divide the sheet equally.

The downward pressure is adjusted by turning the knurled adjusting barrel on top of the pull-out rolls (Fig. 9-75E). To increase pressure, turn clockwise. The pressure should be set very lightly and the rolls should exert equal pressure. To test this, place 1-inch strips of paper under each roll and adjust for light, even tension.

The double sheet detector (Fig. 9-76A) is set to allow only a single sheet to pass at one time. If more than one sheet is picked up and passed to the detector, it actuates a deflector plate (Fig. 9-76E) and passes the sheets into the lower conveyor table.

The detector has a micrometer adjusting knob (Fig. 9-76B). Each click on the knob represents about $\frac{1}{1000}$ of an inch. The detector paper-control wire (Fig. 9-76C) should be $\frac{1}{16}$ to $\frac{1}{8}$ inch above the bottom of the detector foot (Fig. 9-76D). To set, tear a strip of paper 1 inch wide from the stock being run, raise the right hand pull-out roll and insert the strip between the foot of the detector and the lower pull-out roll. Turn on the drive motor and turn the adjusting screw on top of the detector bracket clockwise to lower the rocker (the lower part of the sheet detector). When the rocker touches the paper it will actuate the deflector plate. Turn the adjusting knob counterclockwise one click at a time until the deflector plate stops operating.

Fold the strip of paper in half and insert the cut edge under the detector. If the detector was set carefully, the deflector plate will actuate immediately. Turn the knob counterclockwise one more click and lower the pull-out roll once again.

The conveyor table adjustments must be exactly correct to obtain the proper register. To prevent shutting down the press after beginning the run, spend a few extra minutes adjusting the table before each job. The table permits the sheet to flow on continuous tapes (Fig. 9-77F) as these tapes move down the table to the printing head. Metal straps (Fig. 9-77A) are used to maintain traction on the tapes. To set the table, proceed as follows:

1. Turn on the drive motor and space the conveyor tapes so that they are equally spaced for the sheet to be run. To move the tapes, squeeze the ends of the tape guides together (Fig. 9-78A), and slide the guide along the tightener rod located below the conveyor table. The tape farthest from the stationary guide must not extend

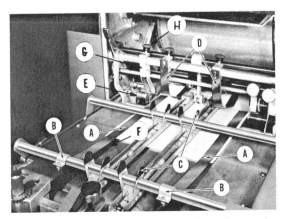

Fig. 9-77. The conveyor table adjustments are made at *A*—metal straps, at *B*—metal strap clips, at *C*—flanges, at *D*—tapes, at *E*—adjusting nuts, at *F*—continuous tapes, at *G*—a jogger spring, and at *H*—a thumb screw.

Fig. 9-78. A close-up view of the tape guides (A) underneath the conveyor table.

beyond the edge of the sheet or the jogger will push against the tape and not the sheet.

2. When all tapes are positioned, move a sheet against the stop fingers making sure that the sheet is squarely against all stop fingers. It should also touch the stationary register guide.

3. Parallel the guide by moving the adjusting nuts (Fig. 9-77E). When properly adjusted, the entire sheet should lightly touch the side of the stationary guide adjacent to it.

4. Place a wide metal strap (Fig. 9-77A) over each of the outside tapes and place the narrower straps over the center tapes. Correct pressure by these is important to the feeding operation. Too little pressure will not move the sheet all the way to the stop fingers. Pressure is regulated by the position of the metal strap clip (Fig. 9-77B). Heavy stocks require more pressure than do thin. Thin stocks will register better if the strap nearest the stationary side guide exerts more pressure than the others. This will have a tendency to pull the sheets rather than push them against the guide. Pushing a thin sheet will cause it to wave. This wave becomes a wrinkle during printing. (Model 251 has glass marbles mounted on marble frames which exert pressure against the tapes (Fig. 9-77D). The frame supports are also movable by squeezing flanges (Fig. 9-77C) with the glass marbles placed directly over a conveyor tape.

5. With the sheet against the stop fingers and register guides, turn the press by hand until the jogger moves toward the sheet.

6. When it has jogged all the way, move the bracket toward the sheet so that the jogger spring (Fig. 9-77G) is slightly depressed by the sheet. A thumb screw on the bracket (Fig. 9-77H) holds the jogger bracket in place. Be sure the spring and bracket do not touch anything in the jogging action.

The upper feed roll (not illustrated) carries the sheet into the gripper mechanism. At a pre-determined time, the upper feed roll descends on the sheet and the lower feed roll, with its stop finger, turns. This propels the sheet into the gripper fingers. No adjustment of the upper feed roll is required because it automatically compensates for various paper thicknesses. The upper feed roll is factory set; *in no instance should it be touched.*

The gripper bar (not illustrated) contains the gripper fingers which receive the lead edge of the sheet. It carries the sheet through the printing cycle and delivers the printed sheet into the receiving tray. The gripper bar requires no adjustment.

The paper catcher (tray, Fig. 9-79) receives each sheet as it is printed. To set:

1. Run a single sheet through by hand until the trailing edge falls into the tray, but has not as yet been released by the gripper bar.

2. Set the paper-catcher side guides (Fig. 9-79D) by loosening the wing nuts in their base. Do not set so close that they bind the sheet as it falls. ⅟₁₆ inch clearance on each side is enough. For short sheets, the paper-catcher stop (Fig. 9-79E) may be moved upward; for long sheets, it may be moved downward towards the end of the catcher base.

The paper retaining wire (Fig. 9-79F) helps to guide the sheets into the paper-catcher and prevents the top sheets from falling onto the floor.

Tinsel cord (Fig. 9-79B) is a strip of tinsel stretched across the press in front of the stripper assembly to aid in the delivery of the sheet. Its primary purpose is to help eliminate static electricity from the paper. The tinsel cord can be lowered or raised by metal flanges (Fig. 9-79C).

Fig. 9-79. The paper delivery consists of: at *A*—ejector wheels, at *B*—tinsel (to eliminate static electricity), at *C*—flanges, at *D*—side guides, at *E*—paper catcher stop, at *F*—paper retaining wire.

Fig. 9-80. The stripper finger (*A*) is adjusted with two set screws (*B*) and the entire assembly can be moved after loosening set screws (*C*) in center of sprockets.

The lower ejector wheels assist the gripper bar in the delivery of the printed sheet. They are equally spaced (Fig. 9-79A) to carry the sheet. To move the wheels, loosen the set screw in the hub of each wheel with a screwdriver, and slide it along the shaft to the desired location.

The stripper finger (Fig. 9-80A) strips each sheet at exactly the same place from the gripper bar, thus assisting in easy delivery. The gripper finger should be as close as possible to the gripper bar without touching it. If it is not close enough, the sheets when released may follow the gripper bar and jam on top of the stripper finger. To set the stripper, place the gripper bar directly above it. Loosen the two set screws (Fig. 9-80B), move the stripper into the desired position and retighten the screws. Check to see that the gripper bar and stripper plate are parallel. The entire assembly may be moved with both hands after loosening the set screws in the center of the sprockets (Fig. 9-80C) and sliding the assembly along the mounting bars.

Correct Impression

Determining the correct amount of packing to be placed under the brass draw sheet (Fig. 9-81A) of the impression cylinder is important to obtain the correct image impression. If it is not correct, improper pressure is applied, and the surface speeds between

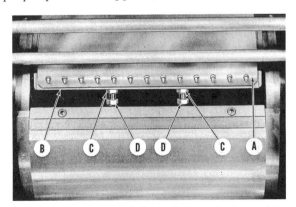

Fig. 9-81. The brass draw sheet (*A*) is shown here on the impression cylinder (*B*) with its two adjustments: at *C*—the lock nuts, at *D*—adjusting screws.

the blanket and impression cylinders are unequal—resulting in an image that is not as clear and sharp as it could be.

The amount of packing which determines this pressure, depends upon the thickness of the paper stock being run. Each change in paper thickness means a change in the packing.

The impression cylinder is undercut .039 inch which means that the outside surface of the cylinder must be raised .039 inch to make the diameter of the upper cylinder twice that of the blanket cylinder in order to print. This .039 inch is obtained by combining the brass draw sheet (a thin sheet of brass, .101 inch, used under the plate to bring the plate up to the correct impression height), the packing, and the sheet being printed. For example: To find the correct amount of packing necessary to run 20 lb. paper stock: first, measure the 20 lb. stock with a micrometer and add this figure to .010 inch (the thickness of the brass draw sheet); subtract this amount from the .039 inch necessary and the result will be the amount of packing required.

Step 1

Add:	.010″	thickness of brass draw sheet
	.004″	thickness of 20 lb. paper stock
	.014″	total thickness

Step 2

Subtract:	.039″	total thickness needed
	.014″	thickness obtained from above
	.025″	packing required

Once the correct amount of packing has been determined, place it under the draw sheet of the impression cylinder as follows:

1. Turn the press by hand until the trailing edge of the impression cylinder is accessible (Fig. 9-81B).

2. Using the larger wrench provided, loosen the lock nuts (Fig. 9-81C) on the tail clamp adjusting screws and turn the adjusting screws (Fig. 9-81D) counterclockwise until there is enough play in the clamp to allow the draw sheet to be released by lifting the clamp.

3. Hold the trailing edge with one hand and turn the press with the other hand until the lead edge is accessible.

4. Insert the packing well up under the lead edge of the draw sheet in the clamp.

5. Refasten the trailing edge of the draw sheet in the clamp. Tighten the adjusting screws equally so that tension is the same on both ends of the clamp. Do not overtighten.

6. Retighten the lock nuts.

On Models 241 and 251, cylinders 221-418AA or 233-2AA, the undercut is .010 inch. Grained plates may be used without any packing or underlay, but when running any other plates, use a micrometer to first measure the thickness of the plate and then add the required sheet or sheets of underlay to bring the combined thickness to .010 inch.

Other Types of Printing

The Davidson Dual is a very versatile press. In addition to being able to print by offset, the press can be easily adapted to relief printing, dry offset printing, dry offset embossing and perfecting.

Relief Printing. Relief printing (letterpress) is the method whereby an image is raised so that only that portion which is to be printed touches the ink rollers. No dampening unit or moisture is needed. On the Davidson press, the image plate prints directly on the paper for relief printing.

The lower or blanket cylinder becomes the impression cylinder and the image to be printed is carried on that portion of the upper cylinder which was regarded as the impression cylinder in offset printing. As the sheet of paper comes between the two cylinders, the letterpress inked image (the medium) which is now located on the impression portion of the upper cylinder, contacts the paper and transfers its image using the blanket cylinder as a platen or impression cylinder (Fig. 9-82).

To convert the press to relief printing, it is important to follow the correct procedure. The first step is to remove the dampening unit:

1. Remove the fountain solution bottle and the fountain solution from the fountain tray.

Fig. 9-82. The Davidson is adapted for relief printing here.

Fig. 9-83. The two mounting screws (A) are loosened and the dampening unit is removed as shown.

2. With the T-handle wrench, remove the two dampening unit mounting screws (Fig. 9-83A) and lift off the entire unit (Fig. 9-83).

To remove the impression segment containing the draw sheet and packing:

With the T-handle wrench, loosen the four screws which hold the segment in place (Fig. 9-84) and remove the segment. Always

Fig. 9-84. The impression segment containing the draw sheet
and packing is removed.

place the segment on its end when removed to protect the surface
from dirt and physical harm.

To remove the plate segment:

1. Loosen the two plate segment holding screws located in the
center of the segment.

2. Once loosened, hold the segment with one hand so that it
does not drop.

The medium offset blanket is satisfactory for relief operation
especially for rubber plate work, but if a great deal of relief printing
is to be done using electros, linotype slugs, etc., better results may
be obtained by a relief blanket with a firmer surface which is
designed for this type of work.

The relief segment (cylinder) is mounted in the position, formerly
occupied by the offset impression segment, identified by the four
holes for the mounting screws located in the segment rings (Fig.
9-85A). To mount the segment:

1. Move the two segment lock nuts (Fig. 9-85B) from their
present position to the opposite side where the relief segment is to
be attached, located on the inside of the segment rings and centered in the slots (Fig. 9-85C).

2. Mount the relief segment onto the upper cylinder, and
tighten the two segment holding screws.

During offset printing the image was transferred to the blanket

Fig. 9-85. The relief segment is mounted into position as shown here in the segment rings (*A*) with lock nuts (*B*) and centered in the slots (*C*).

Fig. 9-86. The relief ejector cam is moved into relief position with a screwdriver as shown here.

and from the blanket to the paper. The sheet was turned over during delivery so that the operator could see the image, but in relief printing, the image is placed on top of the sheet from the upper cylinder; therefore, the sheet does not have to be turned over during delivery. To obtain this relief delivery, it is necessary to adjust the gripper bar so that it releases the sheet before it is turned over.

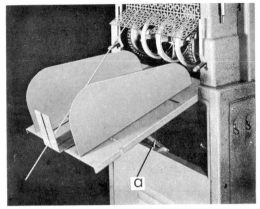

Fig. 9-87. The paper catcher must be raised for relief printing and is supported by a bar (A) as shown here.

1. Move the relief ejector cam into the relief position by loosening the relief ejector set screw with a screwdriver (Fig. 9-86), and slide the cam all the way out toward the center of the press.

Since the sheet is now being delivered as the gripper bar reaches the lower ejector wheels, the paper catcher now must be raised to a new position to receive the sheets. To set the paper catcher:

1. Lift the paper catcher unit from its four mounting pins in the lower position, and mount it on the two upper mounting pins (Fig. 9-88).

2. Place the paper catcher support bar (Fig. 87A) into the plate provided for it on the stand spreader.

Two upper ejector wheels are provided (Fig. 9-88A) to assist in controlling the sheet since the sheet has a small distance to travel to the paper catcher after its release by the gripper bar. Each upper ejector wheel, mounted on the cross bar directly above the lower ejector wheel, must ride directly over a lower ejector wheel. They are held in place by thumb screws (Fig. 9-88B). The upper wheels should be adjusted so that as the sheet passes under them, they turn slightly. To do this means the upper wheels should not contact the lower wheels but should be very close to it. All wheels should be located on the outside of the image area on the sheet. To mount the upper ejector wheels:

1. Loosen the lock nut (Fig. 9-88C) and turn the adjusting

Fig. 9-88. To assist in controlling the delivery of the sheet, upper ejector wheels (*A*) are used and are adjusted by using the thumb screws (*B*), lock nuts (*C*) and adjusting screws (*D*).

Fig. 9-89. Small line clips are used to hold a T-bottom type relief plate.

screw (Fig. 9-88D) until the wheels get ready to turn when paper is feeding and retighten.

When an upper ejector wheel is moved, the lower one must also be moved. Avoid placing an upper ejector wheel directly over a gripper finger.

Letterpress plates. Several types of relief plates may be used; these are mounted as follows:

The T-bottom type is mounted in the rails of the segment and held in place by small line lock clips (Fig. 9-89).

Curved electros are prepared with T-bottom mountings, and slid into position in the rail segment (Fig. 9-90).

Brass-backed rubber plates are mounted on the rail segment

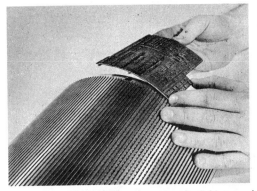

Fig. 9-90. Curved electros with T-bottom mountings is slid into position as shown.

by securing their top and bottom edges with brass sheet retainers (Fig. 9-91A). These retainers are slid into the proper grooves. The sides of the brass back rubber plate are held in place with steel marginal bands anchored at the top and bottom of the segment (Fig. 9-91B). These are attached by placing the anchor hook on one end of the segment, inserting a screwdriver in the loop on the opposite end and applying pressure.

Sticky-back rubber plates are mounted on the rail segment after a brass draw sheet has been inserted and anchored in the same manner as the brass backed rubber plate. The sticky back plate is then mounted by laying it on the brass sheet and applying slight pressure. Positions may be changed by peeling it off and replacing it in a different position.

The rubber plate segment is furnished as standard equipment. When using this segment, the rubber plate should be mounted on a piece of brass the full length of the segment so that it may be anchored at the top and bottom by the clips provided (Fig. 9-92A) and secured by the two marginal bands (Fig. 9-91B).

Sticky-back rubber plates may be mounted on the full-sized brass sheet (Fig. 9-92) by placing them into the desired position and applying pressure with the palm of the hand.

Linotype slugs are used in conjunction with the linotype slug chase. This slug chase is specially ordered and may be installed by following the instructions provided with its purchase.

Impression Adjustment. It may become necessary to increase

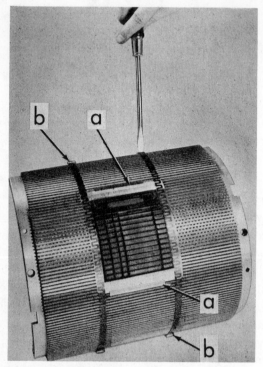

Fig. 9-91. Brassed backed rubber plates are secured in place with brass sheet retainers (A) and steel marginal bands anchored at the top and bottom of the segment (B).

or decrease the amount of impression when converting to relief printing. To do this, the blanket cylinder is used as the impression cylinder. To obtain the correct impression setting:

1. Loosen the two blanket latch holding screws (Fig. 9-93A).

2. While holding the adjusting screw with a screwdriver, loosen the lock nut on the adjusting screw.

3. With a small wrench (Fig. 9-93) turn the adjusting screw counterclockwise to reduce the blanket pressure until it does not print at all. Then turn screw clockwise to raise the blanket and increase the pressure until it is proper for printing.

Dry Offset Printing

Dry offset printing utilizes the letterpress and offset methods to

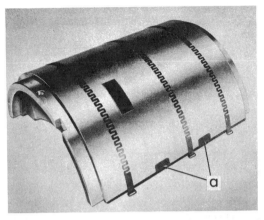

Fig. 9-92. Clips (*A*) are used to anchor the rubber plate mounted on
a piece of brass.

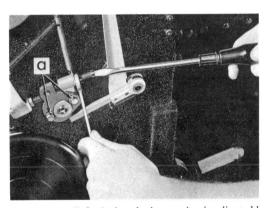

Fig. 9-93. When converting to relief printing the impression is adjusted by loosening screws (*A*) and turning the adjusting screws and lock nuts as shown.

obtain the chief advantages of both. The dry offset metal plate
has the image slightly etched in relief. This raised image is inked
in the normal letterpress manner but unlike letterpress which
prints directly onto the paper, the dry offset plate transfers its
inked image to the blanket which in turn transfers the image to
the paper as in offset printing. Therefore, in dry offset we have
a letterpress type of inking with an offset type of image transfer
(Fig. 9-94).

Dry offset printing has several advantages:

Fig. 9-94. The Davidson Dual fitted for Dry Offset printing is shown

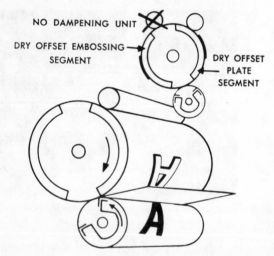

Fig. 9-95. A schematic diagram illustrating Dry offset embossing.

1. No dampening unit or ink and water balance is required, which means less operator attention.

2. Long press runs with a single plate are possible because the offset plate does not touch the paper but contacts the blanket with a very light "kiss" impression.

3. Uniformity of color can be maintained throughout the entire run because there can be no emulsification of the ink.

4. Almost any kind of paper stock with any desired surface texture can be run, one of the chief advantages of the offset process.

5. A lighter layer of ink may be used thereby reducing ink costs.

6. The full selection of inks offered to letterpress can be available when printing by dry offset.

7. Faster makeready of the press is also possible.

Dry offset printing is accomplished by removing the complete dampening unit as done for relief printing and substituting a dry offset segment (containing this relief plate) in place of the standard plate segment.

Complete instructions for dry offset printing are furnished with the purchase of every dry offset segment. Complete instructions for making dry offset plates are also available.

Dry Offset Embossing

The Davidson Dual can be adapted to print and emboss (raise the image from the surface) a sheet of paper simultaneously. This is accomplished by the use of two identical dry offset plates mounted on dry offset segments or cylinders. One is used to transfer the inked image to the blanket and the other is used to press the sheet of paper against the blanket in the corresponding image area (thus transferring the image) and to emboss the sheet at the same time.

On the first revolution of the blanket cylinder, the ink on the raised image of the first plate is transferred to the blanket (Fig. 9-95). On the second revolution of the blanket cylinder, the sheet of paper comes between this inked image and the second dry offset plate. The second plate pushes down on the sheet and transfers the image from the blanket to the sheet and at the same time it pushes down, it pushes hard enough to emboss the sheet in the image area by pushing it into the soft surface of the blanket.

This embossing is done by having the dampening unit completely removed and replacing the plate segment with a dry offset segment and an impression segment with an embossing segment.

Complete instructions are available or furnished upon ordering each embossing segment.

Perfecting on the Davidson Dual

Perfecting is the printing of two sides of the sheet at the same time with a single trip through the press. Davidson has a two-cylinder principle which makes this possible.

As the sheet comes between the two cylinders it is pressed against the blanket cylinder by the draw sheet on the impression cylinder and an image is "offset" from the blanket surface. But if another offset plate was substituted for the draw sheet on the impression cylinder, the sheet would receive another image directly from the plate (direct lithography).

To accomplish this type of printing, merely substitute a second offset plate segment on the impression cylinder instead of the brass draw sheet. The upper cylinder will now have two identical plate segments. The only difference is that the image which is transferred by the direct method must be reversed or "left or wrong reading," so it will print positively. This is accomplished by turning the negative over when making this plate so that the image is made in reverse. Thin base film is excellent for making the negative for this direct plate.

To set up the Davidson for perfecting, simply remove the impression segment and substitute a second plate segment.

Because more impression pressure is required to print both sides at the same time, it will be necessary to add more packing. The plate on the regular offset cylinder should be mounted as usual depending upon the thickness of the plate and whether the cylinder is undercut .006 inch or .010 inch. The direct plate should be "over-packed" an additional .006 inch by underlaying the printing plate with an old printing plate that measures .006 inch.

The press is operated in the usual manner as offset printing with the exception that the ink fountain and water fountain rolls must be set to deliver twice as much ink and water. This is necessary because twice as much image is covered and twice as much non-image is dampened during each revolution.

SPECIFICATIONS TO BE REMEMBERED
DAVIDSON DUAL MODEL 500

Sheet sizes: Maximum 11×15 inches. Minimum 3×5 inches.
Speed range: Model 233-3000 to 5400 impressions per hour
               Models 241, 251-3000 to 6000 impressions per hour
               Model 500-4000 to 8000 impressions per hour
Paper stock: 13 pound to 6 ply card
Printing area: Up to $9\frac{3}{4} \times 13$ inches
Plate size: 10×16 inches
Plate thickness: .004 inches
Blanket thickness: .064 inches
Dimensions: Height, 57 inches, length 64 inches, width 34 inches
Weight: 925 pounds

Review Questions

Instructions

1. Do not write in the book, but on the test sheets provided.
2. Questions are in several forms: multiple choice, true or false, one or a few words, or matching.
3. Place T in the space provided if the statement is true; F if it is false.
4. Select from the list of statements or words the most logical answer.
5. Use one or a few words in the one-word answers.
6. In the matching questions, select the correct letter of the alphabet.

ATF Chief Model 15

1. Maximum sheet size is:

   a. 10×15 c. 11×14
   b. 10×14 d. 11×15

2. Minimum sheet size is:

   a. 4 × 5   c. 3 × 6
   b. 3 × 5   d. 4 × 6

3. Maximum image size is:

   a. 9¾ × 13½   c. 9¾ × 13½
   b. 9¼ × 13¼   d. 9½ × 13¼

4. Speed range is:

   a. 3400 to 7200 impressions per hour
   b. 3500 to 7000 impressions per hour
   c. 3400 to 7500 impressions per hour
   d. 3500 to 7200 impressions per hour

5. The inking unit consists of ten rollers. True or False?
6. The dampening unit consists of four rollers. True or False?
7. The delivery sheet stop halts the sheet as it is delivered into the delivery. True or False?
8. The vacuum control regulates the amount of air delivered to the air blow paper separators. True or False?
9. The paper stack back guides are in a fixed position and are not adjustable. True or False?
10. The vertical positioning of the image is adjustable a full 180 degrees. True or False?

Davidson 500

1. Maximum sheet size is:

   a. 10 × 15   c. 11 × 14
   b. 10 × 14   d. 11 × 15

2. Minimum sheet size is:

   a. 4 × 5   c. 3 × 6
   b. 4 × 6   d. 3 × 5

3. Speed range on the Model 233 is:
   a. 3000 to 5400 impressions per hour
   b. 3000 to 5500 impressions per hour

    c. 3000 to 5000 impressions per hour
    d. 3000 to 5300 impressions per hour
4. Each time the plate cylinder or plate is moved, it is necessary to wash the blanket. True or False?
5. The paper separator does not prevent the suction foot from picking up more than one sheet at a time. True or False?
6. More than one different process of printing is possible on the Davidson. True or False?
7. Line up the right column with the corresponding left column. to complete the sentence.

    a. The paper height control knob ___   a. lifts the top sheet from the stack

    b. The paper separator ___   b. takes the sheet from the suction foot

    c. The suction foot ___   c. prevents the suction from picking up more than one sheet

    d. Paper guide wire ___   d. helps to guide the paper

    e. Pullout Rolls ___   e. allows only one sheet to pass

    f. Sheet detector ___   f. controls the height of the elevator

8. List the printing processes possible on the Davidson press.
9. Only three controls are necessary to regulate the dampening rollers. True or False?

CHAPTER 10

Harris Offset Press
Model LUH-120

What is the Harris? How does it compare to the other presses? Is it much different in operation? Is it more difficult to makeready and operate?

The Harris Offset Press Model LUH-120 (Fig. 10-1), described in this chapter, is larger than those presses described previously. A larger sheet size can be printed on this Harris model (Fig. 10-8) than on the presses in the previous chapters. Better control of the paper can be obtained, especially on critical work where absolute register is necessary. Experienced pressmen, however, consider this a small press.

Up to now, the student or apprentice should have a good knowledge of operating a small press. When confronted with a larger press, he may find it is easier to operate and that adjusting to it is surprisingly fast.

Operating Controls[1]

The Harris-LUH 120 is equipped with three buttons (Fig. 10-2A). The "inch" button allows the press to run as long as the button is depressed. The "inch" and "run" buttons, when depressed simultaneously, permit the press to run continuously. The "stop"

1. The material in this chapter is adapted from The *Harris LUH-120 Instruction Manual.* Material from this copyrighted manual is by courtesy of the Harris-Seybold Corporation.

Fig. 10-1. The Harris LUH-120 is a medium-size offset press.

button is mounted on the same control station and stops the press. The lever (Fig. 10-2B) provided alongside the stop button is a safety lever. This lever, when turned, keeps the press from being accidentally started—the press cannot be started until it is returned.

The speed adjustment handle (Fig. 10-3A) regulates the speed of the press and can be adjusted from 1 to 12. Speed adjustments should only be made while the press is running on "pressure."

To change the speed of the press, pull out and swing the handle until the indicator is at the desired number. The press will maintain this set speed, but as the press "trips" (stops feeding and printing when anything goes wrong with the feeding but continues to run) it will automatically drop back to slow speed. Once the print-

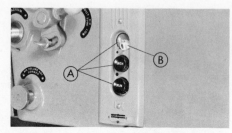

Fig. 10-2. The stop, inch and run buttons (*A*) on the Harris LUH-120 control the running of the press. The lever shown at *B* is a safety lever.

Fig. 10-3. Twelve press speeds are possible on the Harris LUH-120. The speed adjustment handle is shown at *A*.

ing pressure is re-applied, reset the indicator to the previously set number. The indicator will lock in place and maintain the speed.

The feeder latch has two positions besides the "off" position. The first position (Fig. 10-4A) applies the vacuum to the Harris wheel (not illustrated) permitting the sheets to be run without the printing pressure being applied. The second position applies the printing pressure and is attained by pushing the latch to its extreme downward position (Fig. 10-4B).

The manual trip (Fig. 10-4C), which is located above the latch, can be used to disengage the pressure. This can be done by moving the handle toward the delivery end of the press.

The sequence of operation for the feeder and trip latch is:

1. With the press running and the feeder latch "off," turn on the vacuum motor (Fig. 10-5A). When the vacuum slot openings are at the top of the wheel:

2. Engage the feeder latch into the first position, thus allowing

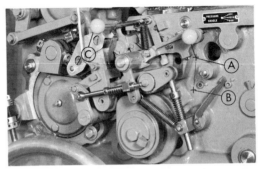

Fig. 10-4. Printing pressure is controlled by the feeder latch—shown in the off-position. The first position (*A*) allows sheets to run without pressure; the second position (*B*) allows sheets to run with pressure applied. The manual trip (*C*) is used to disengage pressure.

Fig. 10-5. The vacuum motor control buttons are shown here at *A*.

the sheets to go down the feed table. When the gripper or lead edge of the sheet has reached the side guide bar:

3. Depress the latch lever into the lowest downward position. The printing pressure is now on.

NOTE: If for any reason the sheet does not reach the front guides in sufficient time to disengage the trip, release the latch quickly to allow the press to trip off automatically. If the latch is held down, the automatic trip cannot operate. If the latch is engaged in the first position and the vacuum slots are not at the top of the wheel, the sheet is likely to be out of timing due to a partial loss of vacuum.

Water Control and Adjustments. Place a plate on the press before setting the dampener rolls. (See "installing the plate"). The dampener rolls have the bushing mounted in the ends of the

Fig. 10-6. Controls and adjustments for the dampening system are shown here.

Fig. 10-7. The working parts of the dampening system are shown here.

roller cores or shaft on which the roller is mounted. These must be thoroughly oiled before installing. The rollers fit into eccentric pins mounted in the hangers. Set screws lock the eccentric adjustments.

The knurled knob (Fig. 10-6A) controls the water "on" and "off." The knob is pulled all the way out by pulling the spring plunger (Fig. 10-6B) causing the ductor to stay against the aluminum vibrator roll at all times. Pushed in all the way, the water is "on" and water is transferred in relation to the setting of the water ductor cam (Fig. 10-6C). Turning the knob counterclockwise gives more water, clockwise gives less water.

The water ductor roller is adjusted as follows:

1. Place two strips of .003 inch paper between the ductor roller and the water pan roller.

2. Back off the adjusting screws (Fig. 10-6D).

3. Place the water control "on" and jog the press until the ductor cam follower is on the "high" of the cam.

4. Using the adjusting screws, adjust the ductor roller until an even tension is obtained on the paper strips.

No adjustments are necessary between the ductor and the aluminum vibrator roll because these are automatically taken care of by spring tension which may be increased if necessary by relocating the round knobs or set collars (Fig. 10-6E).

To adjust the dampeners to the vibrator:

1. Install the lower roller into the eccentric pins.

2. Place strips of .003 inch paper between the dampener and vibrator about 2 inches from each end. Adjust the eccentric until each strip has an identically snug pull between the vibrator and the dampener.

3. Tighten the set screw.

The upper roller is installed and adjusted to the vibrator in the same manner.

The water ductor roller fits into bearing blocks which are installed into ductor hangers. First install the bearings (Fig. 10-6F) on the roll ends and then install this assembly into the hanger. The flat sides of the bearing slide into the hanger and then are turned until the snap pin (Fig. 10-6G) falls into the hole in the bushings, locking it into position.

The water pan (Fig. 10-7A) sets on two rods with clamps (Fig. 10-7B) on both ends which tighten to the rear rod with a thumb screw. The pan roll must first be thoroughly cleaned with plate etch and pumice to remove any dirt or grease. Gum and dry the roll. Place the muslin cover provided with the press over the roller making sure it is smooth and tight. The water pan roll (Fig. 10-7C) has bushings (Fig. 10-7D) which fit into the frame sockets are locked in place with the holding screws (Fig. 10-7E). Be sure the gear on the end engages the mating gear in the water-roll drive mechanism at the bushings and gear side of the press. The oil holes in the bushings should be up, and the thumb screws tightened only by hand.

To adjust the dampeners to the plate:

1. Turn the press until the plate is in position to contact the dampener rolls.

2. Roll the water motion (the unit that contains the whole dampening system, i.e. fountain and all rollers) into the "on" position with the handle (Fig. 10-7F) so that the driving gear meshes with the plate cylinder gear and the detent pawl is engaged in the second notch (Fig. 10-7G). The first notch is the "off" position, but does not disengage the drive gear, allowing the operator to wet the dampeners by running the press.

3. Unscrew the adjusting screw (Fig. 10-7H) at each end of the water motion allowing the dampeners to contact the plate.

4. Back these off just enough to be free from the shaft that they bear against.

5. After the dampeners are wet, sponge off the plate and turn on the press.

6. Check the roller "bounce" as it passes over the gap of the plate cylinder. A slight perceptible movement should be felt at the adjustment screw as the plate cylinder gap passes the rollers.

Ink Control and Adjustments. The ink ductor roller mechanism has three positions, "off," "on," and "automatic." To place the roller in the "off" position, release the knurled lock screw (Fig. 10-8A) and lift the handle (Fig. 10-8B) until it engages in the stop latch (Fig. 10-8C). Retighten the knurled lock screw.

The "on" position permits the ductor to operate continuously whether the printing pressure is on or not. To turn the roller "on" release the knurled lock screw, push the handle down, and retighten the knurled lock screw.

To place on "automatic," release the knurled lock screw and allow the spring to return the handle to its normal position.

The ratchet pawl governs the amount of rotation of the ink fountain roll by the adjustment of a lever. When pulled all the way

Fig. 10-8. The adjustment points for the ink rollers are shown here: at *A*—the ink ductor adjustment, at *B*—the ink ductor control handle, at *C*—the stop latch,. at *D*—the bearing holder for the distributor roller, at *E*—the lock nut for *D*.

back, the action is disengaged. The ink fountain roll can be rotated manually using the handle lever.

The ink fountain blade controls the amount of ink being fed to the fountain roller. In the factory, this blade is exactly paralleled to the roller by the use of stops. *The stops should* not *be moved.* Thumb screws adjust the blade to the fountain roller; when adjusting the thumb screws, work from the center screws out and bring the blade up gradually to the roller. Turning the thumb screws counterclockwise will increase the flow of the ink; clockwise will decrease the flow.

The ductor roller is installed in the bearing holders. End play is removed by pushing the feed pin (Fig. 10-9A) toward the gear side, then tightening the setscrew (Fig. 10-9B). To adjust the ductor roller:

1. Turn the press until the cam follower (Fig. 10-9C) is on the "low" of the cam. As it just starts to leave this low area, the ductor will start to lift toward the fountain roll.

2. Insert two strips of paper between the ductor roller vibrator and use the adjusting screw beneath the fountain to adjust the roller until a light tension against the vibrator is obtained.

To set the ductor against the fountain roll:

3. Jog the press until the ductor cam roll (Fig. 10-9C) is near the "high" of the cam.

4. Release the cap screws at the fountain ends and move the ink fountain all the way back in the screw slots.

Fig. 10-9. Adjustment points for the ductor roller are shown here.

5. Jog the press until the cam follower is on the "high" and the ductor roller has lifted to the extreme amount.

6. Insert paper strips and move the fountain into contact to obtain a light tension on the strips.

7. Retighten the cap screws.

To install the distributor rollers:

1. Mount the bearings on the ends of the rubber distributor rollers and secure with the Waldes rings. A Waldes ring is a type of holder that holds the bearings in place.

2. Release the lock screw (Fig. 10-9D) holding the bracket and, back off the adjusting screw (Fig. 10-9E).

3. Install the lower distributor roller using paper strips to check the tension. The weight of the roller will keep it in contact with the lower vibrator.

4. Adjust until the strips to the upper vibrator have an equal pull between the roller and the lower vibrator.

5. Install the upper distributor in the same manner, equalizing the tension of the roller between the two vibrators.

6. Install the center distributor from the delivery end of the press. This roller sets between the two vibrator rolls.

7. Turn the press until the cutout (the portion cut away to permit the installation of the center distributor roller from the delivery end of the press) on the center shaft is in a position to allow access.

8. Adjust the bracket by releasing the lock nut (Fig. 10-8D) and turn the bearing holder (Fig. 10-8E) to remove the end play. Do not tighten against the bearings because this adjustment limits movement.

Installing the Plate. The plate cylinder is undercut 0.015 inch below the bearer height. Bearers are the round smooth ends of each cylinder that rotate on each other. These bearers are slightly larger than that part of the cylinder on which the plate is mounted; therefore, each plate requires sufficient amount of underlay or "packing" underneath the plate to raise the plate to the height of the bearers. Before each plate is placed on the press, it must be measured with a micrometer to determine its thickness. Once the thickness is determined, packing sheets are added to bring the plate to the correct bearer height. The combined plate and packing must measure 0.015 inch thick. To install the plate on the press:

1. Insert the lead edge of the plate into the front clampbar (Fig. 10-10) and square it with the cylinder using the knurled adjusting screws at the base of the clamp. Inserting the special T-wrench into the cam at the center of the clamp and pressing it down will close the clamp.

2. Install the required packing between the plate and cylinder to a combined total thickness of .015 inch.

3. Engage the pressure lever to allow the cylinders to go on pressure.

4. Using the inch button, jog the press until the rear clamp is accessible and insert the rear edge of the plate into the clamp bar.

Fig. 10-10. When installing a plate, the knurled adjusting screws (*A*) are backed off and a T-wrench (*B*) is inserted.

5. Back off the knurled adjusting screws (Fig. 10-10A) and insert the T-wrench (Fig. 10-10B) all the way to engage the square hole by turning counterclockwise, the clamp is forced against the cylinder body and cocks the spring.

6. Remove the T-wrench part way and lift the clamp locking cam thus closing the clamp against the plate.

7. Insert the T-wrench again into the square hole and turn it clockwise to release the spring tension thus pulling the plate tight against the cylinder.

If the plate requires additional tightening, the knurled screws that were previously backed off are turned in the opposite direction with a pin wrench (Fig. 10-11A).

Installing the Blanket. Before the blanket can be placed on the press, it must be mounted in the blanket clamp bars. To install the blanket, proceed as follows:

1. Remove the screws from the bars and disassemble.

2. Position the larger section of each bar at the ends of the reverse side of the blanket.

3. Measure the diagonal distance to the outer screw holes. When the distances on both sides between these are equal, the bars will be square on the blanket.

4. Mark each screw hole with a pencil then punch out these holes with the blanket punch furnished with the press.

5. Assemble the bars on the blanket and tighten the screws from the center to the outside.

CAUTION: Make sure the stretch direction is around the cylinder as indicated by the blanket manufacturer.

Fig. 10-11. A pin wrench is used to turn the knurled screws (*A*) when the plate needs additional tightening.

Just as the plate cylinder is undercut, necessitating the packing of the plate, so is the blanket cylinder undercut, necessitating the packing of the blanket.

The blanket cylinder is undercut .075 inch below the bearer height. Most blankets are from .062 inch to .065 inch in thickness; packing sheets must be added to bring the blanket to .002 to .003 inch *above,* the bearer height. The combined blanket and packing will measure .077 to .078 inch. The .002 to .003 inch over the bearer height is the impression or printing pressure necessary to obtain the proper image transfers from the plate to the blanket.

6. Install the front edge of the blanket in the slot in the cylinder and secure the screws, Fig. 10-12A. Insert the front edge of the packing between the blanket and cylinder, Fig. 10-12B.

7. Hold the free end of the blanket and turn the press by hand until the reel rod in the cylinder is accessible. The rod on which the blanket is wrapped and which takes up the tension of the blanket by means of a ratchet at the end is the reel rod.

8. Check the packing so that it is not displaced or wrinkled and insert the blanket in the reel rod slot and secure the holding screws.

9. Tighten the blanket with the wrench provided. The ratchet at the end of the reel rod holds the blanket in place.

Feeder Adjustments. To set the feeder, proceed as follows:

1. Fold a sheet of paper stock to be run in half by hand. Place the fold of the sheet in the center of the feed board, thereby center-

Fig. 10-12. To install the blanket, the front edge of the blanket is placed in the cylinder slot and the screws (*A*) are tightened. The packing (*B*) is inserted between the blanket and the cylinder.

Fig. 10-13. Feeder adjustment points are shown here.

Fig. 10-14. After the front corner angle guides (*A* in Fig. 10-13) are properly adjusted, the stock is loaded on the feeder board.

ing the sheet on the press. Use this as a guide to place the rest of the stock on the feedboard.

2. Adjust the front corner angle guides (Fig. 10-13A) to sheet width locating ⅛ to ¼ inch off center toward the side guide being used and load stock in the feeder (Fig. 10-14).

3. Adjust the rear corner brackets (Fig. 10-13B) to contact the edges of the pile.

4. Set the rear pile hold-down (Fig. 10-15A) to hold the rear edge of the sheet to the pile. The counter balance weight will require changing for different stock thicknesses. It should hold stock against the air blast from the blower tubes, but not tightly enough to restrain the vacuum wheel action.

5. Turn on the air motor and adjust the perforated blower tubes (Fig. 10-13C) to separate the top 4 to 6 sheets of paper. These tubes should be positioned near the ends of the air spreader plate, and the air directed out to the corners to keep the sheets separated.

6. Position the air blast tubes (Fig. 10-13D) near the center to blow air toward the air spreader plate on each side of the vacuum wheel. Sufficient air should be used to lift the rear edge of the top sheet slightly from the pile.

7. The air controls (Fig. 10-16A), the perforated blow tubes for the air blast tube valve, the valve (Fig. 10-16B) which controls the

Fig. 10-15. Feeder adjustment points on the rear pile are shown here.

Fig. 10-16. The controls for the air and vacuum system are shown here.

amount of vacuum to the vacuum wheel, and the handle (Fig. 10-16C) that changes the angle of the perforated blow tubes to facilitate their adjustment to the pile are shown in Fig. 10-16.

Depress the handle (Fig. 10-16D) against the spring to disengage the clutch of the automatic pile-elevating mechanism and raise the pile manually to within 1 inch of the spreader plate.

8. Run press to allow the pile to raise automatically, adjusting the pile governor screw (Fig. 10-15B) to stop the pile approximately ¾ inch below the spreader plate (Fig. 10-15C).

9. Adjust the pull-in wheels (Fig. 10-15D) to give a light, even tension to the tape roller. Unequal tension will cause the sheets to feed crookedly. The pull-in wheel shaft (Fig. 10-16D) can be raised to remove sheets from the choke or tape table. (The choke is the micrometer adjustment that prevents more than one sheet from entering the tape table at a time. The tape table is the area of the press on which the sheet of paper is transferred by tapes from the feed board to the point where the paper enters the cylinders for printing.) When the press is idle for any length of time, the pull-in wheels should be raised to prevent flat spots from forming on the rubber tires.

10. Adjust the two-sheet choke (Fig. 10-17A) to stop two sheets

Fig. 10-17. The two-sheet choke (*A*) should be adjusted to prevent two sheets from entering the Feed table. Two knurled knobs (*B*) are used for this adjustment. The vacuum wheel is shown at *C*.

Fig. 10-18. The adjustment points on the feeding system are shown here.

from entering the feed table. The knurled adjusting knob (Fig. 10-17B) is used to make this adjustment.

11. Release the tension of the tape tightener wheel beneath the feed table and position the two center tapes on the tape table approximately ¼ inch from the inside edges of the center tape rollers. The outer tapes can be set to accommodate various sheet sizes. These outer tapes should be set approximately 1 inch from both edges of the sheet.

12. Position the trimming rails (Fig. 10-18A) so that the hold-down wheels (wheels that rotate on the tapes and hold the sheets

down as they pass under the wheels) are centered on the tapes. These should be kept parallel to the tapes and held in place with the set collars to prevent crooked feed sheets.

13. Place the wooden hold-down wheels (Fig. 10-18B) as close to the front edge of the tape table as possible and adjust the spring tension to hold the sheet flat, but also high enough to allow the sheet to be sideguided without buckling.

14. Position the rubber tired hold-down driving wheels (Fig. 10-18C) on the center trimming rails and approximately ¼ inch away from the rear edge of the sheet. These wheels should have sufficient tension to maintain constant sheet travel.

15. Position the flat brushes (Fig. 10-18D) to lay against the rear edge of the sheet to prevent the sheet from bouncing away from the front guides. There are short and long hold-downs on the register plate. Check to be sure that they lay flat against the register plate when left loose and yet do not interfere with the grippers as they close. These hold-downs should be set to .010 inch above the stock thickness being run.

16. Position two of the longer sheet hold-downs at each side of the pendulum (the rod across the tape table on which the sheet hold-downs are mounted) and two alongside each of the front guides. Place two of the shorter hold-downs at the edges of the sheet and the remaining two between the pendulum and front guides.

Make sure all set screws are secured before running the press and make a final check for interference to the grippers and sheet flattening bar before running.

Press Adjustments. To time the feeder to the press:

1. Turn on the vacuum and air, and jog a sheet down the tape table until the front guides are *just* down. Stop and do not reverse the press at this exact point. The sheets should be ½ inch away from the guides at this point. If not, the feeder must be retimed to the press. To retime:

2. Release the Allen lock screw holding the chain sprocket at the extreme gear side of the vacuum wheel shaft, and reposition the vacuum wheel (Fig. 10-17C) in the amount and direction indicated by the sheet position.

Fig. 10-19. The feeder timing system is used to adjust the sheet
feed to the press.

3. Retighten the sprocket and recheck by running sheets.
Repeat the operation if required.

Two push-type side-guides (Fig. 10-19A) allow guiding from
either side of the sheet of the press. The direction of the side-guide
movement is determined by the linkage at the feed side of the tape
table (Fig. 10-19B). To change the side-guide direction, pull the
knurled pin (Fig. 10-19C) and release the snap lock (Fig. 10-19D)
at the other end of the arm, then lift out the linkage arm. The
bracket (Fig. 10-19E) that this arm fits into has two holes. The left
hand hole operates the left hand side-guide and the right hand
hole operates the right hand side-guide. After determining which
side of the sheet is to be guided, set the linkage accordingly then
jog a sheet down to the front guides. Turn the press by hand until
the grippers are nearly closed. At this point the side-guide bar will
be compressed against its stop pin located in the side frame at the
end of the bar. The side-guide should push the sheet ⅛ to ³⁄₁₆ inch.
Move the sheet sideways this amount and install the side guide on

the bar so that it is square to the sheet and the gripper edge of the sheet flush against the front guides.

The sheet flattening bar (Fig. 10-19F) steadies the sheet and prevents buckles from being formed as the sheet is side-guided. To adjust:

1. Jog the sheet down the table until the bar reaches the down position.

2. Loosen the adjusting screw (Fig. 10-19G) against the edge of the register plate and set the bar so that it just contacts the sheet.

3. Lock the Allen set screw.

The sheet detector is positioned so that the sheet will contact the pendulum approximately $\frac{3}{32}$ inch ahead of the front guides. The detector and all parts connected with it are factory timed and should not require adjustment except occasionally to remove the pendulum spring and clean out any accumulated lint or spray powder.

The front guides (Fig. 10-20A) are located over guide tongues in the register plate. When running the maximum sheet size, they are normally located over the two outer tongues. They must be repositioned to the inner set when running a minimum sized sheet. The guides are also adjustable to allow slight changes in the gripper margin or to change the position of the work on the sheet. The adjusting screw (Fig. 10-20B) turns clockwise to give less gripper

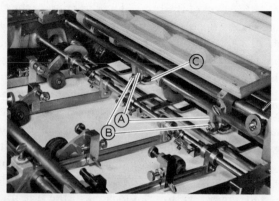

Fig. 10-20. The front guides (*A*) are normally positioned over two outer tongues. The adjusting screw (*B*) is used to relocate gripper margin. The flat spring sheet guide can be adjusted to prevent curl in the sheets being fed.

margin and counterclockwise to give more gripper margin. The guides should be centered by their adjustment or trip, otherwise transfer difficulty will arise. When the guides are centered, the sheet should be flush with the edge of the gripper pads as the grippers close on the sheet.

If the sheet has a tendency to curl beneath the guide, adjust the flat spring sheet guide, located at the bottom of each front guide shoe (the bottom part of the front guide, Fig. 10-20C) to .010 inch above the thickness of the stock being run. A knurled adjusting screw above the guide shoe is used for this adjustment.

The timing of the front guides to the impression cylinder grippers is very important to obtain good register. As the grippers close on the sheet and take it through the cylinders, the front guides should rise at the same time. If the timing is set too short, the sheet will become free and move forward causing misregister. To adjust:

1. Jog the press until the front guide cam roller (Fig. 10-21A) is in the "low" dwell or the indention of the cam (Fig. 10-21B).

2. Turn the press by hand until the cam follower is about 1½ inches from the rise of the cam. An .008-inch clearance should be between the cam follower and cam dwell at this point. If not, release the lock nut and raise or lower the stop screw (Fig. 10-21C) as necessary.

3. Place a sheet at the front guides, releasing the pendulum and slowly turn the press until the grippers lightly close on the sheet.

4. Release the cap screws (Fig. 10-21D) and rotate the cam in the direction of the cylinder travel until the cam contacts the cam roll without lifting the front guides and lock in position.

As the front guides start to lift, they should clear the leading edge of the sheet just fast enough to prevent nicking. When this setting is correct, a pile of sheets in the delivery will show a polished or smooth impression of front guides, even though a single sheet will not show a nicked or marked spot. When heavy stock is to be run, it will be necessary to retime the cam to open sooner.

Impression cylinder grippers that are mis-shaped or have unequal tension may cause misregister or tearing at the transfer to the delivery grippers. This adjustment is, therefore, also important. If adjustment is necessary, proceed as follows:

Fig. 10-21. Proper timing of the front guides to the impression cylinder grippers is necessary to obtain correct register. Adjustment points for timing are shown here.

1. Turn the press until the grippers are closed at the register plate.

2. Mark each gripper location on the gripper pad with a pencil or a dab of ink. This is done to check for equal length and for replacing to original position when necessary.

3. Release the set screws which hold the grippers to the shaft. The gripper shaft is located at the feed-side end of the impression cylinder and inside the gap.

4. Turn the press carefully until a light drag on a .005 inch feeder gage is obtained between the stop lever on the gripper shaft and pin.

5. While in this position, set the grippers to a light even tension with a .002 inch strip of tissue paper.

6. Re-check to make sure that constant tension is kept on the .005-inch feeler gage with the top pin while setting the grippers.

Three delivery gripper bars, consisting of individual spring

Fig. 10-22. The working parts of the delivery system are shown here.

grippers and a master torsion spring, are provided on this press. Periodic cleaning with a solvent and brush to eliminate paper lint and stray dust is recommended. To adjust if necessary:

1. Jog the press until the delivery gripper bar is accessible and remove the screen guard. A master gripper (Fig. 10-22A) which is permanently fashioned to each delivery bar is not to be loosened at any time. Factory set, this gripper controls the height of the cam roller that opens and closes the other grippers.

2. Loosen the cap screws (Fig. 10-22B) holding the individual spring grippers (Fig. 10-22C).

3. Insert a .015 inch feeler gage between the master gripper finger and the contact pad bar (Fig. 10-22D).

4. Set the individual spring grippers to a light even tension using a .002 or .003 inch strip of paper. To check, replace the .015 inch feeler gage with a .020 inch. A strip pulled between the grippers should not be free.

Sufficient tension on the master torsion spring must be maintained to hold the master gripper in contact with the contact pad bar. Do not at any time compress this spring. The procedure just stated should be used until all the gripper bars have been adjusted.

The delivery releasing cam (Fig. 10-22E) controls the time the sheet is released to the pile delivery. An adjustment may be necessary to advance or retard the sheet for various sizes and thicknesses of paper stock. Releasing a cap screw allows the cam to be moved in its slot.

The delivery pile joggers are set to accommodate the sheet size being run. Place a small lift of sheets on the delivery board and jog the press until the side joggers are all the way in. Loosen the thumb screws and place the jogger plates just against the edges of the stock. The rear jogger is operated by the knob at the feed-side opening of the press and is placed against the sheets between the delivery end-gates and the rear jogger plates.

CAUTION: The following are cam operated and are factory set. *Under no conditions are they to be re-adjusted.*

1. The sheet-flattening bar: This is timed to contact the sheet as the side guide pushes and to raise the grippers as they take the sheet.

2. The sheet detector.

3. The master gripper on each gripper bar.

4. The "taking" cam which opens and closes the delivery grippers during the transfer of the sheet to the delivery gripper bars.

Press Maintenance. A chart attached to the vacuum and blower pumps states the recommended oil to use for lubricating. A plate on the press also shows the specifications of all the various types of lubricants used throughout the press.

All moving parts (including springs, spring rods, and others) that do not have oil holes must also be lubricated. *All fast-moving parts should be oiled every 8 hours.* Upon installation, gears are cleaned and lubricated. Paper lint, dust, or spray powder, and old grease should be removed and the gears re-lubricated every one million impressions. Bearings in the ink rollers should be lubricated at the same interval.

The air and vacuum gas pump is used to create the air to separate the top few sheets of paper on the feedboard, permitting one sheet to be picked up and moved forward to the tape table. This pump should not be taken apart to be cleaned. Only an experienced serviceman should clean or replace any parts. Definite assembly and disassembly procedures must be followed or permanent damage may result. Protection from dirt and moisture, proper lubrication and flushing procedures will provide trouble free service.

The pump oiler should be filled every 25 to 50 hours of running time with #105SAE or equivalent pure mineral oil without additives. At the same time add 10 to 20 drops to the bearing oilers. When oiling, check the oil wick and air vent. The pump should be flushed every six weeks or 250 hours of running time. To flush:

1. Remove inlet and outlet accessories and lines.

2. Use a non-inflammable solvent such as DuPont's Perchlorethylene and allow about 1 ounce to be drawn through the unit while running. Feed this in slowly.

3. Clean the felt filters in the same solvent and blow out the lines before reconnecting. Do not allow metal chips or dirt into the filter.

If the air pump is slow in starting, or if the vacuum or pressure builds up too slowly:

4. Examine all connections and lines for leaks.

5. Check for dirty or plugged lines by placing a gage at the pump to note a drop of vacuum or pressure through the line.

6. An excess or lack of oil may cause vanes to be stuck in the rotor shafts.

If flushing does not help, foreign matter obstructing the vanes may be the trouble; in this case, only an experienced mechanic should be permitted to clean or replace the vanes.

SPECIFICATIONS TO BE REMEMBERED
HARRIS OFFSET PRESS

Paper size:	Maximum size 14½″ × 20½″
	Minimum size 8″ × 10″
	Normal size 14″ × 20″
	Maximum thickness .020″
Image size	Maximum size 14⅛″ × 20″
	Normal 13⅝″ × 19½″
Plate size	16⅜″ × 20½″
Blanket size	21″ × 20½″ across
Speed	Maximum 7000 impressions per hour
	Normal 6000 impressions per hour

Ink distribution	Covered form rollers 2—1¾″, 1, 1—⅞″
	Covered distributor rollers 3—2″ dia.
	Vibrating rollers 4—2.666″
	Covered duct rollers 1—1¾″
Water distribution	Covered dampening rollers 2—2⅛″
	Covered duct roller 1—2″
	Vibrating roller 1—2¼″
	Water pan roller 1—2½″
Power requires	Drive Motor 1½ HP
	Feeder Motor ¾ HP

Review Questions

Instructions:

1. Do not write in the book, but on the test sheets provided.
2. Questions are in several forms: multiple choice, true or false, one or a few words, or matching.
3. Place "T" in the space provided if the statement is true; "F" if it is false.
4. Select from the list of statements or words the most correct answer.
5. Use one or a few words in the one-word answers.
6. In the matching questions, select the correct letter of the alphabet.

Harris Offset Press

    a. 14¼ × 20½   c. 14½ × 20½
    b. 14½ × 20¼   d. 14¼ × 20¼

2. Minimum sheet size is:

    a. 8 × 10   c. 8 × 12
    b. 8 × 11   d. 9 × 10

3. The maximum speed is:

    a. 6000   c. 8000
    b. 7000   d. 7500

4. There are ten rollers in the inking unit. True or False?
5. There are five rollers in the dampening unit. True or False?
6. The Harris has ten different speeds. True or False?
7. No adjustment is necessary between the water ductor and the aluminum vibrator roll. True or False?
8. Sufficient air should be used to lift the side edge of the top sheet slightly from the pile. True or False?
9. Different thicknesses of paper stock require the changing of the counter balance weight. True or False?
10. Unequal tension on the pull-in wheels will cause sheets to feed crookedly. True or False?

CHAPTER 11

Printing Paper

How many kinds of printing paper are there? How does one differentiate among them? From what is printing paper made? What processing is needed to make papers? Is offset paper different from letterpress paper? What does paper "grain" mean? In what sizes is paper made? What is meant by the "basic weight" of paper? What are the "standard sizes" of paper?

Thousands of varieties of printing paper are available for the several printing products, such as letterheads, books, newspapers, office forms, booklets, covers, and the like. Printing paper is differentiated from "coarse" or industrial paper; that is, bags, wrapping paper, tissues, and cartons. Printers are not generally concerned with the latter type. Paper is usually made from wood pulp or cotton. Several ingredients are added to the pulp in manufacture. Paper for offset often differs from letterpress paper, because offset is a chemical process, and letterpress is mechanical. Paper has "grain," similar to that found in a piece of wood, and this grain must be considered in printing. The "basic weight" of paper refers to the thickness of the paper, and paper is made in hundreds of standard sizes to suit the needs of printers and the processes they use. This chapter is concerned with printing paper, and it behooves the student of offset printing to know about paper.

Raw Material Used for Paper

Raw material used for paper is cellulose fiber. A microscope shows it to be infinitesimal, hollow, and long. Spruce and hemlock trees are the largest sources of cellulose for the paper making industry, but other fiber sources include hardwoods, flax, cotton, new cotton-cloth clipping from mills, and various plants.

The finer, longer-lasting paper, made from cotton and cloth clippings, is called "rag content," or lately, "cotton content" paper. A page of the Baskerville Bible printed in 1769 is 100 percent rag content, and it is probably as white and as strong now as it was when it was first printed. Rag content is usually 25 percent, 50 percent, 75 percent, or 100 percent.

Recent developments in paper manufacture reveal permanence factors in paper other than rag content. The usual paper ranges from 4 to 5 pH value. A neutral pH value (7.2) of cellulose fiber tends toward permanence, whatever the source of ingredients.

Pulp for Paper. Paper is usually made from wood chips either mechanically ground or cooked with chemicals in a digester to separate the fibers (Figs. 11-1 and 11-2). The fibers are further refined in beaters. (See Fig. 11-3).

Fillers. Most paper contains a filler to fill voids (spaces) between cellulose fibers and give better opacity and printability. The commonly used fillers are China clay, calcium carbonate, and titanium dioxide.

The Papermaking Machine

Pulp is fed to the "wet" end of the papermaking machine, about 99 percent water to one percent cellulose fiber. The pulp flows on a moving copper screen. This screen agitates the pulp to draw away the water, to "felt" the fibers, and to form the paper "grain" (Fig. 11-4). A rubber belt (deckle strap) travels with the wire screen on each side when text papers are made. Pulp is squeezed under the deckle strap and produces, after the paper has left the screen, a ragged edge, which is referred to as a "deckle edge." Most paper is, of course, trimmed on the paper machine.

The paper leaves the screen and is carried by felt blankets to steam heated rollers which turn the fibers into a continuous sheet of paper. Alternate steel and fiber rollers called a "calender stack" further finish and dry the paper (Fig. 11-5), which is wound on rolls. The paper is sheeted later from the roll, and then trimmed to desired sizes on larger paper cutters (Fig. 11-6).

Fig. 11-1. A continuous pulp digester at Hammermill Paper Company.

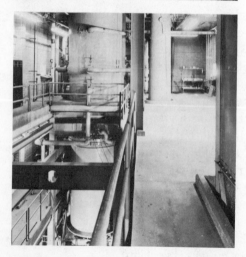

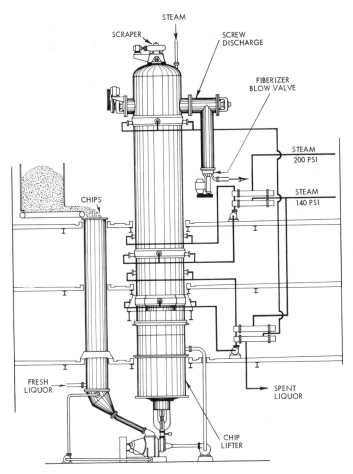

STEAM

SCRAPER

SCREW
DISCHARGE

FIBERIZER
BLOW VALVE

STEAM
200 PSI

CHIPS

STEAM
140 PSI

FRESH
LIQUOR

SPENT
LIQUOR

CHIP
LIFTER

Fig. 11-2. A diagrammatic view of a continuous pulp digester. The digester is used to cook wood chips and chemicals to produce the separate pulp fibers from which paper is made.

Watermarks. Watermarking is done on writing, bond, ledger, and some booktext papers. Watermarked paper is passed under a "dandy roll' while it is still pulp to impress the brand name of the paper into the fibers. The design on the dandy roll is usually made of thin wire which makes the paper thinner at these parts. Watermarks can be seen when holding paper to the light. The offset

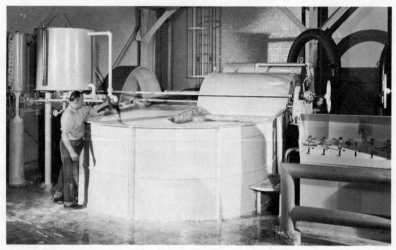

Fig. 11-3. A paper pulp beater prepares the raw material for the papermaking machine.

pressman should print jobs so the watermark can be read the same as the printing, as on a letterhead.

Classification of Paper

Classes of Papers. Paper can be divided into two classes: "fine" paper (also called "writing" and printing paper); and "coarse" or industrial paper. "Coarse" paper includes wrapping, corrugated board, wax, building paper, facial tissues, and the like.

Kinds of Paper for Printing. Generally, offset paper can be printed letterpress, but the offset printer cannot always print well on paper made expressly for the letterpress printer.

Paper for letterpress requires smoothness, compressibility, and bonding strength (necessary to avoid the ink "picking," or removing particles from the paper), and mineral filler.

Offset-coated papers require that coating must not be weakened by the moistening rollers, and must be free of all foreign particles, as slitter dust and coating flakes. Coatings are generally water-resistant caseins, latex, and vegetable proteins.

Fig. 11-4. The wet end of a papermaking machine takes the pulp and forms it into rough paper.

Fig. 11-5. The dry end of a papermaking machine takes the pulp, dries it and forms it into finished rolls.

Fig. 11-6. A 100-inch paper cutter used at the P. H. Glatfelter paper mill at Spring Grove, Pennsylvania is shown here. After the paper is cut, on a machine like this, it is sheeted.

Inaccurate paper trimming (out-of-square) can cause misregister and jamming on presses. Wavy paper edges and curl also cause trouble.

Scumming on offset presses may be caused by piling. Mineral fibers are picked up from the surface of the paper and form an abrasive layer on the press blanket, which wears away the desensitized film.

Coated and Enameled Papers. Paper is coated to provide better printability, particularly for letterpress halftones of fine screen. Coating ingredients include casein, clay, and calcium carbonate. Coating may be applied by rollers, or it may be flowed on. In the latter process, the excess is removed by "air knives," by a "furnish roll" and smoothing bar, with a doctor blade, or by polished drums.

Classification of Paper Stock. A partial classification of paper for printing is shown in the following table.

PRINTING PAPERS

Name	Property	Use
Antique book	Bulky, rough	Books, programs, advertising
Blanks	Thick, smooth finish	Signs, etc.
Bond	Rough, no glare, takes writing ink	Stationery, office forms
Coated book	Smooth, shiny, or "dull" coated	Halftone printing
Cover	Strong, easy folding	Announcements, booklets, catalogs, pamphlet covers
English finish	No glare, slightly roughened finish	Catalogs, booklets, magazines
Gummed	Gummed one side	Stickers, labels
Index Bristol	Writable qualities, thick	Filing cards, records
Ledger	Takes writing ink, strong	Blank books, office forms
Manifold	Thin, strong	Duplicate copies, sales books, etc.
Mimeograph	Roughened surface	Use in duplicating machines
Newsprint	Rough, quick drying of ink	Newspaper, handbills, posters
Offset Book	Not shiny	Advertising, books, booklets, posters
Onionskin	Thin almost to transparency	Typewritten carbon copies, wrappers
Supercalendered book	Smooth	Magazines and booklets
Tagboard	Tough, strong	Tags, etc.

Basic Weights of Paper. Paper is measured for thickness according to weight. Thicker (cardboard) is measured in "points," which mean thousandths of an inch. Paper is referred to as "20-pound bond," "70-pound coated book," "110-pound index bristol," etc. Each kind of paper has a "basic size:"

Bond	17 × 22 inches
Book	25 × 38 inches
Cover	20 × 26 inches
Index Bristol	25½ × 30½ inches

When we say that a particular paper is "20-pound bond," it means that 500 sheets (a ream) of size 17 × 22 weighs 20 pounds. If it is 24-pound bond, then 500 sheets 17 × 22 weighs 24 pounds, etc. However, 20-pound bond can be purchased in other sizes, such as 22 × 34 inches. It is still 20-pound bond, but the 500 sheets weigh twice as much, because the sheet size is twice as large.

Any paper size is usually available—provided over 5,000 pounds of book paper or 2,000 pounds of most other kinds is purchased. When a special color or special weight is wanted, the minimum order is 5,000 pounds.

Bleaching. Seven stages of bleaching are often required to secure the whiteness required for printing paper. The colored matter may be made soluble and washed out, or may be made colorless. Impurities are washed out in the process.

Figuring Paper Cutting

In cutting paper, it is necessary to figure how many pieces of the required size can be cut from the large sheets of standard size. For instance, stock for 1,000 letterheads, size 8½ × 11 inches, is needed. The standard size is 17 by 22 inches. The numbers of the large sheets needed to produce 1,000 letterheads is computed as follows:

$$\frac{\begin{array}{cc}2 & \times\ 2\end{array}}{\underset{8^{1\!/_{2}} \times\ \cancel{11}}{\cancel{17}\ \ \times\ \cancel{22}}} = 4 \text{ pieces, size } 8^{1\!/_{2}} \times 11,$$

can be cut from one sheet 17 × 22 inches. Figuring the number of sheets needed;

1000 divided by 4 equals 250 sheets of 17 × 22 inches

are needed to make 1000 pieces of 8½ × 11 inches.

Another example: 2,000 pieces 6 × 9 inches are needed. The stock size is 25 × 38 inches. Fractions are not considered, as they will not make a sheet that can be used:

$$\frac{\begin{array}{cc}4 & \times\ 4\end{array}}{\underset{\cancel{6} \times\ \cancel{9}}{\cancel{25} \times\ \cancel{38}}} = 16 \text{ pieces, size } 6 \times 9 \text{ inches,}$$

can be cut from a sheet 25 × 38 inches, with waste pieces.

Testing for Grain. If the grain of a paper stock is not known, cut off a square piece and bend it in one hand between the fingers and thumb, both ways—the short and the long way of the large sheet. It folds more easily with the grain than against it. There is no set rule on how the grain of a stock will run; it depends on how the paper is cut at the mill. Another test is by tearing the sheet, which tears easily with the grain, and harder against it. Another way is to wet both sides of a piece torn from the sheet—the curl made as the paper dries will be with the grain.

The grain of a paper works best if it runs across the cylinder of a press, except sheets offset printed on small presses, when the grain should be "long" to prevent curling of sheets on delivery.

In printing index cards that are to be used in a typewriter, the grain should run along the platen of the typewriter.

Humidity

The curling, shrinking, and stretching of paper causes trouble on printing presses. These changes in paper are due to its construction and to changes in relative humidity.

If the stock curls around the felt side, the humidity is high; if it curls around the wire side, the humidity is low. Paper stocks of all kinds are usually made at humidity of 45 to 50 percent. A change from this may cause register trouble in color printing.

Paper should be seasoned for at least forty-eight hours in the pressroom where it is to be printed, so that it can become acclimated to the atmosphere of the pressroom.

Excess moisture in the paper contributes to drying difficulties. Paper should have from five to six percent moisture content for good printing by offset.

Gravure papers are usually mineral-filled, supercalendered book of a high-groundwood content.

Bonds, ledgers, index bristols, antique books, and cover papers are usually printed and run on both letterpress and offset. However, sometimes a bond paper will run well by letterpress, but allow lint to collect on offset press blankets and rollers. The printer should tell the paper dealer what process will be used when paper is purchased.

Paper Questions

1. The raw material used in making paper is _____ .
2. The more permanent papers have _____ content.
3. Most paper is made from _____ .
4. The machine used to separate pulp fibers is called a _____ .
5. The material used to fill voids in paper pulp is _____ .
6. Paper pulp becomes paper by being carried on a _____ .
7. Finishes are placed on paper by _____ rolls.

8. Paper pulp is ———————— to secure whiteness.

9. Watermarks are placed on paper by a ————————.

Four ways by which paper is coated are:

10. ————————————————

11. ————————————————

12. ————————————————

13. ————————————————

Paper is divided into two classes:

14. ————————————————

15. ————————————————

Name two characteristics of paper needed by the offset printer:

16. ————————————————

17. ————————————————

Match the type of paper listed on the left with the use listed on the right:

18. Bond ——   a. Announcements
19. Index Bristol ——   b. Filing cards
20. Ledger ——   c. Letterheads
21. English Finish —— d. Blank books
22. Manifold ——   e. Books
23. Newsprint ——   f. Newspapers
24. Magazines ——   g. Duplicate copies
                       h. Supercalendered

Match the kind of paper on the left with its basic size on the right:

25. Bond ——   a. 25 × 38 inches
26. Book ——   b. 20 × 26

27. Cover ____   c. 17 × 22
28. Index Bristol ____   d. 25½ × 30½

29. A ream of 20 pound bond in its basic size weighs _____ pounds.
30. A ream of 20 pound bond in size 22 × 34 weighs _____ pounds.
31. How many pieces 8½ × 11 can be cut from a sheet 22 × 24? _____
32. How many pieces 6 × 9 can be cut from a sheet 25 × 38? _____
33. Figure the cost of paper for a job of 30,000 with 4% allowance for spoilage, 8½ × 13, to be cut from sheet size 17 × 28. Cost of paper is $9.66 per 1,000 sheets.
34. How much will 253 sheets 17 × 22—20 cost at 42¢ per pound? _____
35. How much will 850 sheets 38 × 50—80 cost at $12.00 per cwt? _____
36. Paper folds more easily against the grain than with it. T or F?
37. There is no set rule how paper grain runs. T or F?
38. The curl created when a small sheet of paper dries is in the direction of the grain. T or F?

CHAPTER 12

Bindery Procedures

Bindery operations usually follow presswork; it is the final process-
ing of a job of printing. How is paper folded? Scored? Perforated?
Round cornered? Die cut? Embossed? Stamped through foil? Stitched?
Bound? Six different ways exist for binding booklets and books. How
and why is paper cut before printing and after printing? What is
"paper ruling?" What is the difference between paper drilling and
paper punching?

The folding and trimming of paper often completes a job of printing. A book, for example, may be printed 2, 4, 6, 8, 12, 16, 32, 64
or perhaps even 128 pages at one time on a large sheet of paper,
and then folded into "signatures," or sections of a book, which are
then gathered, trimmed, and otherwise finished. Scoring is used
to make heavy cover paper behave correctly in folding. At least
six different methods can be used in "binding" a book. Paper may
be cut to size prior to printing a booklet or book, and perhaps even
an office form, and then may be trimmed on three or four sides.
The various processes—paper ruling, drilling, cutting, folding,
scoring, perforating, stitching and other bindery operations are
explained on the following pages. The student of offset printing
should be well acquainted with these processes and methods.

How Sheets of Paper are Fastened

When we have printed matter larger than four pages (which is just
a single piece of paper folded in the middle to make four leaves)

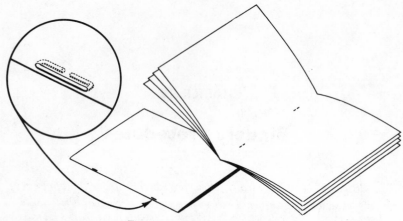

Fig. 12-1. Saddle-wire binding.

we must use some method for fastening the various sections or signatures of the book together. This is called pamphlet binding. Binding methods are saddle wire, side wire, loose leaf, soft-cover sewn, case-bound, adhesive (also referred to as "perfect") and mechanically bound.

Saddle-Wire Binding. For a few pages, and often for many when the pages are made of thin paper, the saddle-wire type of binding is used (Fig. 12-1). This can be done with a simple hand stapler, although in big printing houses this binding is done automatically on great, long machines that gather the folded sheets and carry them along a conveyor which has a stapling unit at the end. Saddle-wired books lie flat when open, and may be folded upon themselves. The inside or gutter margins close to the fold may be small. This is desirable in some cases.

Side-Wire Bindings (Fig. 12-2). This method of fastening sheets together is so called because the sheets are stapled through at the left side. Big catalogs and magazines are often bound this way. Sometimes a cover is glued on the book after it is stapled. Odd-sized pages may be included, and usually such books are made up of single sheets that were printed at different times. One difficulty with a book bound in this way is that it will not readily stay open, and therefore is difficult to hold when reading. In this type of binding the binding edge needs to be wide.

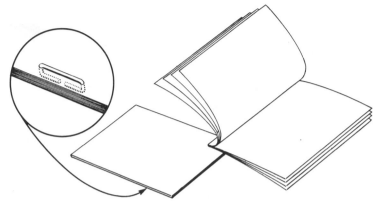

Fig. 12-2. Side-wire binding.

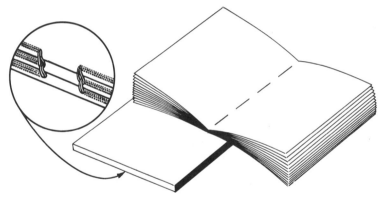

Fig. 12-3. Sewn soft-cover binding.

Sewn Soft-Cover (Fig. 12-3). Perhaps you have in your collection of books some with soft paper or leather covers that are sewn, not wired together. These books are usually machine-sewn, but they may be hand-sewn, too. They lie open, so they are easy to hold to read. The gutter margin does not need to be very large.

Sewn Case-Bound (Fig. 12-4). This is the binding you are already familiar with, because most school books are so bound—in hard cardboard covers. The signatures are sewn, and the book is rounded at the back, which makes a concave part as you turn the pages. These books are bound in this way so that they will last a long time.

Loose Leaf Bindings (Fig. 12-5). We are all familiar with the

Fig. 12-4. Sewn case-bound binding.

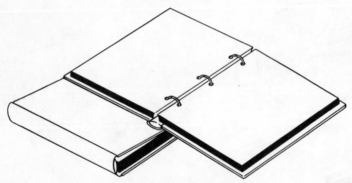

Fig. 12-5. Loose leaf binding.

loose leaf bindings used in school. Some of them have two or more rings, which open like traps and hold the sheets in place. All the bookbinder does here is to punch holes where needed to fit the binding rings. Nowadays sheets for this kind of binding are drilled, perhaps as many as 500 at a time. The drill has a hollow bit.

Mechanical Bindings. This is the very latest method of fastening book, catalog, and program pages together. Sheets of any odd size can be mechanically-bound by using a "wriggle" wire called spiral or by using a piece of plastic cut and bent into a cylindrical form, with tongues to hold the sheets. The spiral bindings can be folded over on themselves but the plastic bindings cannot. (Fig.

Fig. 12-6. Binding post type of loose-leaf binding.

Fig. 12-7. Spiral binding.

Fig. 12-8. Plastic binding.

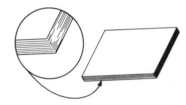

Fig. 12-9. Adhesive "perfect" binding.

12-7.) The plastic bindings are more sturdy, being stiffer than the spiral. Many styles are manufactured. (Fig. 12-8.)

Adhesive binding. Often called "perfect" binding, it can be seen on thick telephone books, a few magazines such as *The Reader's Digest,* thick mail order catalogs, and so-called "pocket books." (Fig. 12-9.) No sewing or stitching is used. First, the folds on the binding edge of the book are cut off, and a milling disk roughens the back. Lint is removed and rollers apply a special adhesive to the back while the pages are compressed. The books advance on the automatic machine to a covering station where the cover is attached (Fig. 12-10). Adhesive bound books lie flat when open despite their thickness, and are less expensive to bind than if sewn. Thick books can be bound by this method when they are too thick to be side wired.

Fig. 12-10. Books being delivered from a Dexter "Perfect" binding machine.

Folding Paper

Paper is usually folded on "buckle-type" machines. Sheets are carried along from automatic feeders, and steel rollers force the sheets into a plate (pocket), which is adjustable to the length of fold. The sheets hit a stop in the plate, "buckle," and are carried between two other rollers which fold the sheets. As many as 64 pages can be folded into signatures, or book sections.

Rotary folders are attached to web presses and fold a 70-inch wide continuous roll at 1600 feet per minute. The end product is a folded signature.

A Mark I Baumfolder (Fig. 12-11), size 20 × 26 inches, can

Fig. 12-11. A Mark I Baumfolder.

Fig. 12-12. A Pitney-Bowes folding
machine.

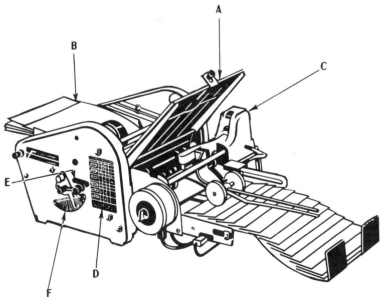

Fig. 12-13. A Flex-o-Fold folding machine.

feed a maximum of 32 inches on parallel folds, may have two, three
or four plates for the parallel section, and two "roll away" sections
to make first and second right angle folds. Scoring, perforating,
slitting, pasting (substituting for saddle wire) and book trimming
may be accomplished when paper is folded.

A Pitney-Bowes folding machine (Fig. 12-12) can handle up to
19,000 sheets per hour. Folds are limited to double-parallel and
11-inch width. Folded sheets may be folded again in the opposite
direction.

Small offset printers find table top folders adequate to their
needs in many instances. The Fairchild Flex-o-Fold (Fig. 12-13)
adjusts at A, holds a half ream of paper at B. Sheets may be
stapled automatically at C, the operator can secure settings at D
for various folds, can change from a single to double fold at E, and
make second fold adjustments at F.

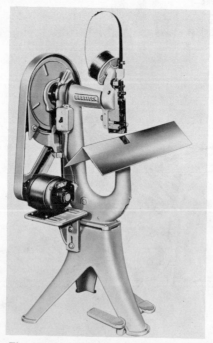

Fig. 12-14. A hand-fed bindery stitcher.

Stapling and Stitching

Stapling is applying made-up staples in the hand-, foot-, and magnetic-powered "automatic" staplers. Stitchers make up their own stitches from coils of wire. Both terms are used loosely. Figure 12-14 illustrates a typical hand-fed power stitcher. Figure 12-15 shows a stitching head (top and left of center) "in-line" with a signature gatherer (right) and three-knife trimmer (left).

Collating and Gathering

Collating refers to gathering single sheets, usually with manual aids. Gathering machines are those automated devices which collect multiple-page book signatures in sets to complete a book. Many different devices are used by printers to automate, or partially automate, the gathering of single sheets or folded sheets. For example, a small, desk-top collator is shown (Fig. 12-16) which will gather sheets from six pockets, size $8\frac{1}{2} \times 11$ inches; A 16-sheet electric collator (Fig. 12-17) which will collate sheet sizes from 4×5 to 17×22 inches. Sheets are thrust forward to be taken by the operator. A rotary type collator (Fig. 12-18) is shown, with 50 stations to hold sheets of one kind in each station. It will collate, count and stagger the delivery of 25,000 sheets per hour. Single

Fig. 12-15. Automatic bindery equipment for gathering, stitching and trimming.

Fig. 12-16. A desk-top collator.

Fig. 12-17. A 16-pocket electric collator.

sheets and multi-page reports from 5 × 8 to 9 × 12 inches can be collated. Automatic stitchers may be added.

Drilling and Punching Holes

Most holes are placed in paper by drilling (Fig. 12-19). The drill bit is hollow and allows the chips to escape to a receptacle. About 500 sheets of 20 pound bond can be drilled at one time. The paper drilling machines have automatic gages which can be preset for accuracy.

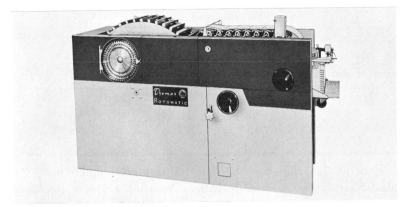

Fig. 12-18. A Thomas rotary collator.

Fig. 12-19. A paper drill.

Fig. 12-20. An electrically-operated punch for plastic binding.

Fig. 12-21. A manually-operated combination slot punching and binding machine for plastic binding.

Punching machines are used for cutting rectangular holes for plastic binding and spiral binding (Fig. 12-20). Other machines are used for placing the punched sheets in the plastic binding (Fig. 12-21). The prongs (top) spread the plastic cylindrical material, allowing the punched sheets and covers to be placed in proper position. Upon release, the binding curls, thus binding the pages.

Jogging Paper

Jogging paper means straightening sheets which have not been delivered in order to be aligned at the edges. It is similar to the operation of "winding," which means handling a lift of paper so air is circulated between each sheet. To jog:

1. Lift about an inch of paper.
2. Lift the far edge of the pile and stand the paper upright.
3. Grip the sides with both hands loosely, then bend the sheets vertically.
4. Grip the sides tightly and straighten the sheets of paper to put air between the sheets.
5. When air is between sheets, thrust inward with both hands.
6. Repeat. Take care to jog a small pile of sheets at a time to prevent breaking or dog-earing individual sheets. Jogging is helped with the use of vibrating table tops known as jogging machines.

Padding

Padding is applying special glue to the straight edges of paper to make scratch pads and to bind office forms in multiple copies.

Padding presses apply the necessary pressure to hold the sheets together when the glue is applied, or a heavy weight (such as a small concrete block), is used. The glue is applied with a brush. Generally, sheets of heavy board are placed between each 100 or so sheets. Individual pads are cut apart when dry with a sharp blade. Cheese cloth is sometimes applied to the glue when it is wet.

Round Cornering

Tickets and cards are often round cornered to prevent the corners from bending. Handbooks are often round cornered on two corners to prevent dog-earing. Round-cornered cards are usually purchased already round cornered, die cut, and absolutely rectangular. Round-cornering machines (Fig. 12-22) range from small hand-operated models to powerful types which will round corner a pile of stock six inches high.

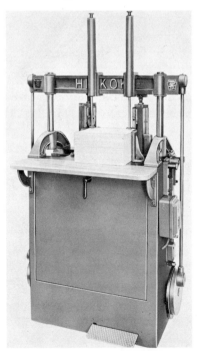

Fig. 12-22. A round-cornering machine.

Perforating

Perforating can be done on letterpress by locking steel perforating rules with the type form. Other devices, actuated by the impression of platen presses, "dry"-perforate (the perforating rule is not inked).

Perforating can be done with small wheels on cylinder letterpress and offset-lithographic printing presses. The perforating wheels cut in the direction the sheet is moving. The perforations are not inked.

Perforating machines allow round-hole perforating, like that found on postage stamps and grocery store stamps. (Fig. 12-23 and Fig. 12-24.) Sheets are automatically fed into the machine which has male and female dies.

Perforating may be done on offset presses through the use of adhesive-backed perforating strips, which can be placed in any direction.

Gold Stamping

Gold or silver stamping requires the use of brass type, or a metal die which carries heat to fuse the foil to the object being stamped. The leaf is usually automatically fed (Fig. 12-25).

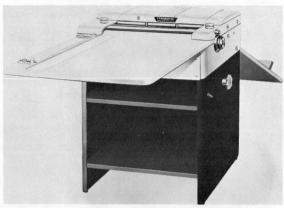

Fig. 12-23. A rotary, hand-fed hole perforator.

Fig. 12-24. A self-feeding rotary perforator.

Fig. 12-25. A hand-operated roll leaf stamping machine.

Cutting Paper

Most paper must be cut to smaller sizes to print jobs, and sometimes is cut after printing. Cutting is done on hand (Fig. 12-26) or power paper cutters (Figs. 12-27 and 12-28) of the guillotine type. A movable gage allows a back gage to be set to measure in the linear system. Automatic electric or hydraulic cutters have sufficient power for bringing down the knife blade and often the clamp. Some are electronically controlled to adjust the back gage to move predetermined distances.

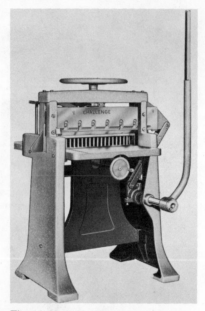

Fig. 12-26. A hand-lever paper cutter.

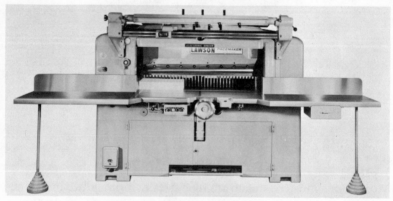

Fig. 12-27. A Lawson automated-spacing power paper cutter.

Three-knife trimmers are paper cutters that trim three sides of a stack of books (Fig. 12-29). Two knives cut at one time, followed automatically by the third knife. Many are self-feeding and self-delivering.

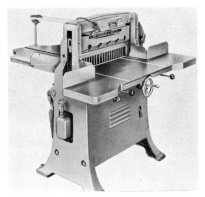

Fig. 12-28. A Chandler and Price power paper cutter.

Fig. 12-29. A three-knife book trimmer.

Paper Ruling

The reader has seen blue, red, and green lines "printed" on bill-heads, statements, index cards, and bookkeeping forms. These lines were "pen" or "disc" ruled on machines similar to the one illustrated (Fig. 12-30). Printers sometimes buy ruled billheads and statements and imprint the space at the top for various businesses.

The pens on a ruling machine are fed with ink from a woolen cloth. The paper is usually automatically-fed and is carried by a belt under strings. As many as nine colors are possible in one pass through the machine. A "striker" lifts the pens and drops them at desired positions on the paper. Other machines place the lines on the paper from discs.

Fig. 12-30. A paper ruling machine.

Embossing

Embossing is a press procedure, minus the ink. The work can be done on letterpresses and on the Davidson offset press. Printed images may be embossed, or the embossing may be "blind" (when no ink is used). A female die is used on the press bed or impression cylinder, and the counter die is made by the pressman from alabastine and dextrine mixed to a putty-like consistency.

Book-Edge Treatment

Edges of sheets of books and also flat sheets of paper may be "marbled" which changes their white appearance. Coloring matter is placed in vats of water and "combed" to distribute the colors. The material to be marbled is placed face down on the liquid. Imitation marbling is sometimes done with a sponge or spray gun. Special platen presses print designs, colors, and advertisements on book edges.

Sprinkling applies specks of colors to book edges with a brush or air gun. Staining is accomplished as in marbling or with a air gun. Gold edging of books is usually done by a hand process with gold leaf.

Review Questions

Match the type of bindings listed at the left with the characteristics listed at the right:

1. Saddle wire
2. Side wire
3. Sewn soft cover

4. Sewn case bound
5. Loose leaf
6. Plastic-type
7. Spiral-type
8. Adhesive ("perfect")

a. Lies flat when open
b. Cutter margin may be narrow
c. Odd-sized pages may be included
d. Does not stay open readily
e. Binding edge needs to be wide
g. Rugged, long-lasting
h. Sheets may be added
i. Sheets may be removed
j. Should be no thicker than ⅜ inch
k. Inexpensive to bind
l. Most expensive to bind

9. Paper folding machines are usually of the _____ kind.

10. What device has taken over the work of the paper punch? _____

11. Round cornering is done to prevent _____

Name five ways to perforate on all types of presses:

12. _____ Steel rule on cylinder and platen presses
13. _____ patented platen press devices
14. _____ Perforating wheels on cylinder and offset presses
15. _____ Perforating round holes
16. _____ Perforating strips on offset presses

17. What process is used to decorate book edges? _____
18. The term for straightening paper is _____
19. Stapling applies to devices using made-up staples. T or F?
20. Stitching applies to devices using coils of wire. T or F?
21. Collating refers to gathering folded book signatures. T or F?

Review Question Answers

Chapter 1

1. c
2. d
3. a-d-e
4. T
5. F
6. Alois Senefelder
7. Strixner
8. Artist
9. Placing image on paper and transferring it to paper
10. Calcareous
11. Hoe
12. 1814, London, England

Chapter 2

1. a
2. a
3. a
4. a
5. a
6. a, b
7. b, d
8. b
9. b
10. c
11. c
12. c
13. d
14. e
15. f
16. a
17. a
18. a, b
19. b
20. c
21. c
22. hand
23. Linotype-Intertype
24. Monotype
25. Ludlow
26. line
27. halftone
28. combination
29. color (duotone)
30. electrotypes (wax engravings)
31. stereotypes
32. molded rubber
33. Daxene
34. stripping
35. gravure
36. screen process
37. offset, screen process
38. electrostatic
39. camera, screen process
40. F
41. T

42. F

43. F

44. T

45. T

46. T

47. F

48. T

49. T

50. T

51. F

52. T

53. a

Chapter 3

1. photos
2. copy
3. size of work
4. color of ink
5. kind of paper
6. diagonal line
7. formula
8. proportional scales
9. pre-printed guide-
   line sheets
10. projected layout guides
11. pre-printed graph material
12. pre-printed artwork
13. border tape applicators

14. pre-printed acetate sheets,
    adhesive-backed
15. scratchboard
16. chemically-treated drawing
    board
17. register marks
18. Varitype 610F
19. Bourges
20. Bourges
21. reproduction proofs
22. T
23. T
24. T
25. F

Chapter 4

1. T
2. F
3. F
4. F
5. F
6. T
7. T
8. F
9. T
10. T
11. F
12. T

13. T
14. F
15. T
16. F
17. T
18. T
19. F
20. T
21. T
22. F
23. F
24. T

25. a, e, f, g
26. c
27. a
28. e
29. e
30. b, c
31. a, b, d
32. a, c, e, g, i, k
33. Fotosetter
34. Protype
35. Hadego Kameratype
36. Photo-Typositor
37. Optype
38. Modification
39. duPont Clarifyer
40. Fotolist
41. Composoline
42. Listomatic
43. Scotchprint
44. Type-to-Litho Film
45. Converkal or Cronapress
46. Silvertype

47. Instant Negative
48. Texoprint
49. Verticon
50. Brightype
51. Scotchprint
52. H_2 Acetate
53. Napconversions
54. di- offset
55. Double offset transfer
56. 18
57. 2
58. 1
59. 2
60. 2
61. 16
62. Alphatype
63. Varigraph, Leroy, Wrico
64. Fototype, Presto
65. Prestype, Craftype, Artype, Letraset, Redi-Kut, Cello-Tak
66. Typro

Chapter 5

1. F
2. T
3. F
4. T
5. T
6. T
7. T
8. F
9. T
10. T
11. T
12. T

13. T
14. F
15. 15a
16. 16b, d
17. 17e
18. 18c
19. 19a
20. 20b
21. 21c
22. 22b
23. 23a
24. 24f

25. 25d
26. 26e
27. 27g
28. 28i
29. 29j
30. 30h
31. c
32. a
33. vertical
34. horizontal
35. darkroom
36. gallery
37. low bed
38. overhead
39. roll film
40. sheet film
41. copyboard
42. lensboard
43. bellows
44. camera back
45. lighting
46. light tight
47. light trap
48. ventilation
49. controlled temperature
50. stainless steel
51. storage area
52. normal light
53. safe light
54. reproduction size
55. extreme enlargements or reductions

56. type of lights used
57. color separations
58. bellows extension
59. carbon arc
60. photo flood
61. fluorescent
62. orthrochromatic
63. panchromatic
64. monochromatic
65. line negatives
66. halftones
67. goldenrod paper
68. tape
69. negative
70. filters
71. slot
72. 68
73. hypo
74. washed in water
75. gelatin silver halide
76. combination
77. drop out
78. f
79. 1; 64
80. continuous
81. scribing
82. diaphragm
83. green
84. none or blue

Chapter 6

1. T
2. F
3. T
4. F

5. T
6. T
7. F
8. Step and repeat machine

9. 24 step gray scale negative
10. Vacuum frame
11. Hydrophilic
12. Moisture
13. 70
14. 14b
15. 15c, d
16. 16a
17. 17e
18. 18d
19. 19c
20. 20f
21. 21g
22. 22b
23. 23a
24. 24d, f, h,
25. 25g
26. 26e, i, j
27. 27c
28. 28b
29. 29a
30. 30c, e, g
31. 31a, f
32. 32h

33. 33d, i, j
34. 34b
35. prolong life
36. repair broken lines
37. remove dirty spots
38. strengthen weak areas
39. adding to the image
40. exposing
41. developing
42. desensitizing
43. gumming
44. hold the image
45. allow water to adhere
46. marbles
47. abrasives
48. distance between lights and frame
49. relative humidity
50. surface coated
51. deep etch
52. dry offset
53. direct image
54. multi-metal
55. xerography

Chapter 7

1. spreading
2. bloom
3. F
4. F
5. F
6. T
7. Vechicle
8. Pigment

9. Dryer
10. Binder
11. Evaporation
12. Absorption
13. Oxidation
14. Linseed oil
15. Litho varnish

Chapter 8

1. T
2. F
3. T
4. 5 Ink, copy, power, elevator, dampener
5. c

6. b
7. b
8. c
9. c
10. a-a, d-c or e, c-b, d-c or e, e-d

A. B. DICK OFFSET DUPLICATOR, MODEL 360

1. b
2. d
3. c
4. T
5. T

6. F
7. F
8. 12
9. Angular, lateral, vertical
10. Adequate buckle control

MULTILITH OFFSET DUPLICATOR, MODEL 1250

1. b
2. c
3. b
4. b & d
5. c

6. ductor, rider, form, fountain
7. ten
8. F
9. T
10. T

Chapter 9
ATF CHIEF MODEL 15

1. d
2. b
3. c
4. a
5. T

6. T
7. T
8. F
9. F

DAVIDSON DUAL MODEL 500

1. d
2. d
3. a
4. T
5. F
6. T

7. a-f, b-c, c-a, d-d, e-b, f-e
8. Relief, dry offset, embossing, perfecting
9. F
10. T

Chapter 10

1. c	6. F
2. a	7. T
3. b	8. F
4. T	9. T
5. T	10. T

Chapter 11

1. cellulose fiber
2. rag, cotton
3. wood, pulp
4. digester, beater
5. filler
6. screen
7. calender
8. bleached
9. dandy roll
10. air knives
11. furnish roll
12. doctor blade
13. polished drums
14. coarse or industrial
15. fine, printing, or writing
16. coating not weak
17. free of particles and dust
18. c
19. b
20. d
21. e
22. g
23. f
24. h
25. c
26. a
27. b
28. d
29. 20
30. 40
31. 8
32. 16
33. $75.348
34. $4.24
35. $32.64
36. F
37. T
38. T

Chapter 12

1. a, b, j, k
2. c, d, e, f, k
3. a, b, f, g
4. a, b, f, g, l
5. a, b, f, h, i, k
6. a, b, c, h, i, k
7. a, b c, i
8. a, b, f
9. buckle
10. drill
11. dog-earing, bending
12. steel rule on cylinder and platen presses

13. patented platen press
    devices
14. perforating wheels on
    cylinder and offset presses
15. perforating round holes
16. perforating strips on
    offset presses
17. marbling, printing, sprinkling

18. jogging
19. T
20. T
21. F
22. F
23. T
24. T

ACKNOWLEDGMENTS

Both authors as well as the publishers wish to acknowledge the following persons and firms for their generous assistance in supplying many of the illustrations in this book.

A. B. Dick Company
5700 West Touhy Ave.
Chicago 48, Illinois
Vernon Anderson, Sales Promotion Manager
Robert P. Balla, Sales Promotion Manager

Addressograph-Multigraph Corp.
1200 Babbitt Road
Cleveland 17, Ohio
W. S. Johnson, Art Supervisor

American Type Founders Co., Inc.
200 Elmora Ave.
Elizabeth, New Jersey
J. R. Greig, Advertising Manager
Robert C. Pierson, Assistant Advertising Manager

Atlantic Numbering Machine Co.
4702–18th Ave.
Brooklyn 4, N. Y.
T. Weiss

Accurate Steel Rule Die Mfrs., Inc.
22 West 21st Street
New York 10, N. Y.
M. Lee Scott

Artype Inc.
127 S. Northwest Highway
Barrington, Illinois
Fred H. Yonkers, Vice President, Sales

A. A. Archbold, Publisher
419 S. Main Street
Burbank, California

Brandtjen & Kluge, Inc.
Corner Gaultier St. at Como Ave.
Saint Paul 3, Minnesota
H. M. Williams

Cerutti Presses of America, Inc.
121 Prospect Street
Westfield, New Jersey
R. G. Marquardt, President

Banthin Engineering Co.
1849–1857 Main Street
Bridgeport 4, Connecticut
W. Krause, Office Manager

Bell & Howell Co.
Baumfolder Division
1540 Wood Street
Philadelphia 2, Penna.
Tex Renz

Bourges Color Corp.
80 Fifth Ave.
New York 11, N. Y.
Jean Bourges, President

W. H. Brady Co.
727 West Glendale Ave.
Milwaukee 9, Wisconsin
J. A. Pescheck, Advertising Supervisor

Chandler & Price Co.
6000 Carnegie Ave.
Cleveland 3, Ohio
Merle D. Kirstein, Sales Manager

Chart-Pak, Inc.
One River Road
Leeds, Mass.
David M. Klein, Advertising Manager

Chemco Photoproducts Co., Inc.
Glen Cove, New York
Burton Kaplan, Advertising Manager

Chemical Products Corp.
King Philip Road
East Providence 14, Rhode Island
Thomas D. McGuire

Commander Engr. & Mfg. Co.
318A North Euclid
St. Louis 8, Missouri
E. J. Walsh, Jr., President

Compugraphic Corp.
175 Amory Street
Brookline 46, Mass.
W. W. Garth, Jr., President

Cottrell Company
Westerly, Rhode Island
Herbert A. Asten, Manager

Craftsman Line-up Table Corp.
49 River Street
Waltham 54, Mass.
Mrs. Eileen M. Foster

Crosfield Electronics, Inc.
47 New York Ave.
New Cassel, Westbury
L. I., N. Y.
Herb Weiss, General Sales Manager

Ditto, Inc.
6800 McCormick Rd.
Chicago 45, Illinois
W. T. Whitehead, Assistant Manager
F. Gregor, Director

Eastman Kodak Company
343 State Street
Rochester 4, New York
J. D. McAlister, Adv. Dept.

Filmotype Corporation
7500 McCormick Blvd.
Skokie, Illinois
B. L. Friedman, General Manager

Foto Graphic Products Co.
311 Fifth Ave. North
Minneapolis 1, Minnesota
Gene Koblas, Sales Manager

General Research, Inc.
572 Division Ave. South
P. O. Box M-956
Grand Rapids, Michigan
Howard J. Niles, Sales Department

Graphic Electronics, Inc.
La Salle, Illinois
John N. Barron

Gregory & Leonard Office Equipment Company
615 Livernois Ave.
Ferndale 20, Michigan
Peter Turgeon, Manager

Copycat Corporation
200 Park Ave. South
New York 3, New York
Miss Gae Olivieri

Craftint Manufacturing Co.
1615 Collamer Ave.
Cleveland 10, Ohio
T. McNeil, Sales

Craftools, Inc.
396 Broadway
New York 13, New York
H. D. Greggs

Didde-Glasser, Inc.
Post Office Box 709
Emporia, Kansas

Dow Metal Products Co.
Div. Dow Chemical Co.
Midland, Michigan
A. B. Fry

Du Pont E. I. DuPont De Nemours & Co.
Wilmington 98, Delaware
E. C. Watson

Fairchild Graphic Equipment Co.
Fairchild Drive
Plainview, L. I., New York
Walter Wilson

Friden, Inc.
San Leandro, California
Bruce F. La Centra, Information Division

General Binding Corp.
Northbrook, Illinois
Kent Elworthy, Advertising Assistant

Gestetner Corporation
216 Lake Ave.
Yonkers, New York
G. S. Barnett

Graphic Systems
Yanceyville, North Carolina
G. Irvin Aldridge, General Manager

Hamilton Manufacturing Co.
Two Rivers, Wisconsin
H. A. Nack, Product Manager

Harris-Seybold Company
4510 East 71st Street
Cleveland 5, Ohio
D. G. Dolesh, Advertising Assistant
W. P. Bourquin, Assistant Advertising Manager

IBM Corporation
545 Madison Ave.
New York 22, New York
D. L. Trownsell, Information Department Manager

Kensol-Olsenmark, Inc.
124–132 White Street
New York 13, New York
Frank J. Olsen

Kreicker & Meloan Inc.
221 North La Salle Street
Chicago 1, Illinois
L. R. Behles

Lawson Company
2011 Hastings Street
Chicago 8, Illinois
Leonard S. Alexander, Advertising Manager

Ludlow Typography Company
2032 Clybourn Ave.
Chicago 14, Illinois
R. Hunter Middleton, Director

Marginator Company
299 So. Lake Street
Burbank, California
John S. Edison

Miehle-Goss-Dexter
2011 Hastings Street
Chicago 8, Illinois
Leonard S. Alexander, Advertising Manager

Minnesota Mining and Manufacturing Company
900 Bush Ave.
St. Paul 6, Minnesota
Paul G. Montgomery, Publicist
D. J. Blomberg, Jr., Marketing Supervisor

Hammermill Paper Co.
Erie 7, Penna.
Mrs. M. L. Gorenflo, Advertising Department

Heidelburg Eastern, Inc.
73–45 Woodhaven Blvd.
Glendale 27, Long Island, New York
J. J. McCall, Advertising Department

Improved Machinery, Inc.
Nashua, New Hampshire
Robert Nivision, Vice President, Sales

Intertype Company
360 Furman Street
Brooklyn 1, New York

Keuffel & Esser Co.
Adams and Third Streets
Hoboken, New Jersey
W. E. French, Advertising Department

Lanston Monotype Co.
G. Street Below Erie Ave.
Philadelphia 34, Penna.
Dominic A. Lorenzo, Administrative Assistant

Lectro-Stik Company
4545 N. Clark Street
Chicago 40, Illinois

Lithographic Technical Foundation
131 East 39th Street
New York 16, New York

Mergenthaler Linotype Company
29 Ryerson Street
Brooklyn 5, New York
Arthur L. Koop, Advertising & Sales Manager

Miller Printing Machinery Co.
1101–1131 Reedsdale Street
Pittsburgh 33, Penna.
E. W. Evans, Advertising Manager

Modi-Graphic Inc.
215 E. Ninth Street
Cincinnati 2, Ohio
Wayne B. Douglas, President

Monsen Typographers, Inc.
22 East Illinois Street Chicago
Chicago, Illinois
Paul J. Bernin, Advertising Manager

Martin J. Weber Studio
171 Madison Ave.
New York 16, N. Y.
Martin J. Weber

New Era Manufacturing Co.
P. O. Box 400
Hawthorne, New Jersey
F. A. Ross, Research and Development Manager

Paillard, Inc.
100 Sixth Ave.
New York 13, N. Y.
Walter Braun, Advertising and Sales Promotion Manager

Photon, Inc.
58 Charles Street
Cambridge 41, Mass.
Wm. Baumrucker, Jr., Vice President

Photo Typositor, Inc.
311 East 46th Street
New York 17, N. Y.
Milton J. Zorin

Presto Process Company
185 St. Paul Street
Rochester 4, N. Y.
H. L. Chapin

Printing Impressions
134 N. 13th Street
Philadelphia 7, Penna.
I. J. Borowsky, Publisher

Remington Rand
315 Park Ave. South
New York 10, N. Y.
D. P. Sheridan, Sales Promotion Manager

Rohm & Haas Company
Washington Square
Philadelphia 5, Penna.
David S. Marston, Editor

Morgan Sign Machine Co.
4510 N. Ravenswood Ave.
Chicago 40, Illinois
Ray F. Morgan

Naz-Dar Company
461 Milwaukee Ave.
Chicago 10, Illinois
J. Nickel, Sales Manager

Nolan Corporation
Rome, New York
Richard G. Sheppard

NuArc Company, Inc.
4110 W. Grand Avenue
Chicago 51, Illinois

P. H. Glatfelter Company
Spring Grove, Penna.
G. M. Markle, Public Relations Manager

Photonews, Inc.
329 Broadway
Bethpage, L. I., N. Y.
Wm. P. Carroll, Vice President

Pitney-Bowes, Inc.
Walnut and Pacific Street
Stamford, Conn.
R. E. Wilkinson, Staff Assistant, Advertising Department

Prestype, Inc.
136 West 21st Street
New York 11, N. Y.
Herb Silver, Secretary-Treasurer

Printing Machinery Company
436 Commercial Square
Cincinnati 2, Ohio
Lee Augustine, President

Robertson Photo-Mechanix, Inc.
7440 Lawrence Ave.
Chicago 31, Illinois
E. W. Hoy, Sales Manager

F. P. Rosback Company
P.O. Box 675
Benton Harbor, Michigan
F. C. Roosevelt, General Manager

Smith-Corona Marchant, Inc.
410 Park Ave.
New York 22, N. Y.
J. F. McElroy

Technical Trade School
Pressmen's Home, Tennessee

Thomson-National Press Co., Inc.
Franklin, Mass.
J. W. Hipple, Jr., Assistant Sales Manager

Underwood Corporation
One Park Ave.
New York 16, N. Y.
Andrew Cerruti, Advertising Division

Varigraph Company
Madison 1, Wisconsin
L. J. Jenson, General Manager

Virkotype Corporation
11 Rock Ave.
Plainfield, New Jersey

Wood-Regan Instrument Co., Inc.
Nutley, New Jersey

Xerox Corporation
Rochester 3, New York
Calvin Rapp, Administrative Assistant
F. James Carr

Shelton Color Corporation
16 Lafayette Street
Hackensack, New Jersey
M. Murphy, Sales Department

Specialties Inc.
235B Robbins Lane
Syosset, L. I., N. Y.

Thomas Collators
100 Church Street
New York 7, N. Y.

Trans-Art, Inc.
237 Huguenot Street
New Rochelle, New York

VariTyper Corporation
720 Frelinghuysen Ave.
Newark 12, New Jersey

B. Verner & Company, Inc.
52 Duane Street
New York 7, N. Y.
G. A. Knudsen

W. O. Hickok Mfg. Co.
Ninth & Cumberland Streets
Harrisburg, Penna.

DICTIONARY OF TECHNICAL TERMS

A

A. B. Dick–A small offset press.

Accelerator–A chemical that makes a solution alkaline.

Achromatic Lens–A lens corrected for black and white photography.

Acid Resist–A coating that does not allow acid to etch away a portion of a plate.

Acetic Acid–An acid used for photographic development in the short-stop bath.

Actinic–A term used for the chemically active components of white light (blue, violet, and ultra-violet) to which lithographic plate coatings are sensitive.

Activate–To set in motion; to start in action.

Air Brush–Photographic retouching with ink and compressed air.

Air Bubbles–Bubbles created when improper coating is applied to an offset plate while whirling.

Agitate–To keep in motion; to stir violently.

Albumin–White of an egg; a protein rich in sulphur used in the coating solution for an albumin plate.

Albumin Plate–A surface-coated lithographic press plate.

Alkali–A compound which has an action opposite to that of an acid; a mixture of alkali and acid will neutralize one another and weaken the stronger.

Alkaline–Having the proerties of alkali—see "Alkali."

Aller Plate–An offset plate made of stainless steel and electrotyped or coated with copper.

Alphatype–A cold type device utilizing magnetic tape to operate a transistorized recorder.

Alum–An ingredient used in the fixing bath to harden the emulsion.

Aluminum Plate–An offset plate made of aluminum.

Ammonium Bichromate–A light sensitive chemical used in plate coatings, also called Ammonium Dichromate.

Ammonium Hydroxide–An ingredient used to form a caustic solution in cleaning offset plates.

Ammonium Nitrate–An ingredient used in the preparation of a press fountain solution.

Ammonium Phosphate–An ingredient used in the preparation of a press fountain solution.

Anti-Halation–Film with a colored coating to prevent the spreading or blurring of the image by light rays.

Aperture–An opening of the diaphragm of a camera.

Aperture Setting–A calibrated setting of the diaphragm. See also "F-number."

Apochromatic Lens–A lens in which corrections for color abberrations are carried out for the three primary colors.

Arc Lamp–A lamp designed to furnish a uniform, high, actinic light by an arc gap between two carbon electrodes. Used for exposing film in a camera or plates in platemaking. Also known as an arc light.

Area Display–Cold type devices that allow the composition of type over a large area. As differentiated from type images made line-for-line.

Artype–Preprinted characters on a transparent wax-backed plastic, used for display lines for offset printing.

Asphaltum–A dark brown heavy liquid derived from coal tar used to make the printed image on a press plate permanently ink receptive and as an overall protective coating when storing zinc plates.

ATF Chief–A make of offset press.

ATF Typesetter–A cold type device for producing negatives of type from 6 to 24 points.

Auto-Screen Film–Pre-screened film for making halftone negatives.

Autosetter–An electronic device which operates line casting machines through the use of printed tape. See also "Teletypesetter."

B

Back-up–Printing the reverse side of a sheet.

Banthin Lithomatic–A make of offset press.

Base–Transparent support for light sensitive coatings as in film, glass, or paper.

Basis Weight–A name given to a sheet of paper in terms of the weight of 500 sheets in a certain size.

Baume–A measurement in density of the amount of chemical dissolved in a liquid, an indication of strength.

BE–Bellows extension (abbr.).

Bearers–Steel rings at the end of a plate cylinder and blanket cylinder to provide a firm base for determining the packing of plate and blanket.

Bellows–The corrugated or accordian-like structure between the lensboard and camera back.

Bellows Extension–The distance between the film holder to the lens at any given setting of the camera.

Ben Day Screen–A mechanical method (laying a screen with dots, lines and other textures on line plates) of producing a shaded effect on a line plate.

Bi-Metal Plate–An offset plate made of two metals using zinc, copper, or aluminum with nickel.

Blanket–A fabric coated with a rubber compound about .064 in. thick which covers the blanket cylinder and transfers the image from the plate to the paper as the paper passes through the press. Also, the impression surface on newspaper rotary presses.

Blanket Cylinder–The intermediate cylinder of an offset press that holds the blanket.

Bleed–A printed image area, an illustration, extending beyond any one or more edges of a sheet; poor inks with water soluble components that mix with the fountain solution and break down and get into the dampening rollers causing scum or tone.

Bleeding–The running or spreading of a pigment color by the action of water or a solvent.

Blind–An area of a plate that has lost its affinity for ink.

Blow-Up–An enlargement.

Body–The general "weight" of ink, the consistency, e.g. an ink with too much body is stiff; the size of type from the bottom to the top of the letter.

Bond–A one-sided rag or sulphite paper noted for its smooth finish, strength, and lack of "fuzz."

Book Paper–kind of paper used for printing books; includes coated, sized, super-calendered, antiqued, machine-finished paper, etc.

Boric Acid–A weak acid used to control the activity of the alkali during the development process.

Brayer–A handled inking roller used to ink forms when proofing.

Brightype–A process of converting type forms to negatives or positives for printing by the offset or gravure process.

Bristol Board–A fine grade of cardboard.

Buckle–Portion of a sheet of paper that is raised by pressure exerted on both ends of the sheet.

Burning In–Exposing a plate through a negative to strong light source.

Butted–Slugs, as from Linotype machines, which are placed end-to-end, allowing lines or widths wider than the machine will cast.

C

Calcareous–Affinity to hold both grease and water.

Calcium Chloride–A chemical used in preparing the deep etch solution for deep etch plates.

Camera–The device by which the copy or original is transposed onto light sensitive material.

Camera Back–That part of the camera which contains the ground glass, film holder and controls.

CE–Camera extension.

Camera Extension–The distance between the lens and the negative.

Canon Rescreener–A device used which permits direct screening of halftone copy without producing any moire pattern.

Caption–Descriptive wording over a picture.

Carbon Tissue–A light sensitive, gelation-coated paper stock used in gravure platemaking.

Catch-Up–A bank of ink appearing on non-printed areas.

Caustic Solution–Mixture of 28 percent ammonium hydroxide and 72 percent water, or a mixture of bicarbonate of soda and water used in making an offset plate.

Cellulose Acetate–A base for film.

Cellulose Fiber–Ingredient used in making paper. The fibrous material remaining after the non-fibrous components of wood have been removed by pulping and bleaching operations.

Cellulose Nitrate–A base for film.

Chalking–The rubbing off of ink after it is dry causing printed forms to offset or scuff in binding operations; improper drying of ink.

Chart Pak–Rolls of pressure-sensitive graph-type material pre-printed in various designs for copymaking in offset printing.

Chase–An iron frame used for locking up type forms which are placed in letterpresses for printing.

Chroma–The degree of intensity from black to white.

Clear Base (Clear Back)–Film without colored coating.

Clip Sheet Art–Advertising illustration service available to offset printers.

Coating–Making an offset plate sensitive to light; the film of sensitive solution covering the plate.

Cold Type–Images of letters created without benefit of molten metal.

Collating–Examining the folded signatures of a book in the process of gathering to verify the number and order of signatures, pages, etc.

Colloid–Egg albumin in water, gum arabic, casein, glue and gelatin.

Collotype–Screenless illustration printing.

Color Blind Film–Sensitive only to blue or ultra-violet light, see "Monochromatic."

Color Filter–A sheet of colored glass or gelatin used on lenses in excluding or transmitting certain colors in color photography. See also "Filter."

Color Form–The form making the second color in a job of printing.

Colors (Primary)–The principle or most important colors of the spectrum (red, yellow, and blue).

Color Proof–An impression or print from a set of reproduction color plates in register.

Colors (Secondary)–Colors formed by mixing two primary colors (orange, green, and purple).

Color Separation–Separating the colors from a colored original using filters and a circular glass halftone screen at different angles.

Copycat Platemaker–A device for making plates.

Combination Plate–The combining of line and halftone work on one plate; the combining more than one job into a flat in offset stripping.

Composition–Setting and arranging types; the product of type, either hand or machine set.

Compositer–One who sets type.

Compound–A substance such as wax or grease used to reduce tack and body of ink.

Contact Print–A print made by placing a transparency or negative against a light sensitive material and shining a light through it.

Contact Screen–See "Magenta Contact Screen."

Continuous Tone Photography–A photograph or a negative made in a camera with a screen that has lines instead of a dot pattern.

Contrast–The quality of an illustration possessing a narrow range in the tone values.

Copyboard–Part of the camera where the original or copy is held in place during exposure.

Copperplate Engraving–Work done from copper engraved dies, engraved intaglio.

Copy–An original or material furnished by the customer for reproduction, may be typewritten manuscript, art work, drawings, etc.

Copyboard Extension–The distance from the lens to the copyboard at any given setting of the camera.

Copy Fitting–Estimating the amount of space taken by a given manuscript in a predetermined size and style of type.

Copy Preparation–The assembling of all copy for a job.

Craftint–Preprinted, wax-backed shading media for offset copy preparation; substitutes for Ben Day shading.

Crop–To cut down in size as directed by "crop marks."

Crop Marks–The cross marks placed on the outside of a photograph, artwork, etc. usually on a mounting or guide sheet to indicate that part of the copy to be reproduced.

Cut–A term used to denote a photo-engraving, electrotype, stereotype in letterpress printing and any picture in offset-lithography and gravure.

Counter Etch–A mild acid solution used for cleaning metal offset plates. In addition to freeing the plate from oxide and dirt, it chemically makes the plate grease receptive or grease sensitive.

D

Dampeners–Rollers that distribute dampening solution to the printing plates on an offset press.

Dampening Rollers–See "Dampeners."

Darkroom–A room where film is handled and developed.

Darkroom Camera–A camera that has its camera back and part of the bellows mounted in the wall so that the camera back is in the darkroom while the rest of the camera is out in the working room.

Davidson–A small offset press.

Daxene–A thermosetting liquid-made rotary letterpress plate.

Decalcomania–Advertisements or signs built up by a series of impressions (screen process or lithographic) on a base. When moistened, the image leaves the paper base and is affixed to glass, wood, metal, etc.

Deep Etch–An offset plate used for long runs. A reversal method is used in making the plate; the image is etched with acid so that it is recessed slightly below the level of the plate surface.

Densitometer–An instrument for measuring the optical density (degree of blackness) of a negative or positive transparency or of a print.

Density–Opaqueness of a negative or opaqueness of an image on a positive.

Desensitize–To make a plate insensitive to grease.

Developer–A chemical solution which renders photographic images visible by reducing the light effected silver halide particles to form metallic silver.

Developing–Making an image by treating an exposed film chemically; the rubbing in an offset plate with an ink, preparing it for the press.

Developing Ink–A black liquid which produces a greasy film on the printing areas of an offset plate and prepares it for receiving the ink.

Detail–Minute or specific sub-divisions of an image.

Diaphragm–A device attached to the lens of a camera for making pre-caliberated openings; an adjustable stop in the form of an iris.

Diazo–An office type reproducing machine-vellum paper with carbon backing reproduced on special sensitized paper.

Dis-Continuous Tone–Graduation of dots as in a halftone.

Display Type–The largest and specially designed type faces used to attract attention.

Ditto–A small offset press; a duplicator.

Doctor Blade–A "knife" of rigid plastic or thin sheet-metal which, presses against the gravure press cylinder, and which wipes away ink from the surface of the cylinder.

Dot Etching–A process by which one changes the tone values of a halftone negative or positive.

Dow Etch–A powderless method of making letterpress line and halftone plates.

Drop Out–Elimination of highlight dot formation in halftone negatives by photographic or chemical methods.

Drier–A chemical compound that is added to ink to hasten drying; the steam-heated cylinder over which paper in the web is passed to be dried.

Drilling–Hollow drilling of holes in paper which has practically eliminated paper punching.

Dry Offset–Printing on a rubber blanket from a shallow-etched relief plate. The rubber blanket transfers the ink to the paper.

Dry-Offset Plate–A metal offset plate that has the non-printing area etched below the image area.

DSJ–Differential Space Justifier (abbr.). A VariTyper term on which proportional characters are used and lines justified by a second keyboarding.

Duograph–A two color reproduction (made by two different half-tone negatives at two different screen angles.) printing in a dark color from one negative, the second color a tint or hue of the first color from the second negative.

Duoplex–Same as "Duograph."

Duotone–A two color reproduction made by two different half-tone negatives at two different screen angles in two different colors.

Duotype–A two color reproduction using the same negative. The first color is dark; the second is a light tone of the first color.

Duplicating–Processes used in offices, lettershops, and small print shops for short production runs. Includes mimeograph, small offset presses (10 by 15 ins.), thermofax, verifax, xerox, etc.

Dummy–Pages of a planned book, catalog, etc. put together to assist in determining the specifications.

E

Electro-Rex Platemaker–A machine that makes offset plates on a photoelectric principle.

Electrostatic Printing–A process of printing on paper as well as on irregular and fragile objects such as sandpaper, rolled cotton, cellophane bags, glass, etc. A dry-ink pigment is attracted by an electrode and fixed on the object, copying the image wanted, without pressure.

Em–The square of the type body of any size.

Embossing–A finish imparted to paper by means of raised or depressed engravings on steel rolls.

Emulsion–Suspension of a light sensitive salt or silver generally in a gelatin solution used for coating plates, films, etc.

Enamel Paper–Paper coated with clay, glue and other substances having a glossy finish.

Engraving–A photoengraving; the process of cutting designs into a plate for the purpose of making impressions on paper; die-stamping and copperplate engraving.

Enlargement–Reproducing larger than original size.

Etch Solution–A desensitizing solution for the nonprinting areas of the plate.

Etching–The fixing of the image areas so that blank areas will accept only water and printing areas will accept only ink; the eating away of metal as in photoengraving; an artistic endeavor accomplished by the intaglio process.

Etch Proof–A reproduction proof.

Exposure–An act of exposing a sensitized surface to light.

F

f#–Symbol for an aperture setting; f-number.

Factor–Number or time by which exposure must be increased when using a filter.

Ferric Chloride–A substance used in preparing the deep etch solution for deep etch plates.

Filling Up–Small openings in letters or halftones being completely inked or blocked up.

FL–Focal length of a camera lens.

Fog–The cloudiness or misty appearance in the transparent portion of a negative that should be absolutely clear.

Font–A complete assortment of all the different characters of a particular size and style of type.

Formula–A definite set or mathematical rule of words or symbols set in abbreviation form to compute an answer.

Fountain–The part of the press that acts as a reservoir for the ink and water solution.

Fountain Roller–Rollers that are mounted in the fountain and, when set in motion, deliver the water or ink to the other rollers in the system.

Front Guide–The part of the press that lines up the sheet squarely to obtain register.

F Stop (f-Number)–Numbers used as indicators to show the particular diaphragm opening.

"f" Value–The "f" value indicates the ratio of the largest aperture of the lens to its focal length.

Feeder–The part of a press which automatically delivers the sheets of paper to the printing unit; a person who hand feeds sheets to a press.

Film–Light sensitive material used to produce a negative.

Film Holder–Part of the camera back that holds the film in position during exposure.

Filmotype–A cold type display device.

Filter–Dyed gelatin sheets inserted into the camera to transmit or absorb certain colors during exposure. See also "Color Filter."

Fixation–See "Fixing."

Fixing–The process of removing unexposed silver salts from a developed plate, film, or print to prevent further reaction to light and to permanently fix the image.

Flash–An exposure during the making of a halftone to expose the black areas of an original to reflected light.

Flash Gun–A lamp used to throw light through the lens and screen to the film in making a flash exposure of the halftone.

Flash Sheet–A white sheet of paper placed over an original during a flash exposure of a negative. Serves the same purpose as a flash gun.

Flat–A stripper's completed work when the negatives or positives are properly assembled and fixed in place on an opaque sheet of paper (goldenrod) and are ready for platemaking; the lack of contrast in a print.

Flexowriter–A tape operated cold type composing machine similar to Justowriter.

Flow–Ink is said to have "flow" when it follows the fountain and levels itself.

Fluff–Separation (accomplished by air blow tubes) of the top few sheets of paper being delivered to a press.

Fotolist–A camera which produces negatives of full pages of directory or catalog work from pre-typed data processing cards.

Fotorex–A photographic display type device used for offset printing.

Foto-Riter–A cold type display device.

Fotosetter–A cold type device based on the circulating-matrix principle.

Fototype–Characters printed on "pads" for assembly of display letters for offset printing.

Fountain Solution–Water made slightly acid with chemicals that react to balance excessive greasiness of ink; deposited on the non-printing areas of an offset plate.

Furniture–Pieces of wood or metal used for filling out the larger blank spaces in a hot type form.

G

Gallery Camera–A camera that is exclusive of the darkroom.

Gathering–Assembling the signatures of a book.

Gamma–A measure of negative contrast resulting from photographic development.

Gelatin–A substance derived from animal tissue, bones, etc.

Gestafax–A device used to make single copies of images and plates for small offset presses.

Gestetner–A duplicating machine which prints through a stencil.

Ghosting–Indistinct image patterns appearing in solids.

Glass Screen–See "Halftone Screen."

Glaze–A hard, shiny surface on rollers or blanket due to oxidation.

Glossy Print–A photographic print having a smooth, glossy finish.

Goetz Lens–See "Gotar".

Goldenrod Paper–A specially coated paper support for negatives or positives used by a stripper for making flats. The colored coating prevents exposure of the nonprinting areas of the plate.

Gotar–A lens by Goetz.

Governor–A chemical used to keep fog to a minimum during the photographic development process.

Grain–The direction in which the fibers lie in a sheet of paper; the high and low areas of an offset plate.

Graining–Roughening the surface of a metal offset plate by means of marbles and an abrasive, to increase its water carrying capacity.

Gray Contact Screen–Same as magenta contact screen, but gray in color instead of magenta. See Magenta Contact Screen.

Gray Scale–Chart to show graduation of tones from white to black.

Gravure–Printing from an etched-out or sunken surface; an intaglio method.

Grippers–Metal fingers on the cylinder of a press which carry the sheets while they are being printed and delivered; the metal clamps that hold the paper against the platen on a platen press.

Gripper Margin–The lead edge of the sheet held by the grippers as they carry the sheet through the press and in which no part of the image can be printed.

Ground Glass–A frosted glass on the camera back of the camera and is used to view the original in the copyboard of the camera.

Guide–Gauges on offset presses that feed the paper into register position.

Gum or Gum Arabic–Pitch from the Acacia tree, used to protect an offset plate.

Gumming–Coating the non-printing areas of an offset plate to prevent oxidation and to desensitize the non-printing areas.

Gum Solution–Gum arabic in water used to preserve plates from oxidation, to desensitize the non-printing areas, and to make up fountain solutions.

H

Hadego–A cold type display device employing hand-assembled "matrices" or images.

Hairline–The fine and delicate lines in a type face design or in an illustration; a hairline rule.

Halation–Spreading or blurring of the image caused by light rays creeping and spreading between the emulsion and the positive or plate.

Halftone–A picture in which the graduation of tone is reproduced by a graduation of dots, produced by the interposition of a screen during exposure.

Halftone Photography–The process by which a continuous tone original is reproduced into a negative consisting of graduations of dots.

Halftone Positive–An illustration made in a camera from a continuous tone negative with a screen interposed between the photographic plate and the lens.

Halftone Screen–The ruled, plate glass dot-forming device used to translate continuous tones into halftones.

Halo–A luminous circle or aura around the halftone dot.

Hand Set–Type or forms set by hand.

Harris-Seybold–A make of offset press.

Headliner–A cold type display device.

Heat Fuser–A device used to make a print permanent in Xerography.

Hickey–Small doughnut-shaped spots obtained during printing (especially in solids) resulting from dirt or other foreign matter getting into the system.

Highlight–The brightest or whitest areas of an original or reproduction or represented by considerable opacity in the negative.

Hot Type–Hand-set and machine-set lines of type created from molten metal.

Humidifiers–A substance or device that controls the amount of water in the air.

Humidity–Moisture content of air.

Hydrochloric Acid–An acid diluted in water to form a counter etch for zinc plates; used in preparing the developing and deep-etch solution for deep-etch plates.

Hydrometer–An instrument to measure relative humidity.

Hydrophilic–Literally "loving water," used in connection with offset plates.

Hydroquinone–A reducing agent used in developing solutions. See Reducing Agent.

Hypo–Fixing agent for plates, film, etc., used in photography.

I

Illustration–Any form of picture, drawing, diagram, etc.

Immerse–To place in or insert under a fluid (either liquid or gas).

Impression–The pressure of type forms or plates on the paper in a printing press.

Impression Cylinder–Cylinder that carries the paper while it is being printed.

Increment–The amount of leading either in points or in decimals of an inch.

Ink–A colored pigment combined with a vehicle and other substances, used to obtain a printed image.

Ink Fountain–The part of the press that holds the ink.

Ink Rollers–Rollers that distribute ink to the plate.

Intaglio–Cut-out or etched-out pictures or type from a plate as in steel-plate engraving or gravure printing.

J—K—L

Jog–To straighten sheets of paper; the mechanical or manual operation of producing a smooth sided pile of paper by knocking the sheets against a smooth, flat surface.

Key Plate–The particular plate used as a guide for registration of other colors; the plate with maximum detail.

Kerning (Kern)–That part of a type face which extends over the side of the type body.

Klischograph–An electronic device for making line plates and halftones.

Laid Paper–Paper having equally-spaced parallel lines watermarked to give a ribbed appearance.

Laketine–A substance used to reduce transparent lithographic inks.

Laminating–Covering printed work with a transparent cellophane; building up paper to a desired thickness or a given surface by joining together two or more web sheets.

Latent Image–The invisible photographic image produced on the light sensitive material during exposure by the camera.

Layout–A drawing containing complete specifications of a job; a preliminary sketch or arrangement showing the position, size, and color of illustrations and text matter.

Lead Edge–Front edge or gripper edge of the paper to be printed; opposite of trailing edge.

Leaders–Periods, dots, or dashes at intervals to lead the eye in tabular matter, content, pages, etc.

Leading–Spacing between printed lines.

Legend–Explanatory type matter under an illustration.

Lens–A precisely ground and carefully manufactured optical glass inserted in the camera for photographic purposes.

Lensboard–Part of the camera that houses the lens.

Lens Cap–A cap that fits snugly over the lens barrel to exclude light and protect the lens when not in use.

Letterpress–Printing from a raised surface, as type and photo-engravings.

Lettershop–Light manufacturer of printed materials, using duplicators and lightweight, cold type devices.

Lift–The quantity of paper that can be lifted (usually the amount one man can lift); when each piece of type in a form stays in place after being locked in a chase, it is said to "lift."

Light–A source of illumination.

Ligature–Two or more connected letters on the same type body.

Light Angle–The angle at which the light source is placed to strike the original or copy.

Light Distance–The distance or space from the original and the light source.

Light Face–A term used for type faces having less impression space on the face.

Light Tight–Allowing no light to penetrate or enter a certain area.

Light Trap–An area that prevents light that enters from one side from going out the other.

Line Copy–Original copy of printed, written or drawn by hand, or typewritten matter.

Line Cut–See "Line Engraving."

Line Drawing–Art work composed on lines or solids of one tonal value. See also "Line Copy."

Line Engraving–A printed plate made up of black and white which has been produced by an etching process.

Line Gauge–A printer's ruler usually having 6 and 12 point graduations. Sometimes with other point scales, as: agate, 9-point, 10-point, etc.

Line Negative–A negative shot without the halftone screen.

Linen Finish–Paper having a finish similar to that of linen cloth.

Line-Up Table–A lighted glass on which lines can be drawn or negatives scribed to indicate alignment of forms or pages and to prepare lines on exposed negatives for form work.

Linofilm–A cold type device.

Linotype–A keyboard machine which casts a line of type from molten metal in one piece; a slug-casting machine.

Listomatic–See "Fotolist."

Litho Chrome–Use of two black ink plates on a two color lithographic offset press. One plate provides low tonal values, the other high tonal values. The result is intense black values heretofore impossible by offset.

Lithography–Printing from stone, now superseded by the offset-lithographic process.

Lithomatic–An offset press.

Lithostone–A specially made stone on which lithography was produced; a stone having an affinity for both grease and water.

Live Form–A printing form still in use.

Logotype–Several letters or a whole cast in one piece of type; name of product or company in a special design used as a trademark in advertising.

Long Ink–Ink that can be drawn out into a long thin string—such ink has considerable tack which will pull a plate clean and sharp but will also tend to pick the paper stock.

Low Spots–Areas that do not print with the rest of the image due to damage of the blanket in that area.

Ludlow–A linecasting (slugcasting) machine for which the matrices are hand-assembled.

M

Machine Composition–Any type composition done mechanically as on the Intertype, Linotype, or Monotype.

Machine Finish–A smooth paper used in printing books.

Make Ready—Preparation of plate, type forms, and press to yield the best register and impression.

Making-Up–Arranging set type and slugs into type form or pages.

Magenta Contact Screen–A variable opacity film screen composed of magenta dyed lines used to make halftones.

Magnesium Nitrate–An ingredient used in fountain solution.

Magnetic Packing Gauge–A device used for a quick and easy method of checking correct packing.

Magnetic Printing–Printing with ink capable of being magnetized to allow electronic devices to "read" numbers on bank checks.

Masking–Process of color correction; blocking out of areas on negative.

Master–A paper plate used on a small offset press; a negative used on devices such as the Verifax to make positive copies.

Master Layout–A ruled sheet, usually on white paper which serves as a guide for stripping identical flats in offset.

Matrix–A mold in which type characters are cast in line-casting machines and individual type making; the paper-like mold used in stereotyping.

Middletone–Intermediate tones between the shadow and the highlight in halftone illustrations.

Miehle–A make of offset press.

Misomex–A step-and-repeat photocomposing machine.

Misprint–A typographical error.

Modifier–A substance that reduces or changes the form or qualities of another substance.

Modigraphic–A device that permits the changing of the original into various shapes and sizes.

Moire–Undesirable, symmetrical, checkered, or patterned formations produced when making a halftone with improper screen angles; overprinting when dots conflict or are out of register; result when re-screening a printed halftone.

Molleton–A specially woven cotton cloth used as a cover on dampening rollers.

Monel Metal–A type of offset plate.

Monochromatic–Color-blind; sensitive only to blue or ultra-violet light; having or consisting of one color or hue.

Monophoto–A photographic, cold type, composition device utilizing the keyboard of the hot metal monotype.

Monotype–A machine which casts individual letters for type cases to be set by hand; body type cast and set as wanted; rule, border, leads, slugs, and spacing material.

Mottling–The appearance of ink that does not dry flat—some areas are dull and others shiny.

Multigraph–A duplicator which prints from specially cast type.

Multilith–A small offset press.

N

ND–New distance of lights from copyboard or vacuum frame.

Negative–Film resulting from photographing copy in a camera. Work areas are transparent on the negative and the white areas are opaque.

NET–New exposure time.

Neutralize–To counteract; to make of no effect; to destroy the characteristics of another.

Nf#–New aperture setting or f-number.

NH–New height.

Nitric Acid–An acid diluted in water to form a counter etch for zinc plates.

Nodal Point–The precise point in the lens where the light rays converge together and spread again to the film.

Non-Offset Gun–A device which spreads fine, white powder onto freshly printed sheets to prevent ink transference from one sheet to another.

NW–New width.

O

OD–Original distance of lights from copyboard or vacuum frame.

OET–Old exposure time.

Offset Plate–A flat sheet of rolled material made of metals, plastics or paper and used on an offset press to transmit an image to a blanket.

OH–Original height.

Oiled Tympan Sheet–A special type of paper used on the platen or bed of the press on which the paper stock being printed is fed.

Offset–Term used to shorten "Offset-lithography;" the smudging of the bottom of a sheet on the press delivery from print on the top of the sheet directly below it.

Offset-Lithography–Producing an image from a plane surface onto a rubber blanket onto the paper; same as offset and planography.

One Stop Method–One exposure (detail) plus flash in making a halftone negative.

Onionskin–A thin, translucent paper usually used in carbon paper work.

Opaque–A water soluble red or black paint used to block out areas on negatives and positives to make them non-transparent; the state of condition of not permitting the passage of light.

Opaquing–Applying the opaque solution to the negative or positive in order to completely stop the transmission of light where desired.

Open Matter–Type lines very widely spread.

Optical Rouge–Substance used to clean the glass halftone screen.

Optype–A cold type device which produces a negative from typewritten copy and simultaneously italicizes or condenses, also justifies the right hand margin.

Orthochromatic–Film or plate sensitive to blue, etc., light. Not sensitive to red light.

Outline Halftone–A halftone in which the background is cut away or dropped out.

Over Develop–Too much time used in developing.

Over-Exposure–Too much time used in exposing.

Overlay–In offset, the transparent or translucent covering on the copy on which directions, specifications or work to be overprinted are placed in conjunction with the original.

Overprinting–Printing on an area that has been previously printed.

OW–Original width.

Oxidation–The process and result of a union of a substance and oxygen.

Oxide–Result of a union of a substance and oxygen.

Ozalid–An office copy-making device. A sensitized paper coated with diazo dye which disintegrates upon exposure to light. By fuming the paper with ammonia gas the image becomes visible.

P

Packing–An underlay of sheets of paper placed under an offset plate or blanket.

Padding–Gluing the ends of sheets as in making scratch pads.

Pamphlet–Several sheets of paper stitched together.

Pamphlet Binding–Binding that produces leaflets, folders, booklets, and soft-covered books.

Panchromatic–Film sensitive to all colors.

Paper Plate–A specially treated paper used as an offset plate.

Paraformaldehyde–See "accelerator."

Paste-up–Fastening parts of galley proofs to a dummy to instruct compositors where components are to be placed. Camera-ready copy consisting of pasted-up reproduction proofs.

Pebbling–A process of graining or crimping gloss-coated paper after printing halftones to give antique paper effect; now generally out of date.

Pen Ruling–Applying lines to paper in various colors, as in notebooks, accounting forms, etc.

Perfecting–A press which prints both sides of a sheet of paper at the same time. Also printing on both sides at once.

Phantom–Areas of a picture which are lighter than others used to bring prominence to the darker areas.

Phosphoric Acid–An acid used in the preparation of a desensitizing etch on zinc plates or aluminum plates.

Photocomposing Machine–See "Step-and-Repeat Photocomposing Machine."

Photoengraving–The process of making line and halftone letterpress printing plates by the action of light on a film.

Photogelatin–See "Collotype."

Photograph–A picture or illustration made by exposing sensitive film to light.

Photography–The art or process of making a picture by exposing sensitive film to light.

Photogravure–See "Gravure."

Photolithography–See "Offset-Lithography," "Offset," or "Lithography."

Photon–A cold type device.

Photostat–A camera for making paper negative and positive prints.

Phototype Composing Machine–A keyboard device for assembling images of type faces photographically on film, rather than in metal type forms. See "Cold Type."

pH Value–The acidity or alkalinity of a solution determined by its hydrogen ion content. Scale is from 1 to 14 with 7 as the neutral point. Below 7 is acid, above 7 is alkali.

Pica–The standard unit of measurement for printing, about ⅙ in.

Pica Rule–See "Line Gauge."

Picking–Spots in printed matter that result from tacky ink; a type of paper stock being run, or dampener lint.

Pigment–The substance used in obtaining color in printing inks.

Pile Up or Piling–The sticking or caking of ink on a plate or blanket.

Pin Holes–Minute transparent spots in negatives.

Planographic–The printing process in which the area to be printed is on the same plane with the blank areas.

Plate–Photoengravings, electrotypes, etc. used in letterpress printing. Plates used in the die-stamping by intaglio methods. In offset, plates are thin and wrap around the cylinder of the press.

Plate Cylinder–The cylinder on a press which holds the printing plate.

Plate Image–The image on the plate to be printed.

Platemaking–Exposing and developing a sensitized plate.

Platen Press–A type of letterpress which makes impressions from a flat surface.

Point–A unit of measurement in printing material and type about ($\frac{1}{72}$ in.); any mark of punctuation such as the period, comma, etc.

Positive–The reverse of a negative. The work appears on the copy the same as it does on the positive film.

Potassium Alum–A photographic chemical used as a hardener in solutions.

Potassium Bromide–The governor agent used in developing. See "Governor."

Potassium Metabisulphite–A weak acid used to control the activity of the alkali during the development process.

Posterization–The interpretation of a continuous tone original as line copy in screen process work. The tonal graduations of the original are converted into a series of printed color or shades, each representing a portion of the tonal values in the photo or wash drawing.

Pre-Etch–To clean and desensitize an offset plate.

Presensitized Plate–An offset plate that has been purchased already sensitized to light and needs no sensitizing in the printer's shop.

Preservative–A chemical that combines with the reducing agent to form a more stable compound.

Press Gripper–Clamps on the platen press that hold sheets flat when printing. See "Grippers."

Pressman–One who operates printing presses.

Press Proofs–Proofs made on regular printing presses, such as reproduction proofs.

Pressure Sensitive–Printed material which can be affixed to objects by peeling off a backing which exposes a quick-sticking material.

Printing–In its general sense, any method of placing an image on objects. Sometimes it is applied to letterpress printing to differentiate from the offset process. See also "Duplicating."

Printing Ink–A thick, pasty, fluid substance used in letterpress and offset processes. Newsprint and gravure ink is more fluid.

Processor D–A device that charges a Xerographic plate in Xerography.

Process Plates–The printing from a series of plates (two or more) in halftone, which makes varying colors possible from the primary colors: yellow, red, blue, and black.

Progressive Proofs–Proofs of color plates used as a guide for the pressman and furnished by the engraver or platemaker.

Proportional Rule–A device for calculating width and depth measurements on reductions and enlargements.

Proportional Scale–A device for calculating width and depth measurements on reductions and enlargements.

Proof–The first print of a type form or offset plate, examined and read to detect errors.

Proofreader–One who examines proofs and marks errors for correction.

Proofreader's Marks–Signs or symbols used by proofreaders to denote errors for correction.

Protype–A cold type display type device.

Pulp–The mass of raw material (cellulose fiber) used to make paper.

Q

Quadding—Spacing out the blank areas in type composed lines.

Quoin—An expanding wedge device used to secure type forms for letterpress work.

R

RCA Electrofax–Both a letterpress and offset platemaking process which eliminates the need for negative by exposing the copy directly on a plate through electrostatic means.

RCA Electro Type Setter–A keyboard operating unit used on Comet Linotype models. See also "Teletypesetter."

Ream–Approximately 500 sheets of paper.

Reducing Agent–A chemical that reduces the silver salt to metallic silver during a development process.

Reduction–In dot-etching, reducing the size of the black half-tone dots on a screen positive; reproducing smaller than original size.

Register–The adjustment of forms or plates so that they will print in correct position over another form or plate as in color printing.

Register Marks–Marks placed on layout sheets or overlays for location of color or other close work in relation to each other.

Relative Humidity–Reference to the amount of water vapor which the air holds compared to what it could hold at a given temperature if it were saturated.

Reproduction–A reproduced copy of an original.

Repro Proof–A proof pulled for camera.

Re-Screening–Screening or making a halftone from copy already containing a screen or already a halftone.

Retouching–Corrective treatment of a negative, plate or copy.

Reversal–The opposite of a positive; printed material in which the background is in the color being printed and the image is in white.

Reverse Plate–A printing plate in which the black and white has been reversed.

Revise Proof–Any proof taken of printing types, forms, or plates after the first as "1st revise." "2nd revise" is used to determine if corrections have been made and on which additional corrections are made.

Rollers–Inking and dampening rollers used on presses.

Roller Stripping–Steel rollers refusing to take ink.

Rolling Up–To cover a plate with a thin layer of developing ink.

Roll-Leaf Stamping–A process of stamping gold, silver, or other colors on covers of books, stationary, etc.

Rotogravure–The process of intaglio (gravure) impressions on a rotary press.

Roughing–See "Pebbling."

Ruling Machine–A device used to pen rule lines in colors on paper.

Ruling Pens–Pens used on a pen ruling machine for ruling colored lines.

Run or Press Run–Number of impressions or copies on a job.

S

Safe Lights–Colored or filtered lights used when processing light sensitive material.

Safety Paper–Paper treated usually by printing a design in a light tint which protects the sheet against forgery.

Saddle Stitch–To fasten a pamphlet or book by stitching it through the middle fold of the sheets.

Salts–Sodium carbonate, ammonium dichromate, calcium chloride.

Scaling–Calculating the percentage of enlargement or reduction of originals; determining proportional width or depth of originals to needed depth or width.

Scanagraver–A device which makes original halftones electronically, without benefit of etching.

Scotch Print–A conversion method employing translucent material on which "proofs" are pulled to convert types forms for offset printing.

Scratchboard–Specially treated white paper to which a coating of black ink is applied and then scratched off to make a drawing.

Screen–Plate glass with cross-ruled opaque lines used in cameras to break continuous tone illustrations and artwork into halftones; the number of lines to the inch on printed illustrations, such as 80 line screen, 120 line screen, etc. See also "Halftone Screen."

Screen Angle–The angle at which the halftone screen is placed to expose different colors.

Screened Snapshot–A photograph containing a screen produced by inserting a small halftone screen into a snapshot camera prior to taking a picture.

Screen Distance–The distance between the ruled lines of the screen grid and the negative coating.

Screen Process–A printing process using a squeegee to force ink through a fine mesh upon which the non-image areas have been blocked out.

Screen Separation–See "Screen distance."

Scum–Ink adhering to the non-printing areas of a lithographic plate.

Selectivity–The ability to confine activity to portions of silver struck by light.

Sensitive Material–An emulsion attached to a film, paper, or dry plate base.

Sensitizers–Materials which make other substances responsive to light; dichromate, potassium, and ammonium make solutions of albumin, glue, gelatin, and casein sensitive to light.

Sensitizing–Making a plate sensitive to light.

Serigraph–Art subjects produced by screen process methods.

Shadow–Shaded or darker portions of a halftone.

Sheet-Wise–Pages imposed in two forms, that is, the same form does not back up itself. See "Work-and-Back."

Short Ink–Ink that breaks quickly when drawn apart; has little tack and will not print as sharp; the opposite of long ink.

Short Stop Bath–A solution of acetic acid used to neutralize the alkaline developer on the negative and to preserve the acid fixing solution.

Side Guide–A device on the press that registers the sheet into position before printing.

Side Stitch–The fastening of pamphlet sheets together side-ways.

Signature–A folded section of a book after being printed; a letter or figure appearing at the bottom of the first page of a signature to guide the binder; dots or squares are often printed at the fold to aid in collating.

Silk Screen–See "Screen Process."

Silver Salts–The light sensitive substance formed when combining a silver nitrate solution with a silver halide mixture and potassium bromide.

Sine–Ratio between radius of circle and a line parallel to a tangent and drawn from circumference to radius.

Size–Water-resisting material which is added to pulp when making paper.

Slitter–A device (a sharp disc) used to cut or slit paper as it passes from a printing press.

Slur–Shadow dots and reverse letter filling up; a blurred or smudged image due to poor impression.

Snake Slip (Snake Stone)–A powdered pumice stone, gum water, and etch worked into a still paste and molded into small sticks and dried, used for removing spots from lithographic plates.

Snap Out Forms–Multiple sheets of paper interleaved with carbon and glued at the top or edge.

Sodium Fluoride–An ingredient used in the preparation of a press fountain solution.

Sodium Hydroxide–An accelerating agent used in developing solutions. See "Accelerator."

Sodium Sulphite–A chemical used as a preservative. See "Preservative."

Solid Matter–Type composition that is not leaded.

Solution–A combination of two or more different liquids or liquids and solid substances.

Splicing–Joining together.

Split Fountain–Dividing the ink fountain into pre-determined sections to run any number of colors of ink from the same fountain at the same time.

Square Four–Four pages imposed so that when printed on both sides and cut, two sections of four pages each are made.

SR–Scale of reproduction.

Standing Matter–Type combination of engravings and other plates held over for another printing.

Stenafax–A device used to make single copies of images and plates for small offset presses.

Stencil–Wax-like sheets which are typed upon for use on mimeograph-like duplicators.

Step-and-Repeat Photocomposing Machine–A device for the printing of the same image in register many times on the same plate for gang or multiple printing.

Stepover–Procedure of repeating the exposure of an offset flat by stepping it along the gripper or lead edge.

Stereotype–A letterpress printing plate cast from a paper matrix.

Stipple–A printing surface on plates which consist of fine dots.

Stream Feed–Automatic feeders which, by the overlapping sheets being delivered to a printing press, allows higher press speeds.

Stripper–One who arranges and affixes negatives or positives on goldenrod paper or acetate sheets into flats, following the instructions on how the job should appear when printed.

Stripping–Arranging the negatives or positives on the goldenrod sheet. See also "Roller Stripping."

Stripping Table–A light, glass-topped table with a light source beneath the glass on which a stripper works when making a flat.

Stylus–An instrument for ruling, drawing, or signing a name on a stencil for mimeographing.

Suckers–Small rubber or metal discs used on presses to pick up the sheets of paper from the stack for feeding into the press.

Suction–The power that picks up the sheet to the suckers.

Supercalendered–Extra smooth paper stock, not coated.

Surface Coated Plate–An offset plate that has thin layer of sensitized solution over its surface.

T

Tack–Amount of stickiness or pull in offset ink.

Tannic Acid–An acid used in the preparation of a desensitizing "Blue" etch for zinc plates.

Tartaric Acid–An acid used in the preparation of a press fountain solution.

Temperature Controlled Sink–A sink that automatically keeps all chemicals and solutions at a constant temperature.

Template–A pattern used as a guide for a pen.

Tension–The force applied for stretching or holding tight.

Thermography–The process of dusting freshly printed sheets with resinous powder. When heated, the powder fuses, forming a raised surface of the print simulating copperplate engraving.

Thermometer–An instrument that records and shows the temperature in a given area.

Thin Base–Film which has a stripping layer that can be peeled off and turned over to give a reversal of the image.

Thiosulphate (Hypo)–An ingredient used in the fixing bath.

Three Stop Method–Three exposures, (detail, highlight, and middletone) plus flash in making a halftone negative.

Tickometer–A device for automatically endorsing and counting checks.

Tint Block–A solid or screened background for printing tints.

Tinting–A light tint appearing all over the sheet.

Tissue–A very thin paper, usually .001 inch thick.

Toptone–Color in ink before it dries on the paper.

Tonal Range–A graduation of the shades of white to black.

Trailing Edge–Bottom edge or back edge of the paper to be printed; opposite of the lead edge.

Transpose–To change a word or letter or groups of words or illustrations from one place to another.

Tray Bail–Metal strip that rests on the printed sheets and prevents them from falling if they fly over the front stop.

Tri-Metal Plate–An offset plate made of three different metals, usually steel or zinc with copper and chromium.

Tusche–A greasy water-soluble black liquid applied to plates for repairing an image.

Tuscher–One who applies tusche to a plate.

Tusching–The operation of applying tusche to plates with a pen or brush for repairing the image when broken or missing.

Two Stop Method–The exposures (detail, highlight) plus flash in making a halftone negative.

Typographer–A master typographical designer of printed matter.

Typography–The art of printing design.

U

Ultra Violet–The rays beyond the violet end of the spectrum.

Underdevelop–Not enough time elapsed in the development process.

Underexpose–Not enough exposure time.

Underlay–A sheet or sheets of paper placed under a form in letterpress printing makeready. Also under the offset plate and blanket in offset printing. Also see "Packing."

Undertone–Color of ink when held up to a light.

V

Vacuum Back–The back of the camera that holds the film in place, during exposure, by vacuum.

Vacuum Film Holder–The flat part of the vacuum back where the film is placed.

Vacuum Frame–A device for holding a plate and negative together during exposure.

VariTyper–A series of keyboard machines for cold type composition from 6 through 18 point sizes.

Varnish–A vehicle used in making printing inks; used also to give a gloss-coated effect to printed work.

Vignette–Photographs, halftones, or prints showing the background gradually fading away.

Virkotype–A thermograph machine.

Viscosity–Having the nature of being sticky, thick, tacky, etc.

Vehicle of Ink–The liquid component of a printing ink which carries the pigment and provides flow properties.

W

Walking Off–Image on plate starting to disappear.

Water Fountain–The reservoir that holds the press water solution.

Waterhouse Stop Slot–The slot in the lens barrel to insert filters used for color work.

Watermark–A faint design pressed into paper during manufacture while the paper is still wet.

Web–A term used for a roll of paper.

Webendorfer–A make of offset press.

Web Offset–Printing by offset, perfecting from one or more rolls of paper fed lengthwise into the press.

White Space–The part of printed matter not covered by type and illustrations.

Whirler–The machine that rotates or whirls the plate during the coating cycle.

Work-and-Back (Sheetwise)–One form is backed up with a different form. The same gripper and side guide are used on the single sheet.

Work-and-Shift–Double sized sheet is fed twice to the same guide and gripper edges.

Work-and-Turn–Both sides of the sheet are printed with one form. The short dimension is used as the axis when the form is turned. The guide, if possible, is shifted for the double sheet.

Work-and-Tumble (Work-and-Flop)–A double size sheet is printed on both sides with one form. The long dimension is used as the axis. The gripper edge used for the second run is printed to the same side guide but opposite gripper. A double sheet is used.

Work Up–Spacing material which rises on the press and prints on the sheet.

Woven Paper–Paper having fine lines running each way on the sheet.

Wrap-Around Plates–Shallow etched relief plates thin enough to wrap around a press cylinder for rotary letterpress.

X

Xerox–A copy making and offset platemaking device.

Xerography–Method of making duplicate copies and offset plates by electrostatic means.

Xylene–A cleaning solution used on the magenta contact screen.

Xylol–A cleaning solution used on the magenta contact screen.

Z

Zinc Etching–A printing plate for letterpress made by photography and the chemical processes of acid. May be line or halftone.

Zinc Plate–An offset plate made of zinc.

Zipatone–Shading media pre-printed on waxbacked transparent plastic; a substitute for the Ben Day shading medium.

Zography–Three dimensional printing.

Appendix

Weights and Measures

Knowledge of weights and measures is an asset not only to an apprentice but also to the experienced individual in offset printing. Today, many of the chemicals used in the printing plant are purchased pre-mixed from the manufacturer. However, due to unforseen circumstances the purchase or shipment of these chemicals may be delayed. It is then that an individual who has the basic knowledge of what ingredients are required, their proportionate amounts, and the ability to mix them, can become an important asset to the printing plant.

The following are the standard tables of weights and measures and conversion tables to assist in the mixing of any formulae required.

LIQUID MEASURE

1 gallon	= 4 quarts	= 128 ounces
1 liter	= 1.057 qts.	= 32.9 ounces
1 quart	= 2 pints	= 32 ounces
1 pint	= 4 gills	= 16 ounces
1 gill	= 4 ounces	

AVOIRDUPOIS WEIGHT

1 pound	= 7000 grains	= 256 drams	= 16 oz.
1 ounce	= 16 drams		
1 dram	= $27\frac{7}{32}$ grains		

METRIC WEIGHT

1 decigram	=	1.54323 grains
1 gram	=	15.43234 grains
1 dekagram	=	5.6438 drams
1 hectogram	=	3.5274 ounces
1 kilogram	=	2.20462 pounds

METRIC—ENGLISH EQUIVALENTS

	Grams	Grains	Kilograms
1 pound =	453.6	7000	0.4536
1 ounce =	28.3495	437.4894	0.02835

U.S. LIQUID TO METRIC

	Drams	Cubic Centimeters	Liters
1 gallon =	1024	3785	3.785
1 quart =	256	946.3	0.9463

OTHER CONVERSION FACTORS

No. gallons	× 3.785	= liters
	× 8	= pints
	× 4	= quarts
	× 128	= ounces (liquid)
	× 3785	= cubic centimeters
No. liters	× 0.2642	= gallons
	× 1.057	= quarts
	× 2.113	= pints
No. pounds	× 16	= ounces (avoirdupois)
	× 256	= drams
	× 7000	= grains
No. ounces (liq.)	× 0.02957	= liters
(avoir.)	× 0.0625	= pounds
(avoir.)	× 28.35	= grams
No. grams	× 0.03527	= ounces (avoirdupois)
	× 15.432	= grains
No. inches	× 2.540	= centimeters
No. centimeters	× 0.3937	= inches
	× 10	= millimeters
No. millimeters	× 0.03937	= inches
	× 0.1	= centimeters

The following are typefaces available for the VariTyper machine discussed in Chapter 4.

12 pt. Alexandria Medium (880-12A)
ABCDEFGHIJKLMNOPQRSTUVWXYZ&
abcdefghijklmnopqrstuvwxyz abcdefghijk

10 pt. Alexandria Light (650-10B)
ABCDEFGHIJKLMNOPQRSTUVWXYZ& AB
abcdefghijklmnopqrstuvwxyz abcdefghijklmn

10 pt. Bell Gothic Light (FL950-10B)
ABCDEFGHIJKLMNOPQRSTUVWXYZ& AB
abcdefghijklmnopqrstuvwxyz abcdefghijklmn

10 pt. Bell Gothic Bold (FL980-10B)
ABCDEFGHIJKLMNOPQRSTUVWXYZ& ABC
abcdefghijklmnopqrstuvwxyz abcdefghijklmn

10 pt. Gothic Bold Condensed (FL970-10B)
ABCDEFGHIJKLMNOPQRSTUVWXYZ& ABC
abcdefghijklmnopqrstuvwxyz abcdefghijklmn

10 pt. Bodoni Book (600-10B)
ABCDEFGHIJKLMNOPQRSTUVWXYZ& ABC
abcdefghijklmnopqrstuvwxyz abcdefghijklmn

10 pt. Bodoni Bold (780-10B)
ABCDEFGHIJKLMNOPQRSTUVWXYZ& ABC
abcdefghijklmnopqrstuvwxyz abcdefghijklmno

10 pt. Bookman (630-10B)
ABCDEFGHIJKLMNOPQRSTUVWXYZ& ABC
abcdefghijklmnopqrstuvwxyz abcdefghijklmno

10 pt. Cartoon Type (940-10A)
ABCDEFGHIJKLMNOPQRSTUVWXYZ A
ABCDEFGHIJKLMNOPQRSTUVWXYZ ABCDEFGHI

10 pt. Caslon (830-10B)
ABCDEFGHIJKLMNOPQRSTUVWXYZ& ABC
abcdefghijklmnopqrstuvwxyz abcdefghijklmno

13 pt. Copperplate Gothic Caps & Small Caps (2000-13A)

ABCDEFGHIJKLMNOPQRSTUVWXYZ&
ABCDEFGHIJKLMNOPQRSTUVWXYZ ABCDEFGH

12 pt. Copperplate Gothic Bold (810-12A)

ABCDEFGHIJKLMNOPQRSTUVWXYZ&
§ † ‡ ⊂ ⊃ ⊏ ⊐ ⊕ □ ◆ ● ▲ ■ ★ ◆ ´ ` ¨ ^ ° ' +

12 pt. Cramer Italic (795-12A)

ABCDEFGHIJKLMNOPQRSTUVWXYZ&
abcdefghijklmnopqrstuvwxyz abcdefghijk

10 pt. Exeter (1010-10B)

ABCDEFGHIJKLMNOPQRSTUVWXYZ& AB
abcdefghijklmnopqrstuvwxyz

10 pt. Garamond Light (620-10B)

ABCDEFGHIJKLMNOPQRSTUVWXYZ& AB
abcdefghijklmnopqrstuvwxyz abcdefghijklmn

10 pt. Garamond Bold (680-10B)

ABCDEFGHIJKLMNOPQRSTUVWXYZ& AB
abcdefghijklmnopqrstuvwxyz abcdefghijklmn

10 pt. Greek (920-10B)

ΑΒΓΔΕΖΗΘΙΚΛΜΝΞΟΠΡΣΤΥΦΧΨΩ ΑΒΓΔΕΖ
αβγδεζηθικλμνξοπρστυφχψω αβγδεζηθικλμνξο

12 pt. Monastery (840-12B)

ABCDEFGHIJKLMNOPQRSTUVWXYZ& AB
abcdefghijklmnopqrstuvwxyz abcdefghijklmn

10 pt. Mathematical Type (710-10B)

ΑΒΓΔΕΖΗΘΚΛΜΝΞΠΡΣΤΦΧΨΩℨℜ ΑΒΓΔΕ
αβγδεζηθκλμνξπρστφχψωд℘ αβγδεζηθκλμνξ

10 pt. Modern Bold (820-10A)

ABCDEFGHIJKLMNOPQRSTUVWXYZ&
abcdefghijklmnopqrstuvwxyz abcdefghijkl

8 pt. Modern Roman (770-8B)

ABCDEFGHIJKLMNOPQRSTUVWXYZ& ABC
abcdefghijklmnopqrstuvwxyz abcdefghijklmno

Index

A

A. B. Dick Model 360
  air-vacuum adjustment 308
  blanket, removing and attaching 317
  buckle control 311
  care, cleaning and lubrication 318
  fountain solution 300
  ink and water settings 315
  inking 298
  paper feed 301
  paper stack adjustment 308
  plate, attaching 312
  receiving tray 309
Accelerator 181
Acid, etching 17
Alphatype 99–101
Aperture setting 143, 150–151
Artype 59, 108, 109
Artwork 47
Artwork, pre-printed 56–57
Asphaltum 221
ATF Chief "15" Adjustments
  blanket-to-paper 395
  chain delivery 381
  delivery chute 383
  fountain and water settings 375
  image position 385
  ink and ink system 373
  ink-form roller 393
  paper feedboard 379
  paper platform 377
  plate-to-blanket 394
ATF Chief "15" Inking system 366
ATF Chief "15" Operating controls 367–372

ATF Computer 15, 131
ATF Photographic typesetter 93–95

B

Bellows 144
Bellows extension 150, 152
Berger system 90, 91
Bindery procedures
  book-edge treatment 508
  collating and gathering 498–500
  cornering 503
  cutting paper 505
  drilling and punching 500–502
  embossing 508
  fastening, methods of 491–495
  folding paper 496–498
  gold stamping 504
  jogging paper 502
  padding 502
  perforating 504
  ruling paper 507
  stapling and stitching 499
Bista plate 20
Bourges 63
Brady tape pen 58

C

Calcareous stone 2
Camera, adjustments of 150–156
Camera projects 187
Carbon arc lights 156
Carbon ribbon 74
Care and cleaning of offset plates 245–247

Caustic soda 17
Caustic solution 220
Cello-Tak 112–113
Chandler-Price Automatic 25
Chart Pak 57
Chase 23
Clip-books 59
Coating solution 212–213
Cold and hot type compared 70–71
Cold type forms machine 52
Cold type, growth of 71–72
Collotype 35
Color separation
   duotones 174–176
   duotypes 176
   filters 171–174
   screen angles 170
Colotone 63
Combination halftone and line 176–178
Composing stick 13
Compos-O-Line 130, 131
Computers 40–43
Conversion devices 132–133
Copy board 142, 143
Copyboard extension 150, 152
Copy defined 46
Copy preparation 46–47
Counter etch 212
Cost, comparison of letterpress and offset 9
Craftint board 61
Craftype 108
Crop 47

D

Darkroom 179–181
Darkroom requirements 180
Davidson Dual "500"
   blanket, changing 406
   cylinders, paralleling 418
   dampening unit 398
   dampening unit pressure 409
   dry offset 444
   dry offset embossing 447
   feeding and delivery 421
   image positioning 407
   impression 435
   inking unit 400

inking unit pressure 415
   perfecting 448
   plate-to-blanket pressures 419
   relief printing 437
Decalcomania 35
Deep etch plates 231–233
Desensitizer 220–221
Developing ink 219–220
Development, fixing and washing 181–187
Diaphram 142, 143
Diagonal line method of scaling artwork 48–49
Diatype 124
Die-cutting 39
Die stamping 33
Differential spacing 81–82
Directories, offset printing and 12
Ditto Offset Duplicator
   air blow control-valve adjustment 293
   air blow tubes 292
   blanket pressure control 282
   control panel and switches 275
   ejector mechanism 284
   feed table adjustments 289
   form-roller adjustments 293
   fountain solution and water settings 277
   image adjustments 286
   inking and ink settings 280
   ink-form roller adjustments 295
   ink roller cleaning and care 290
   master plate 284
   receiving tray 284
   variable speed control 289
Doublebold 76
Dow etch process 17
"Dragon's blood" 17
Dropout halftone 179
Dry offset 31
Dycril plates 15, 17, 18

E

Electronic photographic typesetting 89–90
Electrotypes 16, 21, 29
Elgramma 20
Emery 3
Employment in graphic arts 9

Engravings
  combination 16
  copperplate 33
  halftone 16
    (*See also Offset photography*)
  line 16
  wax 16
Enlargements and reductions 47–50
Etching acid 17
Exposure time (camera) 151–156
Exposure time (platemaking) 213–215

F

f numbers 143
Fairchild Morisawa 126, 127
Film holder 144, 145
Film types of 148–150
Filmotype Photo-Compositor 117
Flatbed cylinder presses 15
Flatbed press, lithographic 3
Flexographic 9, 31–32
Flexoprint 131
Finiguerra, Maso 1
Focal length 144
Form 23
Formatt 109, 110
Formliner 54
Forms machine, cold type 52
Forms, reproduction proofs of 52–53
Formulas, developing 185–187
Foto-Chase 66
Foto-Drafting 95
Fotolist 129, 130
Fotosetter, Intertype
Fotorex 119
Foto Riter 114
Fototronic, Intertype 89
Fototype 90, 107
Furniture 23

G

Gallery type camera 146, 147
Goss rotary press 28
Governor (developing) 182
Graining, plate 209
Graph and chart material 56–59

Graphic layout board 55
Gravure 33, 34
Graphic arts, employment in 9
Growth of cold type process 71–72
Guideline sheets, pre-printed 52–55
Gum arabic 221

H

Hadego 121–123
Halftone negative analysis 187–192
Halftone photography
  aperture setting 161–162
  care of glass screen 159
  care of magenta contact screen 164–165
  contact screen 163–164
  exposure 162–163
  Kodalith 165
  mounting the screen 158
  rescreening 167–169
  screen distance 159–161
  snapshots, screened 167
Harris brothers 4
Harris Company 4
Harris Offset Press, LUH-120
  feeder adjustments 463
  ink control and adjustments 458
  installing the blanket 462
  installing the plate 461
  operating controls 452
  press adjustments 468
  press maintenance 474
  water control and adjustments 455
Harris Wrap-Around 27, 28
Hermes Ambassador 75
Hoe, R. and Company 4
Horizontal cameras 145, 146, 147
Hot and cold type compared 70–71
Hydroquinone 181

I

Illustration medium 63, 65
Illustrations, combination 176–178
Industrihuset 125
Inks, offset 264, 271
Instantex 61, 62

Intertype 13
Intertype digital computors 41–42
Imposition 24

J

Jet Scriber 53
Job case 13
Justa-Meter 80, 81
Justigage 77
Justowriter 82–83, 84

K

Kameratype 123, 124
Klischograph 20
Kluge press 25, 26

L

Layout 46–50
Layout guides 55–56
Lens barrel 143
Lensboard 142, 143
Leroy lettering device 105
Letraset 110
Letterphot 124
Lettering devices 104–107
Letterpress and cold type compared 69
Letterpress printing 12
Letterpress, use in offset printing 11–12
Letterset 9
Line-cast type 13
Line composers, photographic 95–99,
    114–128
Linofilm 95–99
Linotron 42
Linotype 13
Lights (offset photography) 156
Lithography defined 1
Lithography, early methods 3
Low bed camera 145
Ludlow Typograph 3

M

Magnascop 124
Makeready 15, 24

Marginator 76
Mechanical 47
Megatype 119–120
Metalphoto 39
Mentype 13
Miehle Vertical 26
Modigraphic 128–129
Modular art 56–59
Monel metal 35
Monochromatic film 150
Monotype 14, 15
Monsen Transadhesive Tape 110, 111
Multilith, Model 1250
    auxiliary equipment 357
    blanket, attaching 350
    cam adjustment 354
    dampening system 322
    inking system 324
    ink unit adjustment 344
    paper feed 331
    plates, attaching 326
    plate-to-blanket pressure 351

N

Newspapers, use of offset for 5–6
NHM system 83–84
Numbering devices 28–29

O

Office copiers and platemakers
    Electrostatic 36–37
    Xerography 37–38
    Xography 37
Office forms 50–53
Offset blankets 260–264
Offset, dry 31
Offset photography 141–206
Offset plate 207
Offset platemaking
    care and cleaning 245–247
    caustic solution 220
    coating solution 212–213
    counter etch 212
    deep etch plate 231–232
    desensitizer 220–221
    developing ink 219–220

gum arabic 221
materials and qualities of plates 233
photocomposing machine 216
plate graining 209
pre-sensitized plates 230
steps in 208
zinc plate 221–230
Offset printing 5
Offset process 4–5
Optaliner 56
Optiset 113
Optiskop 113
Optype 125
Original Heidelberg 25, 26
Orthochromatic film 149
Overhead camera 146

P

Panchromatic film 149
Paper
basic weights 561, 562
bleaching 479
classes of 484, 485
coated and enameled 484
digester 480, 481
figuring 486
filler 479
grain, testing for 487
humidity 488
machine for making 483
pulp 479, 480
raw material 478
watermarks 481
weights, basic 486
Paper and plastic type 107–114
Paper ruling 35–36
Paraformaldehyde 181
Paraliner 54
Pasco 127–128
Photocomposing machines 6, 216–219
Photoengravings 15, 16–21
Photogelatin process 35
Photographic typesetting 93–104
Photographs 47, 48
Photo-Lathe 20
Photo-mechanical process 5
Photon 42, 101–104, 131

Photopolymer plate 17, 18
Phototypositor 125
Plastic and paper type 107–114
Plastic halftone plates 19
Platemaking, offset
care and cleaning 245–247
caustic solution 220
coating solution 212–213
counter etch 212
deep etch 231–232
desensitizer 220–221
developing ink 219–220
gum arabic 221
materials and qualities of plates 233
photocomposing machines 216
plate graining 209
pre-sensitized plates 230
zinc plates 221–230
Platen press 25
Plates, letterpress 15–16
Plates, plastic 19, 20
Potassium bromide 182
Powderless etching 17
Powderless etching machine 17, 18
Precautions in developing 184
Pre-printed artwork 56–57
Pre-sensitized plates 230–231
Preservative 182
Press fountain etches 256, 257–260
Presses, rotary newspaper 5
Presto paper type 107, 108
Printing processes and methods 8–45
Printing, typical products by type 10–11
Print-O-Stat 107
Process camera, parts of 142, 143–145
Projected layout guides 55–56
Projects, photography 201–202
Proofreaders marks 43
Proof press 69
Proportion scale 49–50
Protype 121
Pumice stone 3

Q

Quantity, influence on choice of printing
method 8–9
Quoins 23

R

Raphael typewriter 82
Reading machines 42
Reducing agents 181
Reductions and enlargements 47–50
Remington electric typewriter 75
Reproduction proofs 68
Reproductions, kinds of 141–142
Review Question Answers 511–523
Roll film cameras 147, 148
Ross drawing board 61
Rotary presses, letterpress 28, 29
Rubber plates 15, 20
Rubel, Ira 4

S

Scan-a-graver 19
Scan-a-sizer 19
Schematics, pre-printed 58
SCM "250" 75, 76
Scratchboard 61
Screen process 34–35
Screens 17
Selectric 73, 74
Senefelder, Alois 1
Senso lettering guide 106–107
Sequential card camera 12, 129–131
Shading media 59–60, 63
Sherwood, Alex 4
Short stop bath 183
Siemag typewriter 59, 60
Sign machines 29–31
Silk screen 34–35
Silver salt 181
Sine 155
Small shop industry 9
Snopake 91
Solotone 63, 65
Star Autojustifier 42
Starlettograph 126

Stereotypes 21–22
Strike-on composition 73–83
Stripping the flat 192–200
StripPrinter 117–118
Strixner 2
Stylus 19

T

Tape, Monsen Transadhesive 110, 111
Tape pen 58
Tatoo 3
Technical advancement 10
Thermography 32, 33
Times of London, *The* 4
Transfer type 111–112
Transopaque 63
Twistype 129
Types of cameras 145–148
Typewriter accessories 75–78
Typewriter corrections 91
Typewriters 73–83
Typewriters, proportional spacing 82–83
Typit 77, 78
Typographic layout 46–50
Typro 116, 117

U–Z

Ultra-violet light 17
Universal Dynamic Phototypesetter 121
Vacuum printing frame 213
Varigraph 104
VariTyper 75, 78–79, 91, 115, 116
Vertical cameras 146, 147
Waterhouse stop slot 143–144
Wax engravings 16
Weber process 200–201
William Blake 1
Wrico Lettering Guide 105, 106
Zinc plate solutions 258–260
Zinc plate 221–230